Potential Civilian Markets for the Military-Electronics Industry

CONVERSION OF INDUSTRY FROM A MILITARY TO CIVILIAN ECONOMY

A Series Edited by Seymour Melman

Also available in this series:

THE DEFENSE ECONOMY: Conversion of Industries
and Occupations to Civilian Needs
edited by SEYMOUR MELMAN

THE CONVERSION OF SHIPBUILDING FROM
MILITARY TO CIVILIAN MARKETS
by DANIEL M. MACK-FORLIST AND ARTHUR NEWMAN

CONVERSION OF NUCLEAR FACILITIES FROM MILITARY TO
CIVILIAN USES: A Case Study in Hanford, Washington
by ARIS P. CHRISTODOULOU

THE CONVERSION OF MILITARY-ORIENTED RESEARCH
AND DEVELOPMENT TO CIVILIAN USES
by MARVIN BERKOWITZ

PRAEGER SPECIAL STUDIES IN
U.S. ECONOMIC AND SOCIAL DEVELOPMENT

Potential Civilian Markets for the Military-Electronics Industry

STRATEGIES FOR CONVERSION

Edited by
John E. Ullmann

Foreword by
Seymour Melman

PRAEGER PUBLISHERS
New York · Washington · London

The purpose of Praeger Special Studies is to make specialized research in U.S. and international economics and politics available to the academic, business, and government communities. For further information, write to the Special Projects Division, Praeger Publishers, Inc., 111 Fourth Avenue, New York, N.Y. 10003.

PRAEGER PUBLISHERS
111 Fourth Avenue, New York, N.Y. 10003, U.S.A.
5, Cromwell Place, London S.W.7, England

Published in the United States of America in 1970
by Praeger Publishers, Inc.

Library of Congress Catalog Card Number: 76-105415

Printed in the United States of America

FOREWORD

This book is part of a five-volume series, entitled "Conversion of Industry from a Military to
Civilian Economy," which evolved from a graduate seminar on industrial economics in the Department of Industrial and Management Engineering at Columbia
University. During the period 1961 to 1968, government officials, officers of military-industrial
firms, trade union leaders, and officers of engineers' unions--as well as economists, managers, and
engineers with a professional interest in the conversion problem--addressed this seminar. The graduate
engineers in attendance subsequently produced most
of the material included in the series. This volume,
the one exception, was prepared by a team of engineers at Hofstra University under the direction of
John E. Ullmann.

It is my hope that the series will contribute to
the national capability for coping with the varied
and often special problems of conversion. Americans
will increasingly discover that conversion to civilian economy is the indispensable requirement for industrial, technological, and human renewal of the
quality of American life.

This study of the military-electronics industry
and its prospects for entering alternative civilian
markets reflects the strengths and weaknesses of all
military industry.

The strengths include large managerial and engi-
neering-scientific staffs, with varied military product experience; demonstrated capacity for developing
complex electronic systems; a work force that has
been trained for product flexibility; and an array of
large and small firms capable of maintaining product
standards with great division of labor. As a potential candidate for "going civilian," the weaknesses
of the military-electronics industry include engineering talent that has become specialized in serving
the unique needs of the military; a trained

incapacity in many firms for designing and manufacturing for the civilian market as against a "cost is no object" military and NASA customer; and underdeveloped civilian-marketing capability.

The market potentials outlined in this book can only be translated into market and production operations insofar as particular firms develop capability for surmounting the constraints that are traceable to the long military-serving experience. On the marketing side, for example, U.S. military-electronics firms will have to overcome the leads developed by European and Japanese firms that have long specialized in civilian, rather than military, market development.

Many firms will be unable to make the transition to civilian work. Therefore, occupational conversion will pose a problem for many men in this industry. This requires attention to the options described in the section on occupational conversion in the volume, THE DEFENSE ECONOMY, which is part of this Series of of books. Even where managements can succeed in "going civilian," there is no automatic assurance of employment for the oversize engineering and allied staffs that have functioned on behalf of the military.

Given a reduction in the level of military activity, it is reasonable to expect that only the fittest in the military-electronics industry will survive. Professor Ullmann and his associates have a prescription for developing appropriate fitness.

Seymour Melman

PREFACE AND
ACKNOWLEDGMENTS

This volume is intended to measure the internal
capability of the electronics industry to generate
markets that can offset cuts in its current high commitment to defense spending. It demonstrates that
the prospects of making up the entire market are poor
and that, therefore, interindustry transfers of employees and resources may be necessary.

In writing about an industry faced with a market that is subject to political controls (hence unpredictable), and a rapidly changing technology, the
danger is always present that some of the findings
will turn out to be obsolete by the time of publication. We do not expect that this book will be an exception. It is rather our hope that it will be a
modest foundation from which to proceed to more detailed investigations, leading to the formulation of
public policies and conversion plans of individual
firms.

This book results from the continuing series of
graduate seminars conducted by the School of Business
of Hofstra University. Its contributors are largely
engineers or other professional employees of technically oriented firms, some of them major defense contractors. Each student was responsible only for his
own contribution, and the employers of the participants were in no way involved either in the study or
in its conclusions. A first edition of this report
was completed in 1964 and was circulated by Hofstra
University.

Since its publication, there have been several
other reports on the subject, but none of them has
provided the same sort of detailed market-by-market
review. In bringing it once more before the public,
it is the conviction of its authors and editor that
it fulfills a purpose not served by other works. We
have brought statistics up to date, and as a result,
chapters with major statistical components have been

largely rewritten. We have also in each case sought out references to the newest products and embodied these in the various chapters.

Two chapters of the original report, that on the marketing function, by Clarence R. Rydberg, and that on a network model of the conversion process, by James E. Baird, contain material of significance to the conversion process in general rather than only to the electronics industry. For this reason, they have been included in THE DEFENSE ECONOMY, another volume in The Conversion of Industry from a Military to Civilian Economy series.

The original report appeared on the same day that sustained bombing of North Vietnam was started-- hardly a propitious moment to be concerned with conversion. For a time, indeed, it looked as if the word "conversion" might usefully be abandoned and replaced by the World War II term "post-war planning." It is clear, however, that interest in the field remains widespread and that the task of making provision for a hopefully more peaceful future is still being given active consideration.

All of us would like to express our appreciation to the many members of the electronics industry who provided us with information. We are particularly indebted to Malcolm Rowe of Airborne Instruments Laboratory, a division of Cutler-Hammer corporation and to Professor Seymour Melman of Columbia University, who addressed our seminar. Neal A. Irwin and Sheldon Rice of Traffic Research Corporation gave us valuable information on characteristics of traffic control systems. Terence McCarthy, Consulting Economist, and Michael Averko of Electronic News helped us with the financial and market analyses. The Audio-Visual Programming section of Republic Aviation Corporation gave us important cost information on their activities. Our thanks also go to Dr. N. Goldfarb and Mr. L. McKee of the Computer Center of Hofstra University for their assistance with the analysis of the financial data.

We were supported throughout our endeavor by Dr. Harold L. Wattel, Dean of the School of Business. Mrs. Irene Bettum, Mrs. Dorothy Callis, Miss Joyce Frattarole, and Mrs. Gloria Stevenson did splendid service in preparing the manuscript for publication.

We are grateful to John Baima and Stephen Gideon, who did a substantial degree of reworking of their papers, and to several of the other original participants, who, re-evaluated their papers and made suggestions for bringing them up to date. We express our deepest appreciation to John Aloisio, Edward Hoffman, Philip Kantz, Edward Stepina, Alan Thierman and Martin Weiss, who collaborated on the revisions in the various chapters. Dr. George N. Gordon, Director, Communications Center at Hofstra University, gave his most valuable comments on the prospects of instructional devices. Finally, we record our gratitude to Mrs. Adelaide Berg for her able assistance in preparing the manuscript for publication.

We very much regret having to report the death of Mr. Anthony Malito, Jr., the original author of Chapter 2, shortly before this revision was put in hand.

John E. Ullmann

CONTENTS

LIST OF TABLES

LIST OF FIGURES

LIST OF ABBREVIATIONS

ACDA	Arms Control and Disarmament Agency
ADA	Automatic Data Acquisition
AMA	American Medical Association
ASDE	Airport Surface Detection Equipment
AT&T	American Telephone and Telegraph Co.
AUDREY	Audio Reply
CDC	Control Data Corporation
CIA	Central Intelligence Agency
COBOL	Common Business Oriented Language
COMSAT	Communication Satellite Corporation
CRAM	Card Random Access Memory
CRIS	Command Retrieval Information System
CTC	Centralized Traffic Control
DME	Distance Measuring Equipment
DORIS	Direct Order Recording and Invoicing System
ecg or ekg	Electrocardiograph
EDP	Electronic Data Processing
eeg	Electroencephalograph
EVPI	Expected Value of Perfect Information
FAA	Federal Aviation Administration

FCC	Federal Communications System
FORTRAN	Formula Translator
GRACE	Graphic Arts Composing Equipment
IDP	Integrated Data Processing
INTELSAT	International Telecommunications Satellite Consortium
KWIC	Key Word in Context
Medlars	Medical Literature Analysis and Retrieval System
MICR	Magnetic Ink Character Recognition
NSF	National Science Foundation
PCQ	Productivity Criteria Coefficient
RCA	Radio Corporation of America
SIC	Standard Industrial Classification
SMSA	Standard Metropolitan Statistical Area
SPA	System and Procedures Association
TACAN	Tactical Aid to Navigation
TRA Analogue	Traffic Response Average
TRA Digital	Traffic Response Average
TRD Digital	Traffic Response Detailed
UNICORN	Unidensity Coherent Light Recording
VOR	VHF Omnirange

PART **I** THE PRESENT
INDUSTRY

CHAPTER **1** THE NEED
FOR CHANGE

by John E. Ullmann

OBJECTIVES

The rapid growth of the American electronics industry has been one of the most prominent economic
developments of the last twenty years. From a relatively small industry, in which a few consumer items
accounted for much of the volume, it had grown by
1968 to annual sales of almost $14 billion, with more
than a million employees. The securities of its companies are sometimes known as "glamour stocks," although a term commonly used before 1962, i.e.,
"growth stocks" is heard less frequently these days,
and with good reason. In the course of its rapid
growth, the industry has come to depend more and more
on defense and allied markets and thus has become affected by changing patterns in the nation's military
involvements and resultant emphasis of other kinds of
defense expenditures. In an industry which has been
growing rapidly, even the prospect of reduced growth
rates is a disturbing one; when perhaps 60 percent
or more of the total industry volume is involved, a
search for alternatives is essential. In view of
the importance of the industry to the economy and
its current preemption of a large share of the nation's inventive genius, it is appropriate to inquire
into its capabilities for conversion to nondefense
products.

Such an inquiry must attempt to answer two principal questions:

1. What increases in nondefense markets can be
expected from a continuation of past trends in those
areas depending mainly on private initiative?

2. What increases in nondefense markets can be
stimulated by increased governmental support of

3

research and development, procurement, or a combination of them?

The total of these two new sources of market
growth is an indicator of what can be done in converting the industry within the constraints of its
present general characteristics both in manpower and
production facilities. If these projected volumes
are insufficient to replace the present market commitments to defense electronics, the solution of the
conversion problem would require inter-industry rather than intra-industry transfers, a much more complex
problem in planning and execution.

It is the central hypothesis of this report that
this is the case. Plausible increases in nondefense
markets now in prospect or capable of being stimulated under "forced draft" will be shown to be insufficient to make up for a sharp cutback in defense
procurement. The realignment required of the industry in these circumstances is thus likely to be a
critical challenge not only to the firms involved,
but to the economy as a whole.

THE GENERAL ISSUE OF CONVERSION

Until recently, conversion of defense industries was regarded by many as an exercise in economic speculation, of importance only in the event of
agreement on general and complete disarmament. Since
this possibility was widely held to be remote, little
effort developed even at the academic level to come
to grips with the subject in modern terms. Managements of the firms concerned held aloof almost without exception, for in an environment of sharply
rising defense budgets and increasing shares of electronics within the procurement sector, there appeared
to be little to worry about.

A hiatus in defense procurement, accompanied by
the closing of a substantial number of military bases
during the period 1963-1964, followed by the escalation of the Vietnam war, which shifted the nature of
defense procurement, all served to change this view.
A series of studies was put in hand under the aus-
pices of the U.S. Arms Control and Disarmament Agency
(ACDA), which clearly indicated that even the limited
dislocation caused by these developments had a considerable impact on firms and communities. For

example, the post-layoff experiences of the workers
of the then Republic Aviation Corp. (now part of
Fairchild-Hiller) showed extensive misery, public
callousness, and long-term unemployment.[1]

Another study looked into the experiences of
firms that had tried to diversify and found a mixed
bag of results; in general, the top managements of
all but a few firms gave lukewarm support to such
projects, and several of them foundered as a result.[2]
Other studies limit themselves to identifying the requirements for successful conversion and concentrate
on quantifying the impact of various rates or modes
of defense cutbacks on the defense industry. There
have been two major studies of the electronic industry which take this approach.[3] Through the latter,
especially, there runs the understanding that much
of any cut would be made up by other defense-related
projects.[4] Whether or not this is realistic
is, of course, impossible to forecast. We can, as
noted at the outset, estimate the industry's capability of generating internal commercial-industrial
growth, which will balance some of the cutbacks.
Beyond that, we make no attempt to forecast what will
happen.

PLAN OF THE STUDY

The present study is divided into two main parts.
The first part gives an overview of the industry in
its present state. First a chapter analyzes its
structure; then its production facilities, problems,
and its product design practices are reviewed. This
is followed by a financial analysis of the principal
firms in the industry, designed to assay their changing profitability over time.

The second part of the study is the major market
analysis. It defines the problems and considers predictions of markets based on a variety of economic
interpretations. In effect, it delineates the
limits of natural growth. This is followed by an
identification of those products in which government
intervention in the form of research support or procurement could effectively stimulate additional market potential. The former products are mainly those
associated with automation; accordingly, four chapters deal with the possible systems for the automation of offices, distribution, processes, and the

manufacture of piece parts. The areas in which
government intervention would be essential for meaningful market breakthroughs are controls for road,
rail and air traffic, communication systems, education, library systems, medical diagnostic and monitoring devices, and medical prosthetics.

The summary then spells out the total effects
on the industry's volume and establishes the implications for employment as well as managements.

THE REQUIREMENTS OF A MARKET STUDY

The second part of this study deals with twelve
different classes of products in the nondefense sector which are considered to have generally favorable
prospects as objectives in a conversion effort.
These items fall into the two broad categories of industrial and commercial products on the one hand, and
consumer products on the other.

It is, however, also necessary to distinguish
between two types of demand: that due to natural
growth and that capable of stimulation by the public
sector. The first type of demand is encountered
largely in the area of automation equipment and consumer products. Stimulated demand is to be found in
communications, aircraft and marine equipment, and
medical electronics, in which either legal requirements are controlling or in which public support is
an accomplished fact or growing in importance.

The market for technical products has always
had a very strong economic component. Technical
products are frequently sold to a clientele with considerable technical sophistication, able to judge for
itself analytically what the product is likely to be
worth in its operations.

At the consumer level also, competitive pressures have tended to introduce economic factors as a
determinant of product design. An extensive treatment of the criteria of change in the design of industrial products appears in a previous study by the
author.[5] An evaluation of the design history of several industrial products showed that most design
changes were cost saving. Similar results were obtained in a later study of automotive safety devices
which are, in essence, consumer products.[6] The

criterion of success, in short, is the ability of a
new product to perform a certain function at lower
cost than an incumbent product, with other characteristics of the performance being equal.

It is, of course, recognized that this may at
times oversimplify matters. However, the defense
electronics industry would only be guilty of dangerous complacency if it were to assume that any demon-
strable higher quality or reliability of its product
would be salable unless it actually produces a demon-
strable advantage to the prospective user.

To perform such a cost analysis for a product
would require, first of all, the identification of
its function and the assignment of values to these
functions, perhaps on the basis of weighting of some
kind, but preferably on a common cost basis. An analysis of a new product then would have to compare the
cost of fulfilling the purposes of the product by the
new and the old methods. In this way, it is speedily
demonstrated whether or not the new product can mount
a significant challenge to the present products. The
concept of cost per unit of performance has been
found to be useful as a predictor of shifts in the
utilization of raw materials and processes as well as
finished products.[7]

Such studies for the multiplicity of products
that would be involved in converting the defense
electronics industry are clearly beyond the scope of
the present report, although they would have to be
made in detailed market studies. However, throughout
the market analysis, a concerted attempt has been
made to examine the cost parameters of new products.

This is a requirement, because the existence of
other ways of performing a given task in effect con-
strains the permissible cost of the new electronic
product. To use a simple example from Chapter 6, the
allowable cost of a system for shopping by closed circuit television is limited by the cost of a good mail-
order catalogue. Under these conditions, it then
becomes possible to make estimates of the worth of
having a certain function performed, even if the products involved do not yet exist.

A second major issue in the conduct of the market analyses of this report lies in where to draw
the line between feasible and nonfeasible products
in the time generally considered appropriate here,

that is, the next five to ten years. This is an important issue, because in the electronic industry, as in many others, growth has traditionally depended on new products. It follows from this that if certain new products are ignored in the market studies or, on the other hand, their prospects overestimated, grave errors are the result. This is probably unavoidable, and the authors of this report make no claims of infallibility. Nevertheless, there are cases in which it is possible to draw the line.

When a product, for example, obviously meets only one part of a problem which it was designed to solve and makes others worse, its prospects must be regarded unfavorably. As the result of such an evaluation, for example, electronic highways were discarded as a feasible product. It might, of course, be possible to build such an installation, but its usefulness can only be regarded with reserve. An electronic highway, as conceived by its proponents, would enable the motorist or truck driver to set his vehicle on "automatic pilot." It would then be guided both with respect to direction and proximity to other vehicles by various electronic systems installed partly on the road and partly on the vehicle.

At first, of course, this sounds attractive; however, this system must be viewed against broader issues of transportation planning. First, it is doubtful if even the most optimistic electronic engineer would view the reliability of his product so highly that he would recommend the abolition of the driver altogether and leaving the control of the vehicle entirely to automation. Thus far, this has not even been done for railroads in which the technology is infinitely simpler. Without eliminating the driver, a major incentive for such a system is gone, and the relatively wasteful utilization of manpower in road traffic continues. Even the present simple automatic aids to driving have aroused the concern of automotive-safety experts because they reduce the need of the driver to pay attention to the driving situation.

Secondly, another major problem in road traffic is the greater usage of fuel (about three times that for rail). Obviously, a guidance system makes no contribution to the solution of the problem nor does it reduce air pollution. It also does nothing to eliminate the great space requirements of modern roads and the resultant squeeze on urban and

suburban land.   Indeed, to the extent that the electronic highway would encourage more automobile traffic, it would make all these conditions much worse.
This case has been discussed in some detail here because it symbolizes a type of projection of electronic progress which can only be regarded as
unrealistic. Of course, none of this rules out substantial new markets for electronics in fields as yet
unkown or dimly discerned; we shall consider some of
these in the final chapter.

LIMITATIONS

    The approach to the problem set forth in this
chapter and particularly in the last section necessarily leaves some problems unanswered. The first
limitation concerns regional impacts of the industry..
Pending the release of authoritative data on industry
distribution by the 1963 Census of Manufactures, data
on industrial location of the industry are too frag-
mentary for any but the most cursory examinations.
Further, the smaller the geographic subdivision for
which the impact is to be studied, the more the
problem becomes one of specific firms and communities. This type of analysis is beyond the present
scope of the study. However, it is considered in
proposals for further work included in the summary
chapter.

    The second limitation also results from the con-
cern of this study with macroeconomic rather than
microeconomic phenomena. On the basis of a study
largely based on limited interviews and the published
literature, one cannot examine the capabilities and
motivations of individual managements or aggregations
of workers. Put another way, there is no method by
which one can predict that a given firm is able or
willing to take advantage of the business opportunities described here or to further their potential
by forceful advocacy of suitable government action.

    Such studies, of course, must ultimately be
made on behalf of those charged with the support of
such firms as continuing enterprises, whether they
be potential customers, the bankers, or other financial supporters of the firm or government agencies
awarding contracts in the nondefense field. Again,
proposals for further work of this kind are included
in the final chapter. In an environment in which

conversion with limited dislocation will be possible
for only a few firms, clearly the race belongs to the
swift. Managerial capabilities for such determined
action are likely to become the principal determinants of corporate survival.

NOTES

1. U.S. Arms Control and Disarmament Agency,
Post Layoff Experiences of Republic Aviation Workers
(Washington, D.C., 1966); see especially pp. 69-82.

2. U.S. Arms Control and Disarmament Agency,
Defense Industry Diversification (Washington, D.C.,
1966).

3. U.S. Arms Control and Disarmament Agency,
The Implications of Reduced Defense Demand for the
Electronics Industry, (Washington, D.C., 1965).

4. Electronics Industries Association, Requirements Committee, The Post Vietnam Defense and Space
Market Environment (Washington, D.C., 1968) 2 Vols.

5. John E. Ullmann, Criteria of Change in Machinery Design (doctoral dissertation, Columbia University, January 1959).

6. John E. Ullmann, "Some Economic Aspects of
Automobile Safety Devices," Passenger Car Design and
Highway Safety (Mt. Vernon, N.Y.: Association for the
Aid of Crippled Children and Consumers Union of U.S.,
Inc., 1962), pp. 248-264.

7. John E. Ullmann, Criteria of Change in Machinery Design.

CHAPTER **2** CHARACTERISTICS
OF THE
ELECTRONICS
INDUSTRY

by Anthony E. Malito, Jr.

INTRODUCTION

The electronics industry is engaged in "that
branch of science and technology which deals with
the study and application of techniques to direct
and control the condition of electricity in a gas,
vacuum, liquid or solid-state material. Electron
tubes and semi-conductors are combined with resistors,
capacitors, transformers and similar components in
equipments which detect, measure, record, compute
and communicate information."[1]

The industry serves four major markets: military and space products, industrial and commercial
products, consumer products, and components. The
latter in turn may be divided into items installed
in original equipment and spare parts. Originally
installed components are properly part of their end-
use categories, but, unfortunately, not all data
sources make this secondary distribution.

In this chapter, the structure and pattern of
change is first discussed followed by an examination
of the firms and establishments of the industry,
their organization, and size distribution. Lastly,
there is an analysis of the employment patterns of
the industry and of its geographic distribution.

At the present time, the task of arriving at
meaningful industry data is handicapped to some extent by the rather poor coverage which the industry
as an entity has had in the past, in the Census of
Manufactures and elsewhere. As shown in Table 2.1,
there are seven four-digit industries in the Standard Industrial Classification (SIC) of 1958 with

11

TABLE 2.1

Major Electronic Industries, 1958

SIC four-digit industries with at least $25 million in electronics shipments each and with electronics shipments representing half or more of the value of total shipments.

Industry number	Industry title
3651	Radio and television receiving sets, except communication types.
3652	Phonograph records[a]
3662	Radio and television transmitting, signaling, and detection equipment and apparatus
3671	Radio and television receiving type electron tubes, except cathode ray
3672	Cathode ray picture tubes
3673	Transmitting, industrial, and special purpose electron tubes
3679	Electronic components and accessories, not elsewhere classified

SIC four-digit industries with at least $25 million in electronics shipments each, and with electronics shipments representing less than half of the value of total shipments.

Industry number	Industry title
1925[b]	Guided missiles, complete
3571	Computing and accounting machines, including cash registers
3611	Electric measuring instruments and test equipment
3622	Industrial controls
3661	Telephone and telegraph apparatus
3693	Radiographic X-ray, fluoroscopic X-ray, therapeutic X-ray, and other X-ray apparatus and tubes
3721	Aircraft
3722	Aircraft engines and engine parts
3729	Aircraft parts and auxiliary equipment, not elsewhere classified
3811	Engineering, laboratory, and scientific and research instruments and associated equipment
3821	Mechanical measuring and controlling instruments, except automatic temperature controls
3842	Orthopedic, prosthetic, and surgical appliances and supplies
3931	Musical instruments and parts

[a]Phonograph records are not uniformly considered to be an electronic product. They are treated as electronic in this report chiefly because the shipments estimates of the report are based upon figures of the Electronic Industries Association, which include phonograph records.

[b]This industry is a special Census grouping and is part of SIC Industry Number 1929--Ammunition, not elsewhere classified.

Source: U.S. Bureau of Labor Statistics, Employment Outlook and Changing Occupational Structure in Electronics Manufacturing, Bulletin 1363 (November, 1963), p. 46.

more than $25 million in electronics in which elec-
tronic shipments made up more than half of the
shipments of the industry. There are a further
thirteen industries in which electronic shipments
were more than $25 million in 1958 but less than
half of the total of each industry. Even though
this information may be obsolete with respect to
some of the figures, qualitatively the situation
is still as shown.

MARKET STRUCTURE

The electronics industry has four major sectors:
military-space, industrial-commercial, consumer products and components. Since the only independent
part of component sales is for spares for other products, just the first three sectors merit detailed
discussion. The military-space sector is by far
the most important one, in sales as well as in employment.

As shown in Table 2.2, there has been impressive growth in all sectors except component parts.
Consumer products have more than tripled in volume
since 1955. Industrial products increased 7.3 times
in that period, and government products almost qua-
drupled. In fact, since 1952 there has been a virtually unbroken exponential rate of change in all
these sectors, with great regularity, as shown in
the following tabulation of compound growth rates
and coefficients of correlation computed from
Table 2.2:

Sector	Growth rate 1952-1968 Percent per annum	Coefficient of Correlation, r
Consumer	9.0	0.9673
Industrial	17.3	0.9928
Government	10.2	0.9878
Total	10.8	0.9960

As to changes in the relative shares of its
principal components, the electronics industry has
recorded some rather interesting trends. First,
consumer products had a long relative decline from

TABLE 2.2

Industry Summary of Factory Sales by Selected Years, 1950–1968

(In Millions of Dollars)

Year	Consumer Products	Industrial Products	Government Products	Replacement Components	Total
1950	1,500	$ 350	655	$200	2,705
1951	1,400	450	1,193	270	3,313
1952	1,300	500	3,100	310	5,210
1953	1,400	600	3,230	370	5,600
1954	1,400	650	3,100	470	5,620
1955	1,500	750	3,332	525	6,107
1956	1,600	950	3,595	570	6,715
1957	1,805	1,300	4,130	610	7,845
1958	1,660	1,405	4,725	475	8,265
1959	2,002	1,676	5,373	530	9,581
1960	2,018	1,980	6,124	555	10,677
1961	2,020	2,585	7,190	580	12,375
1962	2,435	2,915	8,080	620	14,050
1963	2,604	3,325	8,841	590	15,360
1964	2,940	3,568	8,775	620	15,903
1965	3,658	4,265	8,969	630	17,522
1966	4,574	4,949	10,132	640	20,295
1967 est	4,700	5,100	12,100	600	22,500
1968 est	4,700	5,500	12,700	600	23,800

14

Percentage of Total Electronics Shipments

Year	Consumer Products	Industrial Products	Government Products	Replacement Components	Total
1950	55.5	12.9	24.2	7.4	100.0
1951	42.3	13.6	36.0	8.1	100.0
1952	24.9	9.6	59.6	5.9	100.0
1953	25.0	10.7	57.7	6.6	100.0
1954	24.9	11.6	55.2	8.3	100.0
1955	24.6	12.3	54.5	8.6	100.0
1956	23.9	14.2	53.4	8.5	100.0
1957	23.0	16.6	52.6	7.8	100.0
1958	20.1	17.0	57.2	5.7	100.0
1959	20.9	17.5	56.1	5.5	100.0
1960	18.9	18.5	57.4	5.2	100.0
1961	16.3	20.9	58.1	4.7	100.0
1962	17.3	20.7	57.6	4.4	100.0
1963	17.0	21.6	57.6	3.8	100.0
1964	18.4	22.4	55.3	3.9	100.0
1965	20.9	24.3	51.2	3.6	100.0
1966	22.6	24.4	49.9	3.1	100.0
1967	20.9	22.7	53.7	2.7	100.0
1968	21.0	23.1	53.4	2.5	100.0

Source: Electronic Industries Yearbook 1967 (Washington, D.C., 1967), p. 92. Letter from EIA (Mar. 29, 1968).

15

1950 and reduced its share till 1961. Since that
time there has been some recovery so that, taking the
period 1958-1968 as a whole, one can say that the
share has remained fairly stable. Industrial products have recorded the biggest relative advance, although here too, there is evidence of stability within
the past five years. Government products hit a peak
in 1961 and have generally declined since. The small
upswing in the last two years is mainly a reflection
of Vietnam demand. As expected from their stagnant
overall volume, the share of component parts had declined steadily since 1954.

The foregoing data cannot be accepted as a full
description of the dependence of the electronics industry on government business, because many industrial-commercial products, notably instruments and
computers, have important and at times sole markets
in the Department of Defense, NASA, and other security-connected agencies. Even if the products are not
sold directly to these agencies, their main markets
may lie with prime contractors. The result is an
understatement of the market. On the other hand,
there is a small market in government agencies that
are not security-connected, such as the Federal Aviation Administration (FAA). This is included in the
government sector and would thus tend to overstate
the military market.

A breakdown of the government market in electronics is given in Table 2.3. Virtually all of it,
as noted, is security-connected, except for a small
portion of the communications field. Within the last
five years, missiles have lost some of their previous
dominance in the field, by declining from 22.5 to 12.9
percent of the total. Aircraft which had for years
given ground to missiles in this market declined considerably less, as the need for them increased in the
Vietnam war. The share of space has markedly increased, although by 1968 this field reached a limit.
The prospect of nonmilitary space markets is thus
rather clouded at present.

In the industrial-commercial market, computers
have been the leading growth area. As indicated in
Table 2.4, the market share of computers in the industrial commercial market rose more than fourfold in
1955-1966 and accounted for almost one eighth of the
total electronics market. These figures actually
understate the full impact of computers because a
portion of the market is represented by equipment

rentals, although usually equivalent sales value is counted. Digital computers are by far the biggest sellers, with major users being banks, utilities, and insurance companies.

The communications share of the industrial market has also shown increases since 1955. Commercial sound equipment and land-mobile radio head the list of products.

The shares of the other market segments have declined considerably, although, of course, there have been considerable absolute increases. Test and measurement include instrumentation, of which some 75 percent is used by the electronics industry itself, the rest being largely sold to communications companies and research laboratories.

Industrial controls are used by manufacturing firms in most manufacturing industries, utilities, and in such fields as traffic control and local government. The aircraft and marine equipment is used by aircraft manufacturers, shipbuilders, airports, and harbor authorities. Medical and therapeutic products in turn are used by hospitals, physicians, laboratories, and universities. Hearing aids, a major segment of this market, are virtually consumer products, although usually prescribed through physicians.[2]

A more detailed analysis of the markets is given in Table 2.5. It is clear that in some of the major segments there are individual products which dominate the field. For example, in data processing, digital computers account for 76.8 percent of the market. In medical electronics, X-ray equipment and hearing aids, between them, account for 76.8 percent of that sector. Aircraft requirements are greater than marine needs by a factor of 6.25. The markets for communications, tests and measurements, and industrial controls are more fragmented with rather less dominance of any single component.

A detailed examination of the industrial sector, however, yields the finding that many of the market components are heavily dominated by the government sector, mainly because commercial products may be bought by government directly or at one remove through government contractors.

TABLE 2.3

Market Sectors in Government Electronics, 1962 and 1966[a]

Item	Volume $ million		Percent of total government		Percent of total electronics	
	1962	1966	1962	1966	1962	1966
Missiles	3,146	2,630	40.4	25.5	22.5	12.9
Aircraft	1,570	1,844	20.2	17.9	11.2	9.6
Ships	333	498	4.3	4.8	2.4	2.4
Communications	1,300	2,152	16.7	20.9	9.3	10.0
Surveillance	835	744	10.7	7.2	6.0	3.7
Space	607	2,435	7.8	23.7	4.3	12.0
	7,791	10,303	100.0	100.0	55.7	50.6

[a]Government sectors largely DOD, NASA, and other security-connected agencies.

Source: Electronic Industry Marketing and Distribution Chart, Electronic News (1962 ed.).

TABLE 2.4

Industrial Electronics

A. Size of the segments of the industrial electronics market in millions of dollars, 1955, 1959, 1962, and 1966.

Market segment	1955	1959	1962	1966	Percent increase 1962-1966
Communications	95	365	580	715	23.3
Computers	72	360	1,290	2,520	93.8
Test and measurement	145	315	365	569	56.4
Industrial controls	85	200	240	416	77.7
Aircraft and marine	65	180	145	276	90.3
Medical and therapeutic	110	165	215	307	42.8
Total	572	1,585	2,835	4,803	69.4

B. Size of the segments of the industrial electronics market as a percent of the total, 1955, 1959, 1962, and 1966.

Market segment	1955	1959	1962	1966
Communications	16.6	23.0	20.5	14.8
Computers	12.6	22.7	45.5	52.4
Test and measurement	25.4	19.9	12.9	11.8
Industrial controls	14.8	12.6	8.5	8.6
Aircraft and marine	11.4	11.4	5.1	5.7
Medical and therapeutic	19.2	10.4	7.6	6.7
Total	100.0	100.0	100.0	100.0

C. Size of the segments of the industrial electronics market as a percent of total electronics sales, 1955, 1959, 1962, and 1966.

Market segment	1955	1959	1962	1966
Communications	1.6	3.8	4.2	3.5
Computers	1.2	3.7	9.2	12.3
Test and measurement	2.4	3.3	2.6	2.8
Industrial controls	1.4	2.1	1.7	2.1
Aircraft and marine	1.1	1.8	1.0	1.4
Medical and therapeutic	1.9	1.7	1.5	1.5
Total industrial percent of electronics market	9.6	16.4	20.4	23.6

Source: Electronic Industry Marketing and Distribution Chart, Electronic News (1962; 1966 eds.).

TABLE 2.5

Details of Industrial and Commercial
Electronics Market, 1962 and 1966

Item	Shipments $ millions		Subtotals $ millions	
	1962	1966	1962	1966
Total, industrial and commercial			2,695	
Data processing			1,290	2,520
Digital computers	960	1,250		
Analog computers	30	70		
Peripheral equipment	300	1,200		
Magnetic tape units	100	180		
Memory and data storage units, external	50	220		
Printers	40	185		
Punched-card-reader and punch units	17	60		
Paper-tape-reader and punch units	8	25		
Data transmission and collection equipment	20	160		
Character and code sensing units	9	45		
Visual display devices and plotters	3	55		
A-to-D and D-to-A converters	32	120		
Other	21	30		
Communications			447	715
Land mobile	130	170		
Microwave	75	75		
Telemetry	35	125		
Facsimile	6	16		
Radio relay	25			
Closed circuit TV	6	12		
Commercial Sound	110	165		
Intercoms	40	90		
Theater	20	35		
Other	50	40		
Broadcast equipment	60	152		
FM transmitters	5	11		
AM transmitters	3	13		

Item	Shipments $ millions		Subtotals $ millions	
	1962	1966	1962	1966
TV Transmitters	10	12		
TV cameras	20	25		
Other broadcast equipment	22	59		
Test and measurements			373	125
Oscilloscopes	65	110		
Ultrasonic test	6			
Signal generators	35			
Spectrum analyzers	10			
Microwave test	25			
Analyzers (engine testing)	25			
Calibrators	21			
Voltage, current, and power meters	15			
Bridge and decades	10			
Instrument panel meters	20			
Frequency meters and counters	50			
Spectrometers	18	16		
Digital voltmeters	15	25		
Components testers (Tubes, semiconductors, etc.)	18	23		
Radiation detection instruments	40	50		
Monitoring instruments	5			
Portable instruments	7			
Count-rate meters	2	30		
Power supplies	7	50		
Pulse height analyzers	4			
Amplifiers	4			
Dosimeters	4			
Other	7	30		
Industrial controls			225	416
Numerical controls	30	55		
Ultrasonic controls	8	10		
Ultrasonic cleaning	10	11		

(continued)

TABLE 2.5 (continued)

Item	Shipments $ millions		Subtotals $ millions	
	1962	1966	1962	1966
Infrared controls	25	33		
Infrared ovens	20	20		
Closed circuit TV	10	20		
Railroad traffic controls	6	9		
Vehicular traffic controls	15	25		
Photoelectric controls	7	11		
Industrial X-Ray	12	21		
Nuclear reactor controls	30	25		
Remote controls	40	16		
Other miscellaneous controls	12	20		
Aircraft and marine			145	276
Aircraft	125	237		
Communications	45	88		
Navigation	25	47		
Test equipment	10	15		
Radar	12	7		
Flight control	13	33		
Other	20	28		
Marine	20	39		
Radiotelephones	8	16.5		
Depth sounders	4	5		
Radar	3	7		
Automatic pilots	1	2		
Direction finders	2	2.5		
Loran	1	3		
Other	1	3		
Medical			215	307
X-Ray equipment and accessories	110	150		
Hearing aids	55	50		
Electro-cardiographs	8	14		
Electro-encephalo-graphs	4	4		
Electro-myographs	1	1		
Electron microscopes	6	8		
Ultrasonic devices (Cleaning & therapeutic)	6	6		

Item	Shipments $ millions		Subtotals $ millions	
	1962	1966	1962	1966
Oscillographs and Oscilloscopes	5			
Closed circuit TV	3	3		
Other standard and custom equipment	17	25		
Lasers		1		

Source: Electronics Marketing and Distribution Chart, Electronic News (1962).

TABLE 2.6

The Market for Consumer Electronics

A. Size of the segments of the consumer electronics market in dollars (millions), 1955, 1959, 1962, and 1966

Market segment	1955	1959	1962	1966	% increase from 1962
Television	1,091	850	1,045	2,642	152.8
Consumer electronics equipment	146	720	1020	1375	34.8
Radio	283	430	493	563	14.2
Total	1,500	2,100	2,558	4,580	80.0

B. Size of the segments of the consumer electronics market as a percent of the total, 1955, 1959, 1962, and 1966

Market segment	1955	1959	1962	1966
Television	71.6	42.5	40.9	57.7
Consumer electronics equipment	9.8	36.0	39.8	30.0
Radio	18.6	21.5	19.3	12.3
Total	100.0	100.0	100.0	100.0

C. Size of the segments of the consumer electronics market as a percent of total electronics sales, 1955, 1959, 1962, and 1966

Market segment	1955	1959	1962	1966
Television	18.0	8.7	7.5	13.0
Consumer electronics equipment	2.5	7.4	7.3	6.7
Radio	4.8	4.4	3.5	2.8
Total consumer share of electronics market	25.3	20.5	18.3	22.5

Source: Electronic Industry Marketing and Distribution Chart, Electronic News (1962, 1967).

TABLE 2.7

Details of Consumer Electronics Market,
1962 and 1966

Item	Shipments $ millions		Subtotals $ millions	
	1962	1966	1962	1966
Total all consumer electronics			2,558	4,580
Television			1,045	2,642
Monochrome	930	781		
Color	115	1861		
Radio			493	563
Auto radios	174	267		
Portable radios	108	160		
Transistors	95	n.a.		
Other	13	n.a.		
Table radios	63			
Clock radios	56			
Amateur equipment	30	25		
Citizens Band radio	62	40		
Other			1,020	1,375
Tape recorders	80	112		
Electronic organs	120	120		
Records	260	370		
Phonographs	430	528		
Electronic toys	10	10		
Hi-Fi components	70	52		
Amplifiers	15	17		
Speakers	12	18		
Tuners	13	17		
Other	30	133		
Electronic kits	50	50		
Total, all consumer electronics			2,558	4,580

Source: Electronics Marketing and Distribution
Chart, Electronic News (1962, 1966).

TABLE 2.8

International Trading Account of the
U.S. Electronics Industry, 1961 and 1966

Item	Imports Amount (millions)		Percent		Exports Amount (millions)		Percent	
Military	---	---	---	---	257.9	895.5	41.9	65.0
Industrial	17.3	216.0	9.7	29.7	104.6		17.1	
Consumer	147.7	298.9	82.3	41.1	81.4	46.3	13.4	3.0
Components	14.3	212.9	8.0	29.2	169.0	440.4	27.6	32.0
Total	179.3	727.8	100.0	100.0	612.9	1382.2	100.0	100.0

Source: Electronics Industries Association, 1962 Yearbook, (Washington, D.C., 1962) p. 1; 1967 Yearbook, p. 64-65.

26

Three sectors are particularly affected: data processing, test and measurements, and industrial controls. Much of the early work on digital computers was done on behalf of the government, and although the government and its major contractors have now completed much of their computerization, there is still considerable support for new installations, especially the more complex ones, such as a national data bank which has been the cause of concern on libertarian grounds.

In test and measurements, it is clear that a major indirect government market is involved. For example, microwave test instruments had a $25 million market in 1962, whereas civilian microwave equipment had sales of only $75 million. Obviously, a major part of the test instruments must have gone to military microwave in which the markets were enormously greater. In industrial controls, there has been major government procurement of numerically controlled machines, especially the contouring type. Unfortunately, there are no complete estimates of the error that would be introduced here by taking the total industrial market at its face value.

The last major sector comprising finished products is that of consumer items. As shown in Table 2.6, this group has three major components: television, radio, and other consumer products, such as phonographs, stereo, tape recorders, electronic musical instruments, etc. The group as a whole has recorded sizeable gains in relation to the rest of the industry, but its share declined for a number of years. The fact that this trend has been reversed is due very largely to color television, a fact which is illustrated even more strongly in Table 2.7, which gives greater breakdowns of the market. Between 1962 and 1966, for example, monochrome television declined in sales volume by 16 percent while color television increased 16.2 _times_, the most impressive growth of any component of the electronics industry. The inclusion of records in statistics on this sector is sometimes criticized, because the electronic content of the industry is small compared with plastics technology, packaging, and, of course, its artistic component. If they are excluded, the volume has to be reduced by 7.5 percent on 1966 volume. The radio market continues to be dominated by the portables (other kinds have declined in value recently), and although these score impressive gains in numbers of units, their value per unit continues to decline so

their overall share of the market has also shown a
drop (See Table 2.6, part C).

The electronics industry also has an important
part in international trade. As shown in Table 2.8,
the trade balance is favorable. This tabulation,
however, is subject to certain important qualifica-
tions. According to the Electronics Industry Association:

> Significant quantities of electronic
> imports are included in nonelectric
> product categories in governmental
> data. Therefore, the import figures
> in Table 2.8 are understated. Fur-
> ther, U.S. electronic firms have
> established many plants abroad dur-
> ing recent years, and this invest-
> ment is an import item in our
> balance of payments. Official ex-
> port statistics understate our total
> electronic export activity because
> they do not reflect the electronic
> equipment incorporated in major
> weapons systems included in our large
> military assistance programs, the
> substantial revenue U.S. firms de-
> rive in the form of license payments
> for their export of electronic know-
> how, or profits from the overseas
> operations of U.S. firms.[3]

Thus, in 1961, an estimated 41.9 percent of
American exports were military in nature. Although
later data are unavailable and military, commercial,
and industrial items are now listed together, the
proportion is still great. However, as the table
shows, imports and exports both grew impressively
in the period 1961-1966. Consumer products, especially radios, dominate imports, as do transistors
among components. Japan and Hong Kong are principal suppliers of these. The American industry
does a sizeable business in industrial equipment,
with one third of the military, industrial, and
commercial sector consisting of computers. Most of
the noncommunist industrial countries are customers
for these. The growth of the electronics industry
abroad and its competitive strength are illustrated
by the changing ratio of exports to imports, which
was 3.3 in 1961 and had declined to 1.9 in 1966.
Imports increased 4.0 times and exports 2.2 times in

that period. An increase in both import and export trade, coupled with a declining (and from the viewpoint of balance of payments, worsening) ratio between the two, is a common feature of many American products.[4]

THE FIRMS IN THE INDUSTRY

The following discussion of the firms in the industry is largely based on some rather early data. It still is germane, however; in fact, the merger and concentration movement has only picked up speed in the last few years. The electronics industry consists of about 10,000 firms, including a significant number of small firms as well as some of the nation's largest. At the top of the size pyramid may be found such firms as General Electric, Radio Corporation of America, and International Business Machines Corporation. All of these, however, also produce a good deal of nonelectronic equipment, such as nonelectronic appliances, industrial equipment, and office machines.

The firms in the electronics industry cover a considerable range of sizes, but in all of the significant components of the industry there are firms in the largest category, that is, with 2,500 or more employees. As shown in Table 2.9, in most categories the largest firms exceed 10 percent of the total. Many of these are multi-product and multi-plant companies so that there is considerable overlapping among the industries listed, especially in the larger firms. Of course, small business has long been active in the electronics industry. Men with good ideas have set up smaller firms and have successfully gone into the business of making subsystems and components. As shown in the table, these firms are also numerous. Indeed, with one exception, the firms with less than fifty employees are by far the most numerous. This reverse-J distribution is, of course, what is to be expected in the size distribution of most industries. The role of the smaller companies cannot however, obscure the fact that there is a high degree of concentration in the various parts of the industry. These are usually measured by concentration ratios, which are defined as the percentage of value of shipments accounted for by a specified number of the largest companies of the industry.

TABLE 2.9

Size Distribution of Companies in the
Non-defense Electronics Industry, 1958

SIC four-digit industries with at least $25 million in electronics shipments each, and with electronics shipments representing half or more of the value of total shipments (1958 data).

Industry number	Industry title	Total	Number of employees						
			1-49	50-99	100-249	250-499	500-999	1000-2499	2500+
			Number of companies						
3651	Radio and television receiving sets, except communication types	138	75	19	14	7	4	12	7
3652	Phonograph records	85	64	10	4	2	2	1	2
3662	Radio and television transmitting, signaling, and detection equipment and apparatus	472	304	40	35	15	19	15	44
3671	Radio and television receiving type electron tubes, except cathode ray	71	54	6	-	2	-	1	8
3672	Cathode ray picture tubes	72	54	8	1	1	1	-	7
3673	Transmitting, industrial, and special purpose electron tubes	40	11	4	3	3	2	4	13
3679	Electronic components and accessories, not else-where classified	1348	942	156	112	44	23	31	40

SIC four-digit industries with at least $25 million in electronics shipments each, and with electronics shipments representing less than half of the value of total shipments (1958 data).

Industry number	Industry title	Total	Number of employees						
			1-49	50-99	100-249	250-499	500-999	1000-2499	2500+
			Number of companies						
3571	Computing and accounting machines, including cash registers	119	74	6	3	7	6	5	18
3611	Electric measuring instruments and test equipment	476	357	30	34	11	10	12	22
3622	Industrial controls	205	155	15	11	6	2	3	13
3661	Telephone and telegraph apparatus	67	45	6	4	1	2	3	6
3693	Radiographic X-ray, fluoroscopic X-ray, therapeutic X-ray, and other X-ray apparatus and tubes	124	106	5	5	1	2	1	4
3811	Engineering, laboratory, and scientific and research instruments and associated equipment	542	435	33	26	14	9	5	20
3821	Mechanical measuring and controlling instruments, except automatic temperature controls	586	452	41	34	18	11	13	17

(continued)

TABLE 2.9 (continued)

SIC four-digit industries with at least $25 million in electronics shipments each, and with electronics shipments representing less than half of the value of total shipments (1958 data).

Industry number	Industry title	Number of employees							
		Total	1- 49	50- 99	100- 249	250- 499	500- 999	1000- 2499	2500+
					Number of companies				
3842	Orthopedic, prosthetic, and surgical appliances and supplies	553	471	33	22	11	6	4	6
3931	Musical instruments and parts	253	191	24	20	11	3	4	-

Source: U.S. Bureau of the Census, Concentration Ratios in Manufacturing Industry 1958 (Washington, D.C.: U.S. Government Printing Office, 1962), Table 6.

The results for the industries and product classes mostly affected by electronics are given in Table 2.10. It should be observed that, in most categories, the largest 50 firms account for most if not substantially all of the value of shipments. The four largest companies in most industries generally account for 40 percent or more of the shipments, again with few exceptions. Further, in an industry as original as electronics, there are undoubtedly additional concentrations not shown.

In interpreting the results, several difficulties must be borne in mind which may have the effect of either overstating or understating the concentration. Aside from inaccuracies in census gathering, one problem is that the ratios relate to the nation as a whole, and greater concentrations may, therefore, exist locally. However, since most electronic firms sell nationally this is perhaps not a major problem.

A major source of understatement, however, arises from the defining of many of the industries and product classes in terms so broad as to include nonsubstitutable products. This means that though the overall concentration ratio may be low, within the grouping, virtual monopolies may exist with respect to specific products. Conversely, where the definition of the industry is too narrow, the concentration ratio is overstated. Lastly, only the domestic market is considered. However, except for portable radios, the impact of imports of specific electronic products is limited.

The firms of the electronics industries have also been active in mergers. In Table 2.11, the rates of acquisitions of those electronics firms included among the 500 largest manufacturing firms are given. Two groups, electrical equipment and communication and electronic equipment, both exhibited higher acquisition rates than the average for the whole group, but this modest difference is very small compared with the 66 acquisitions per firm in the dairy-products industry. Of course, there are industries in which the rate of acquisitions is very much lower, for example, natural gas and sugar, each of which has 0.7 per firm.[5]

In making these acquisitions, the electronics firms have generally stayed close to their specialties with virtually all the firms acquired, making

TABLE 2.10

Percent of Values of Shipment in Each Industry and Product
Class Accounted for by the Largest Companies, 1958

SIC	Class of product	Value of shipment $million	Percent of value accounted by			
			4 largest companies	8 largest companies	20 largest companies	50 largest companies
A.	Industries with at least $25 million in electronics shipments in each four-digit classification and with electronics shipments representing half or more of the value of total shipments.					
3651	Radios and TV sets	1,516	38	57	76	91
36511	Radios	549	34	53	81	99
36512	TV sets	727	55	81	99	100
36513	Other audio equipment	240	17	30	54	80
3652	Phonograph Records	136	74	81	88	97
3662	Radio, TV communication equipment	1,991	36	52	70	83
36621	Radio and TV communication equipment	399	48	61	79	94
36622	Radio and TV broadcasting equipment	54	50	63	79	93
36623	Intercommunication equipment	130	40	54	75	91
36624	Electronic navigational aids	203	54	76	95	100
36625	Electronic aircraft and missile equipment	918	46	71	89	98
36626	Other equipment	288	58	67	79	92

SIC	Class of product	Value of shipment $million	Percent of value accounted by			
			4 largest companies	8 largest companies	20 largest companies	50 largest companies
36710	Electron tubes, receiving type	337	76	94	99	99+
36720	Cathode ray picture tubes	177	69	85	96	99
36730	Other tubes, exc. X-ray	225	52	69	94	(D)
3679	Electronic components, n.e.c.	1,481	12	21	36	53
36791	Solid state devices	237	46	64	92	99
36792	Capacitors	184	40	57	83	96
36793	Resistors	147	43	60	84	99
36794	Coils, transformers, etc.	205	24	34	51	73
36795	Other components	699	15	24	38	55
B. Selected other products.						
35711	Computers, including cash registers	1,039	77	84	93	98
3611	Electric measuring instrument	588	21	35	53	71
3622	Industrial controls	447	54	68	80	90
3661	Telephone & telegraph equipment	1,139	(D)	98+		
3693	X-ray and allied equipment	73	52	65	80	93
38111	Aircraft navigational equipment	648	47	70	88	97
38112	Other scientific instruments	264	30	41	60	76

(continued)

35

TABLE 2.10 (continued)

SIC	Class of product	Value of shipment $million	Percent of value accounted by			
			4 largest companies	8 largest companies	20 largest companies	50 largest companies
38211	Aircraft engine instruments	55	54	77	97	100
38213	Industrial process instruments	403	25	38	58	78
38220	Automatic temperature controls	320	68	78	94	99
38424	Hearing aids	39	64	86	98	100
39312	Organs	79	61	79	97	99

(D) Deleted to avoid individual disclosure

Source: U.S. Bureau of the Census, Concentration Ratios in Manufacturing Industry 1958, Washington, D.C.: U.S. Government Printing Office, 1962), pp. 153-163.

TABLE 2.11

Acquisitions by Firms Engaged in
Electronics Manufacturing, 1951-1961

SIC no.	Industry	Acquisitions per firm 1951-1961
357	Office machines	6.0
361	Electrical equipment	8.0
363	Applicances	3.0
365	Radio and TV sets	4.1
366	Communication and electronic equipment	8.3
380	Instruments and related products	4.3
	Average for all industries	6.8

Source: U.S. House of Representatives, Select Committee on Small Business, Mergers and Superconcentrations, 1961, 88th Congress, 1st Session.

TABLE 2.12

Types of Firms Acquired by
Firms Engaged in Electronics Manufacturing,
1951-1961

No. of firms acquired	Primary business of acquired firm
7	Machinery (including computing machines)
7	Electrical machinery
6	Instruments and related products
1	Chemicals
1	Retail store (misc.)
1	Stone, clay and glass products
1	Fabricated metal products

Source: U.S. House of Representatives, Select Committee on Small Business, Mergers and Superconcentrations, 1961, 88th Congress, 1st Session.

other forms of machinery or being part of the industry itself (Table 2.12). Exceptions were relatively
few and in at least one case had mainly a financial
basis rather than one of product diversification.

LOCATION AND EMPLOYMENT

The electronic industry employed almost 800,000
workers in 1961. As shown in Table 2.13, about 36
percent each were in military and components manufacture and only 11 percent in consumer items. This
tabulation, however, does not break down the component sector into replacement parts and original
equipment and, therefore, overstates its importance.
The industry has maintained a considerable rate of
increase in its employment. The smallest rate of
change is to be found in the military sector and the
largest in the industrial products.

The industry also exhibits a sharp variation in
the proportion of production and nonproduction employees within its sectors. As shown in Table 2.14,
all sectors have increased their proportion of nonproduction employees between 1958 and 1961. However, in the military and industrial sector, here
shown combined, the nonproduction employees begin
to outnumber the production employees in that period.

The location of the industries shows some re-
markable regional concentrations which differ greatly
among the various sectors, as shown in Table 2.15.
Unfortunately, no information is available separately
for industrial and military products, but by merely
considering the locations of the major firms in the
industrial field, it is clear that the high concentration in the Pacific Coast area (almost all in
California) is largely military, whereas industrial
electronics are more concentrated in the Middle
Atlantic states and the East North Central region.
The South Atlantic region is also almost exclusively
military.

The regional concentration of consumer items is
sharply at variance with this distribution. More
than 90 percent of that industry is concentrated in
the Middle Atlantic, Pacific, and East North Central
regions, with the latter accounting for almost one-
half of the total. Indeed, except for the Middle
Atlantic region, the distribution among the two

TABLE 2.13

Employment in Electronics Manufacturing
by Product Category, 1958, 1961, 1966

Product	Employment (thous.)			Percent of total employment			Percent increase	
category	1958	1961	1966	1958	1961	1966	1958-1961	1961-1966
Military	245.6	283.0	327.0	40.3	36.4	30.3	16.1	15.5
Industrial	86.3	126.0	169.0	14.2	16.2	15.7	46.0	25.5
Consumer	72.7	88.7	144.0	11.9	11.4	13.3	21.9	62.3
Components	205.2	280.0	440.0	33.7	36.0	40.7	36.3	57.1
Total	609.8	777.7	1080.0	100.0	100.0	100.0	27.6	36.0

Source: U.S. Bureau of Labor Statistics, Employment Outlook and Changing
Occupational Structure in Electronics Manufacturing--Bulletin No. 1363 (Nov., 1963),
p. 28. EIA 1967 Yearbook, p. 69.

TABLE 2.14

Nonproduction and Production Workers in
Electronics Manufacturing by Product Category
1958 and 1961

Product category	Employment (thous.)		Percent total employment	
	1958	1961	1958	1961
Military and industrial				
nonproduction	158.3	214.3	47.7	52.4
production	173.6	194.7	52.3	47.6
Consumer				
nonproduction	19.0	23.8	26.1	26.8
production	53.7	64.9	73.9	73.2
Component				
nonproduction	51.7	76.2	25.2	27.2
production	153.5	203.8	74.8	72.8
Total				
nonproduction	229.0	314.3	37.6	40.4
production	380.8	463.4	62.4	59.6

Source: U.S. Bureau of Labor Statistics, Employment Outlook and Changing Occupational Structure in
Electronics Manufacturing, Bulletin No. 1363 (November,
1963), p. 36.

TABLE 2.15

Employment in Electronics Manufacturing by
Industry Sector and Region
January, 1961

Region	Total		Military-space and industrial-commercial		Consumer		Components	
	Number (000)	Per-cent	Number (000)	Per-cent	Number (000)	Per-cent	Number (000)	Per-cent
Total	616.9	100.0	293.2	100.0	97.2	100.0	226.5	100.0
Middle Atlantic	192.2	31.2	89.9	30.6	29.8	30.7	82.0	36.2
Pacific	130.6	21.2	80.3	27.4	10.6	10.9	30.1	13.3
E. North Central	121.7	19.7	34.1	11.6	47.7	49.0	39.9	17.6
New England	74.6	12.1	25.0	8.5	2.8	2.9	46.8	20.6
South Atlantic	40.6	6.6	30.7	10.5	n.a.a		8.9	4.0
W. North Central	22.6	3.7	15.2	5.2	2.2	2.2	5.2	2.3
W. South Central	16.9	2.7	14.4	4.9	0.8	0.8	1.7	0.8
E. South Central	11.9	1.9	3.2	1.1	2.3	2.4	6.5	2.8
Mountain	5.8	0.9	0.4	0.1	n.a.a		5.4	2.4

Note: Because of rounding, sums of individual items may not equal totals.

aCombined total 0.9 and 1.0 percent.

Source: U.S. Bureau of Labor Statistics, Employment Outlook and Changing Occupational Structure in Electronics Manufacturing, Bulletin No. 1363 (November, 1963), pp. 8-11.

41

groups is almost completely lopsided. Components manufacture has yet another distribution. Again the Middle Atlantic states lead, in fact, by a bigger margin than the other groups, but New England is in second place.

It is clear, therefore, that any major disturbance in the industry, whether from cutbacks in defense electronics or the elimination of separate components as the result of integrated circuits, would fall heavily on certain specific regions.

SUMMARY

The markets in the electronics industry are still heavily dependent on the military sector. Though for some years the proportion had been declining slightly, the requirements of the Vietnam war has again raised the proportion of military business, including space, to about 55 percent of the total in 1968. Missiles, communications (military), and space are three of the largest single markets; only television sets (in which industry the rather expensive color sets now predominate) and computers can boast shares of this magnitude.

The firms in the industry vary greatly in size, but large firms exist in all of its major constituents. The effect is seen in a high concentration ratio in most of the industries and product classes involved. There have also been a considerable number of mergers within the industry, with the firms in electrical equipment and communication and electronic equipment maintaining a higher than average acquisition rate.

The industry employed 1,080,000 workers in 1966. There are considerable differences in the occupational make-up of these employees with the proportion of nonproduction workers markedly higher in military electronics than in the rest of the industry. The employment is heavily concentrated in the Middle Atlantic states and California, with the latter predominantly in military electronics.

NOTES

1. Electronics Industries Association, _1962 Yearbook_, (Washington, D.C., 1962), p. 1.

2. Electronic Industries Market and Distribution Chart, 1962, _Electronics News_, 1962.

3. Electronics Industries Association, _op. cit._, p. 55.

4. J. E. Ullmann (ed.), _Product Innovation in Selected Industries_ (Hempstead, N.Y.: Hofstra University Yearbook of Business, 1967), Ser.3, Vol.3, _passim_.

5. U.S. House of Representatives, Select Committee on Small Business, _Mergers and Superconcentrations_, 88th Cong. 1st Session, 1961.

CHAPTER **3** MANUFACTURING PRACTICES
AND THE PROBLEMS
OF CONVERSION

by Eugene Foley

INTRODUCTION

If firms in the electronic industry are to
shift successfully to the manufacture of new products
for the commercial, industrial, and consumer markets,
an assessment of their technology of production is
necessary. The way the firms concerned have coped
with present problems in the production of equipment
for military and space markets bears importantly
on their probable ability to make the transition to
nonmilitary markets successfully.

In the present analysis, three major areas are
considered: product design, production processes,
and production management. Product design includes
the development of new components and assemblies and
the problems of constant change due to new designs,
standardizations and simplification, and the problem
of extravagance in design. A discussion of production processes must look beyond new ways of making
things to plant layout, training methods, an aging
stock of machines, and a possible transfer of some
activities to entirely different technologies. Some
progress has been made in modern quantitative models
of production processes but not enough to eliminate
the job shop problem of relative inefficiency in the
use of labor and plant.

Most of these issues become crucial mainly in
small-quantity production, taken here to mean lots
of less than a thousand. Larger ones than these
would be turned out by mass production of a type
relatively seldom found in major military systems
today. The manufacture of appliances as an alternative for the military-electronics industry is

therefore not considered here. Rather, this chapter
mainly envisages a new product mix of special computers, machines, test apparatus, and other new
products, as described in Part II of this report.
This is done in order to take a conservative view of
probable difficulties. If it should turn out that
the industry can maintain a substantial volume with
mass products, the main result would be to simplify
the task greatly.

PRODUCT DESIGN

In electronics, as in all industries, product
design determines production methods. In electronics, these now range from the conventional machine
shop to elaborate and precise chemical processes,
comparable in complexity to those found in pharma-
ceuticals. New components and assemblies have been
developed to meet the high accuracy and quality
control requirements of the industry. These new
developments are likely eventually to save costs,
but they have also caused instability in processes
and in the organization of production. The result
of rapid design advancements is the general failure
of manufacturers to standardize and modulize their
products.

In this section, the problems of components and
assemblies are first examined, followed by a discussion of two issues common to both: standardization and simplification and extravagance in design.

Components

One of the most important developments in the
industry is microelectronics. The main advantages
anticipated are increased reliability, reduced cost,
greater flexibility in design, shorter time cycle
for development and production and reduced size,
weight, and power supply.[1] The extreme miniaturization and combination of devices reduces the number
of interconnections that are principal sources of
potential trouble. New test equipment and especially
the development of new accelerated life tests have
brought reliability to what might otherwise have
been too unpredictable a product. The savings realized by manufacturers have been in equipment,
production engineering, logistics, and maintenance.

It is possible, for example, to use microcircuit
modules in a building-block technique where various
combinations can provide complex circuitry while
allowing redundancy and self checking because of the
reduced size, weight, power consumption, and the
relative low cost of the module. The use of the
microcircuit allows the electronic engineer to spend
more time on developing applications rather than
creating basic circuitries provided by microcircuits.

There are three basic types of microelectronics:
isolated components, integrated assemblies, and
transition or hybrid systems. The latter are really
assemblies and are discussed in the next section.
Isolated components, in turn, are of two main types.[2]
There is the pellet type, where all the components
are made in the same cyclindrical shape to permit
higher packaging, and the micromodule, which origin-
ated in the packaging of conventional components
into a uniform size or shape. The micromodule method
can use a relatively wide range of components,
including transistors, diodes, several types of
semi-precision and precision resistors, capacitors
of the electrolytic and ceramic types, and some inductors and transformers. Pellets are mainly
restricted to transistors, diodes, resistors, and
capacitors.

Assemblies

Advances in the use of microelectronics on
assemblies have also been made. The building-block
technique of utilizing microcircuits on plug-in
printed circuit boards has made large advances
within the electronic industry. The advantages of
utilizing printed circuit assemblies are many,
including high reliability, ease of trouble shooting,
rapid replacement of defective circuit board, and
redundancy. The increase in use of microcircuit
assemblies has additional benefits of reduced power
supply requirements and greater maintainability
within a system aspect.

The use of plug-in printed circuit assemblies
also lends itself to computerized wiring in association with wire-wrap connections. With the mechanical
standardization of card files the programming
associated with computerizing the wiring has been
simplified. The quantity required to use computerized

wiring economically has been reduced to the point
where it can be used on small-quantity electronic
equipment.

Flexible cabling has also made an important
contribution to electronic assemblies. This cabling
is made of conductors between two pieces of Mylar.
It is used to replace harnessing, having the advantage of space and weight. A strip of tape 3 inches
wide can easily carry 24 conductors. It can be
rolled, folded and preformed to fit the shape of any
package and also provides greater reliability at
lower cost.

Another new technique is Weld Pack, which is
not limited to repetitive circuitry.[3] Components
are mounted by their axial leads between two printed
circuit boards. The package can be made smaller
because of the use of .an electrical resistance welder
for making the electrical connections instead of
soldering, which would require clearance between
components. Such assemblies can also be made to
assume many different shapes compared with conventional groupings of circuit boards and components.
The Weld Pack can be used in conjunction with microcircuits on plug-in printed circuit boards providing
an even larger variety of circuits.

Of these new techniques, microelectronics and
its derivatives have by far the greatest potential
impact and are likely to change radically the prospects of component and systems firms now in the
industry, even without any major changes in markets.
Some observers now believe that functional integrated
circuitry, an outgrowth of microelectronics, will
replace the component and system maker.[4] The
resulting instability has influenced every area of
the electronic industry as it exists today.

The introduction of microelectronics has affected
the manufacturers of components, such as resistors,
capacitors, coils, and inductors. The growth rate
of these industries which averaged 9.5 percent from
1957 to 1962 is expected to fall to 3.8 percent for
the period of 1967-1972.[5] The active element,
which included tubes and semiconductors, had an
average growth of 10.9 percent from 1957 to 1962.
This rate is expected to fall to 3.3 percent for the
period of 1967-1972. The growth of integral circuit
packages is expected to be at the rate of 36 percent
per year for the next five years, and continue after

that at a rate of 21 percent. Obviously, the component manufacturer can no longer expect to specialize
in one or two types of components but will have to
move towards integrated circuits if he expects to
survive. Similarly, systems producers tend to
diversify back into components, since the obvious
differences between them are diminishing steadily.
Either way, it means large investments for new
machines and the development of different skills
within the firms. Not all are equal to the task. As
will be seen, these uncertainties have contributed
to the lack of standardization, which is the bane
of the industry.

Standardization and Simplification

Standardization is the reduction of sizes in
which a product is made to certain specified values.
Simplification is the reduction in the number of
standard sizes to the minimum required for adequate
coverage of the needs of customers. The combination
of components into standard assemblies called modules
carries this process one step further. To be meaningful, simplified standards must be industry-wide.
One firm, to be sure, can do a lot by standardizing
and simplifying its product. It can exercise
effective control over proliferation of new parts
and consequent difficulties in production management.
However, to realize the full potential of simplification, industry-wide participation is essential.
This is far in the future except in limited aspects,
e.g. in a few components. For the individual firm,
however, there are also advantages:

1. A halt to proliferation of parts.

2. A simplification of production tooling and
test equipment.

3. Larger production lots, resulting in
economies of scale.

4. Simpler assemblies through use of more
widely applicable tooling.

5. Simplified packaging and shipping.[6]

An account of savings and reorganization with
standardization has been given by the Cenco Company,
a large job shop in the field of scientific and

industrial instruments as well as electronics.7 It
markets 8,000 products and introduces 50 new ones
each year. The company made a department-by-depart-
ment check of all its assemblies, and each was
broken down into its machine and subassembly costs.
If the costs were high, a redesign of the product
began, maximizing use of standard parts. On new
products the engineering staff would work with Production Control, which would supply cost data from
cost accounting. Using selling prices, estimated
manufacturing costs, and annual estimated sales,
Production Control determined the manufacturing lot
size. If it was bigger than one year's sales, the
item was redesigned. The breakdown of the cost
showed the economy of large production runs and of
holding machine parts in inventory while cutting
stocks of subassemblies and assemblies.

The program was highly successful. Although
sales of Cenco increased 2.3 times from $12.6 million
in 1956 to $28.7 million in 1962, inventory increased
only 5 percent.

As noted, however, the real point of standardization is cross-industry or, at least, cross-equip-
ment simplification. It may be too much to hope for
at this time that circuit modules could be made
interchangeable in the manner of screws and other
simple hardware, yet clearly this could eventually
be done in many cases. Even within firms, however,
different departments dealing with widely varying
products often make little effort to find common
elements that could lead to single long production
runs of certain components. The electronics industry
has far to go, even in standardizing what might be
called its external relations. There is, for example,
still no common computer language, although the
variety of punched cards and tape has fortunately
remained limited. A successful shift of major effort
to nonmilitary products would involve serious attention to these problems on the part of the industry.

Extravagance of Design

In the successful conversion of a product line
from military to nonmilitary products, the cost
consciousness of the new customers typically conflicts
with the more tolerant cost criteria of military
customers. Ullmann has noted the view, especially

among engineers working on weapons development, that
economic criteria of design selection can be altogether unimportant.

> The specification of product function
> need not have an economic basis, to
> be sure, but once several alterna-
> tives for achieving a specified ob-
> jective are available, the selection
> will turn upon cost. . . . To sup-
> pose otherwise is to believe in
> infinite inputs of money and effort
> and this is manifestly absurd.[8]

The new cost consciousness does not imply the introduction of a cultivated shoddiness into the design.
On the contrary, simplicity and ruggedness are at a
premium in commercial products. Continual changes
in the product, overdesign, the profligate use of
special rather than standard components, and excessive administrative routines associated with the
design function must, however, be avoided. In some
respects, this is a function of the work habits of
the engineers involved as much as of company policy.

PRODUCTION PROCESSES

The product requirements have made necessary
significant changes in production processes. The
industry has had to develop new methods of manufacture, plant layout, and training devices. Nevertheless, its machinery has been getting older, thus
sharing a characteristic of all American metalworking
In response to these problems many companies have
added a substantial effort in basic research on
production to supplement both product research and
routine manufacturing engineering.

For example, the Western Electric Engineering
Research Center was established in 1958 to conduct
research and development on improving the production
of electronic and communications equipment. The
four stated objectives of the Center are to increase
the engineering capability of the company, to pursue
broad-scope manufacturing development, to establish
an information center on manufacturing processes,
and to ease the transition between product design
and manufacture.

The center does research and development in three basic areas:

1. Mechanization studies in the development of new concepts of manufacture for new and existing telephone apparatus.

2. System studies using mathematical techniques, automatic data processing, and computers to plan and control production.

3. Process studies which use chemistry, metallurgy, and physics in the development of new or better processes and materials.

Among the achievements of the Center to date has been the development of a new vacuum machine which promises to cut the cost of some electronic circuitry by 90 percent.[9]

Chemical and Metallurgical Technology

The new products described in the section on product design have resulted in a whole new group of processes based on chemical and metallurgical technology rather than on mechanical manufacture and assembly. Both areas have seen advances and have had as research objectives the reduction of cost in small quantity production and the maintenance of high quality standards. Taken by and large, success has been greater in the latter set of objectives than in the former.

One of the most important replacements of an essentially mechanical process by a largely chemical one was the introduction of printed circuit boards. This substantially reduced the complexity of wiring found in electronic equipment. The printed circuit board is a laminate of paper, phenolic plastic, or epoxy resin bonded to copper foil. A circuit is etched into the board by a solution bath. Components are assembled through predrilled holes in the board. Soldering of the components is done by hand or automatically by a dip or wave soldering machine.

Given reliable circuit boards, the assembly of components and the testing of the completed circuit unit readily lent themselves to automation. Of course, reliability is still not easy to assure, at

least in commercial production where the high military inspection costs and rejection rates are
unacceptable. Still, there were profound changes
in production methods. New soldering, welding, and
fastening devices were developed to aid in assembly.
The first assembly machines used in electronics
were little more than stapling machines, attaching
components to circuit boards. Miniaturization
further helped in reducing handling problems.

The transistor also opened up a new method of
making components.[10] It is made by a chemical-metallurgical process; the crucial task is growing the
silicon and germanium wafers used. After that,
assembly, while also a precise task, is less important. Assembly and testing of transistors have been
greatly speeded up. The experience gained was in
turn applied to the older components. For example,
tubes can now be tested by a machine at a rate of
1,800 per hour.

The increasing use of the simplified circuits
described in the introduction to this chapter has
further added to the chemical-metallurgical incur-
sions into manufacturing technology. Dip soldering,
film deposited components, multilayer components,
pellets, and complete circuits have required the
development of new materials for the components
themselves, adhesives, etc.

Electronic components of all kinds have bene-
fited from these advances. For all of these methods,
the full realization of their cost-cutting potential
depends on the increase of lot sizes, which only
standardization and simplification can bring. However, the tooling necessary is often simple enough
to permit wide flexibility and thus contributes to
a solution of the cost problems of production in
small lots.

Machine Tools

The electronics industry, of course, also uses
conventional and special machine tools and metalworking equipment. Changes in the performance and
efficiency of these machines are, therefore, of
interest. It is difficult to make a standardized
comparison for machine tools overtime because of the
different types of change that took place in their

design and operation. One method, that of the productivity criteria coefficient (PCQ) attempts to get
around this difficulty by an empirical rating of
changes.[11]

The PCQ is determined by weighting the changes
in critical features of the machines, such as automatic controls, changes in feeds and speeds, bed and
way improvements, etc., for each machine and dividing
the total by the number of machines surveyed in the
sample and then multiplying the answer by 10:

$$PCQ = \sum \frac{\text{Weighted critical criteria X 10}}{\text{Number of machines of each kind}}$$

Table 3.1 gives the PCQ for the machines used
most often in the metalworking industry. Table 3.2
permits an interpretation of the change in these
characteristics by showing the ratios of change in
each five-year period from 1940 to 1960. It is
clear that there has been consistent improvement;
that is, none of the ratios is less than one. It is
also evident that several machines have been unable
to match in the 1950's the progress that was made in
their design in the 1940's. For others, progress
appears to have been more rapid in the latter period.

There are, of course, important limitations to
this type of analysis. First, there is the matter
of cost. Before a new machine can be bought, no
matter how high the savings it generates, it must be
justified in terms of the rate of return on investment. High machine prices make such justification
difficult, and the prices of machine tools and metal
working equipment have been rising much more rapidly
than most other things that manufacturers have to
buy.[12]

Secondly, machines have been getting heavier
and more powerful, and the ability to remove large
quantities of metal at high rates has been a characteristic of machine performance. With the present
and continuing emphasis on miniaturization, these
advantages of modern machines are sharply reduced in
practical importance insofar as they are due to this
increase in power and rigidity. Further, the
development of precision casting, plastic molding,
and other forming methods reduces the need for
large-scale metal removal. When used for light

TABLE 3.1

Productivity Criteria Quotient for
Metalworking Machines, 1940-1960

Machine	1940	1950	1955 PCQ	1958	1959	1960
Horizontal boring and milling machines	6	172	276	364	382	472
Vertical turret lathes	140	190	405	505	630	640
Jig borers	0	94	124	173	196	249
Sensitive drills	4	8	22	48	52	70
Radial drills	10	32	67	103	115	165
Engine lathes	10	170	280	290	309	380
Turret lathes	8	188	311	373	383	465
Surface grinders	23	50	80	115	118	152
Cylindrical grinders	0	145	180	227	247	272
Milling machines	6	80	150	168	174	198
Contour saws	20	63	77	90	90	93
Cut-off saws	0	12	32	72	86	96

Source: "Productivity! How Do Your Machines
Rate?" American Machinist/Metalworking Manufacturing
(November 11, 1963), pp. 111-142.

TABLE 3.2

Rates of Change of Productivity Criteria Quotient
of Metalworking Machines 5-Year Periods,
1940-1960

| Machine | PCQ Ratio: End ÷ beginning of period | | |
	1940-1945 1945-1950 (ave.)[a]	1950-55	1955-60
Horizontal boring and milling machines	5.5	1.6	1.3
Vertical turret lathes	1.1	2.1	1.6
Jig borers	--	1.3	2.0
Sensitive drills	1.4	2.8	3.2
Radial drills	1.8	2.1	2.5
Engine lathes	4.1	1.6	1.4
Turret lathes	6.1	1.7	1.5
Surface grinders	1.5	1.6	1.9
Cylindrical grinders	--	1.2	1.5
Milling machines	3.7	1.9	1.3
Contour saws	1.8	1.2	1.2
Cut-off saws	--	2.7	3.0

[a]Obtained from the square root of the ratio PCQ
(1950)/PCQ(1940).

Source: Table 3.1.

finishing cuts, the power of most machines can only
be fully used by working on many pieces simultaneously. It has been shown that, in practice, there
usually is not enough room on the machine tables
for this.[13]

In all, there are limitations to the advantages
which modern technology has brought to the machine
tools of the electronics industry. This fact applies
even to numerical controls, which, as shown in
Chapter 8 have thus far had to face economic limitations. Numerical controls, themselves a product of
the electronics industry, can produce great savings
in machine time. However, they too must be justified
in relation to the hitherto rather high cost of
certain kinds of such equipment. In two-coordinate
tape control, however, as used in drills, borers,
etc., tape control shows promise for the industry
in such tasks as the location of holes for components
and the like. These machines appear to have approached the closest in cost to widely and readily
applicable innovations. A major reason, of course,
is their flexibility and ease of conversion to different outputs.

The problems in introducing new machines are
worsened when they are combined with a lack of flexibility and risk of quick obsolescence of expensive
new equipment. Firms have delayed purchase of new
machines, hoping to take advantage at some time in
the future of a real breakthrough in productivity at
reasonable capital cost.

As a result, the electronics industry, like the
rest of metalworking, has a gradually aging inventory
in metalworking machinery, in spite of its rapidly
developing product technology. Cabinets, gear trains
punchings of all kinds, electromechanical details,
etc., are produced on these machines, and thus these
important components have been subjected to ever-
rising cost trends.

The machines of the electronics industry are,
in general, younger than those of many others. Table
3.3 shows that electrical machinery and equipment
which includes electronics has a lower rate of obsolescence than the other metalworking industries in
the United States.[14] The data are for 1963; the 1968
survey not being available at the time of revision,
but the situation has remained essentially the same.

TABLE 3.3

Age Distribution for Machine Tools for the
Nine Major Industrial Groups

	Units	Percent 10 years old and over	Percent 20 years old and over
Ordnance and Accessories	28,943	65	23
Furniture and Fixtures	43,067	50	14
Fabricated Metal Products	633,998	65	21
Machinery, Except Electrical	951,901	67	22
Electrical Machinery & Equipment	328,548	54	14
Transportation Equipment	450,079	66	23
Precision Instruments	124,521	56	15
Misc. Manufacturing Industries	77,955	61	20
Total	2,808,530	64	21

Source: "The Ninth American Machinist Inventory of Metalworking Equipment," American Machinist/Metalworking Manufacturing (1963).

Only 54 percent of its machinery is more than ten
years old. However, the machine inventory has been
aging steadily, especially when communications
equipment, a new industrial classification, is considered separately. The percentages of machinery at
least ten years old during the period 1949 to 1963
has changed as follows:[15]

	Years			
	1949	1953	1958	1963
	Percent over 10 years old			
Electrical equipment	37	51	57	59
Communications	n.a.	n.a.	42	39

The rate of obsolescence in the electrical equipment
industry has thus increased from 37 percent in 1949
to 59 percent in 1963. Only in communications has
there been an improvement over time.

This deterioration of the machine inventory
over time is part of a national problem. At present,
64 percent of the American stock of equipment is
more than ten years old. Recent studies in Western
and Eastern Europe indicate comparable percentages
in other leading industrial countries as follows:
United Kingdom, 59 percent; France, 58 percent;
Italy, 57 percent; West Germany, 55 percent; and
USSR, 50 percent.[16] If the equipment of the electronics industries of these countries follows a
similar age distribution, the United States is clearly
in a poor position for making up in higher productivity what it now must spend in higher wages. The
increasing utilization of numerically controlled
machine tools (Chapter 8) has thus far made only a
small difference in this situation.

Plant Layout

The electronics industry has also turned its
attention to plant layout and training devices to
cope with the need for a flexible production system.
Often the necessary changes were only made after
difficulties had developed with a previous system.
For example, the Merrimack Valley Works of Western
Electric Company, a producer of telephone carrier
equipment for the Bell System, designed a plant to

the requirements of small-quantity production. The
following needs had to be met:

1. Three thousand types of equipment.

2. Two to three hundred at a time of any particular type.

3. Five to twenty operations performed on each
type with the average amount of operations twelve.

4. Eighteen thousand stock parts required for
component manufacture.[17]

Due to this combination of many types of products
with small-production lots, the company found itself
building up large quantities of in-process work in
order to cut the number of setups and keep workers
on the same operation as long as possible. This led
to parts shortages and heavy expenses for emergency
orders.

In order to overcome the problems, four steps
were taken:

1. It was decided that straight line production
was not flexible enough for use in small quantity
production. The straight-line production was
replaced with small progressive lines where the volume of production would show them to be economical.

2. A mechanical handling system was designed
to eliminate the maze of wagons, hand trucks, etc.
This eliminated handling of mixed skids as well as
large areas having to be assigned for drop areas. To
reach an optimum, it was decided to use drag-line
trucks.

3. The storeroom for electronic components was
unsuitable because it occupied too much space and
required an excess of record keeping. These problems
were overcome by using a mezzanine type storeroom
serviced by a continuous belt conveyor and run on the
basis of dispatch central control with all entries
and withdrawals handled by a punchcard system.

4. The component-manufacturing area was split
into four parts, each with its own dispatch center

with full control of the shop operations, inventories,
schedules, and materials. In-process inventory time
was saved by the use of conveyor belts to deliver
equipment and parts to the various stations within
a dispatch center. After each operation, the part
was returned to the dispatcher, who could keep a
close control before shipping to the next station.

The system provided an easily controlled and
supervised assembly line. It allowed for work to be
better balanced, constantly reviewed, and evaluated.
It also supplied a method for manufacturing and
engineering problems to be quickly brought to attention and solved. From this example it follows that
much can be done merely by a rearrangement of existing
equipment and a change in control methods.

Training

The problem of training is exacerbated by the
need for frequent product changes. Several firms,
for example, Hughes Aircraft Co., have successfully
used audio-visual aids synchronized with the assembly
operations concerned.[18] In this manner, learning
time is greatly shortened, and the errors otherwise
frequently found in the assembly of complex circuitry
are materially reduced. However, this type of
technique is most useful in cases in which lots are
relatively small so that they cannot be conveniently
subdivided into unit operations. In commercial
equipment, such situations are generally less common
than in defense products.

PRODUCTION MANAGEMENT

The current prevalence of small lots and diverse
product in the electronics industry has led to the
job-shop type of production system. From the viewpoint of programming production, this poses difficult and still largely unsolved problems in effective
control. Muth and Thompson defined the job shop
scheduling problem as follows:

> A plant is said to consist of several
> work centers, all with different
> capabilities. Sometimes duplication
> of facilities is allowed. There is

a list of products to be completed.
The routing for each product is a
simple order: the first operation
must be completed before the second
may be started, and so on down the
list. A specific machine is designated to carry out each of these
operations, with dates for the
completion of each of the products
possibly having been assigned. How
shall the products be scheduled to
machines in such a way that (a) due
dates are met whenever possible, or
(b) the total time to complete all
jobs is minimized, or (c) some other
criterion function is optimized?[19]

A generally applicable and practical resolution of
this problem has thus far eluded the many management
scientists that have worked on it.

The industry still largely has to go by a random choice of work sequence on each machine or by
the formulation of simple loading rules which may
or may not lead to the desired efficiency. Moreover,
as Pound has pointed out, a good deal of difficulty
is normally removed from the problem by having an
excess of equipment and quoting long lead times to
the customers. In fact, the determination of capacity
of a job shop has, thus far, eluded successful
analysis.[20]

One approach to better job shop scheduling has
been by integer-linear programming.[21] However, this
method involves such substantial computations that
they are beyond the practical capacity of present
computing equipment in any but the simplest cases.[22]
The solutions do not converge rapidly enough to
lead to an optimal result. Fortunately, it often
happens that there is relatively little difference in
costs and elapsed time between a number of feasible
solutions. Methods based on the complete enumera-
tion of feasible solutions as a step towards optimization, have been improved by devising sampling and
Monte Carlo techniques. There is also the heuristic
approach in which an attempt is made to improve a
given first feasible solution. Most of these are
still at the stage of the formulation of theoretical
models and not of practical application.[23]

In spite of the savings in tooling and other operations possible by the use of numerically controlled machine tools from an organizational standpoint, the simplest remedy for job-shop operations is still to depart from them in the direction of large-quantity production.

There has been much better progress in the scheduling of large unique projects. The methods and applications of network scheduling and control systems are widely known and have been extensively applied though, thus far, mainly on military contracts.[24] Even there, however, some technical work remains to be done in order to have available a method which can take trade-offs between time and cost more readily into account.

SUMMARY

The manufacturing methods of the electronics industry are now undergoing considerable changes. The most important appears to be the development of miniaturized, integrated circuits, which have brought a gradual change in mechanical manufacturing and assembly of components to a variety of chemical and metallurgical processes. Several of these are highly successful. Others still require improvement to the point where the process yield is suitable for commercial production in which the high scrap rate in defense work is unacceptable. This development is likely to pose considerable difficulties for the assembly-type systems producer without competence in the new manufacturing techniques of components. As a physical reality, components and systems are becoming hard to distinguish.

A second important element is the fact that the industry has has been slow to standardize its product in spite of the fact that basically it lends itself ideally to such techniques as modulization. It is true that such policies are difficult to put into effect in a new and rapidly changing industry. Certain items of software, such as cards and tapes, have been standardized, but aside from some forward looking programs of a few manufacturers acting individually, there has been little activity outside of connectors and similar hardware.

In its conventional machine-tool equipment, it was shown that the electronics industry has the same aging machine stock as the rest of American metal-working. While it is better off than some older industries in the group, its showing is still poor by comparison with the national average of other major industrial nations.

Lastly, it was shown that management science has not thus far been able to formulate a basic and effective control system for the job shop. Hence, the industry probably pays a considerable price in excess equipment and long lead times, in the usual manner of the troubled job-shop industries.

NOTES

1.   George T. Jacobi and Samuel Weber, The Impact of Microelectronics (New York: McGraw-Hill Publishing Co., 1963), p. 8.

2.   Ibid., p. 75.

3.   P. J. Klass, "Welded Modules Reduce Component Size," Aviation Week (Aug. 24, 1959), pp. 104-5.

4.   George T. Jacobi and Samuel Weber, op. cit. p. 8.

5.   George T. Jacobi and Samuel Weber, op. cit. p. 15.

6.   B. Miller, "Uniform Component Packaging Offered," Aviation Week (Oct. 24, 1960), pp. 93-94.

7.   "System Proves Small Lot Runs Can Still be Profitable," Iron Age (Aug. 2, 1962), pp. 37-39.

8.   J. E. Ullmann, "Criteria of Change in Machinery Design," (doctoral dissertation, Columbia University, 1959), p. 235.

9.   "Fact Sheet" Western Electric Engineering Research Center (Princeton, N.J.: Jan. 9, 1963).

10.   U. S. Bureau of Labor Statistics, Employment Outlook and Changing Occupational Structure in Electronic Manufacturing, Bulletin No. 1363

(Washington, D.C.:   U.S. Government Printing Office,
1963), p. 33.

11. "Productivity! How do Your Machines Rate?"
(American Machinist/Metalworking Manufacturing, Nov.
11, 1963), pp. 111-142.

12. S. Melman, The Peace Race (New York:
Ballantine, 1961), Ch. 6.

13. J. E. Ullmann, op. cit. p. 108 ff.

14. "The Ninth American Machinist Inventory of
Metalworking Equipment" (American Machinist/Metal-
working Manufacturing, June 10, 1963), p. 7.

15. Ibid., p. 8.

16. Ibid., p. 4.

17. J. R. Mandel, "Job Shop Challenges Materials Handling System" (Mechanical Engineering,
April, 1958), pp. 77-80.

18. P. J. Klass, "Video-Sonics Cut Production
Defects," Aviation Week (Jan. 4, 1960), pp. 75-76.

19. J. F. Muth and G. L. Thompson (eds.),
Industrial Scheduling (Englewood Cliffs, N.J.:
Prentice-Hall, 1963).

20. W. F. Pounds in Ibid., p. 5.

21. A. S. Manne in Ibid., p. 185 ff.

22. A. S. Manne, Economic Analysis for Business Decisions (New York: McGraw-Hill, 1961), p.
108 ff.

23. J. F. Muth and G. L. Thompson, op. cit.,
p. xi.

24. H. L. Wattel (ed.), The Dissemination of
New Business Techniques: Network Scheduling and
Control Systems (Hempstead, N.Y.: Hofstra Univer-
sity Yearbook of Business, vol. 2, Jan. 1964).

4

TRENDS IN
PROFITABILITY

by Fred Halmos

The past profitability of the electronics industry bears importantly on its ability to sustain
itself in any difficulties which it might face in
the future. It is accordingly pertinent to inquire
into the performance of the industry and into the
ways in which it has chosen to allocate its overall
capital. The first edition of this work included a
comprehensive review of the financial statements of
128 firms in the electronics industry, divided into
components producers, systems producers, and large
diversified companies. All of them were, of course,
public corporations.

The most important conclusion drawn from an examination of the profitability of the firms from
1953 to 1961 was that the industry exhibited a generally declining trend in profitability. This was
based both on a consideration of net profits on net
sales and, even more strongly, on an analysis of net
profit on invested capital. Accordingly, the present revision of the chapter focuses on this aspect
of the industry's performance.

As shown in Table 4.1, the ratio of net profits
to invested capital for the components group has continued its decline. Median net profit rate in 1967
was less than one-half what it had been in 1953, and
the upper decile also shows a lower value than in
any of the other three years listed. The lower
decile shows some improvement but is still at def-
icit level. A very similar picture emerges from
Tables 4.2 and 4.3 which present the same information for the systems group and the large diversified
companies. Finally, Table 4.4 presents a summary
for all firms in the sample and, again, demonstrates
a generally declining picture of profits.

TABLE 4.1

Ratio of Net Profit to Invested Capital for
Components Group 1953, 1957, 1963, and 1967

Ratio of net profit to invested capital percent	1953		1957		1963		1967	
	No. of firms	Per-cent	No. of firms	Per-cent	No. of firms	Per-cent	No. of firms	Per-cent
Deficit	1	3.8	7	18.4	12	23.1	4	11.1
0 – 9	5	19.3	7	18.4	9	17.3	18	50.0
10–19	12	46.2	18	47.3	22	42.3	11	30.6
20–29	6	23.1	2	5.3	5	9.6	3	8.3
30–39	1	3.8	–	–	1	1.9	–	–
40 and over	1	3.8	4	10.6	3	5.8	–	–
Total	26	100.0	38	100.0	52	100.0	76	100.0
Median, percent	15.4		12.5		12.1		7.3	
Lower decile	3.2		-20		-13.4		-2.9	
Upper decile	29.0		42		27.6		18.4	

TABLE 4.2

Ratio of Net Profit to Invested Capital for
Systems Group 1953, 1957, 1963, and 1967

Ratio of net profit to invested capital percent	1953		1957		1963		1967	
	No. of firms	Per-cent	No. of firms	Per-cent	No. of firms	Per-cent	No. of firms	Per-cent
Deficit	—	—	2	5.1	11	22.4	3	8.6
0 – 9	2	8.3	9	23.1	10	20.4	20	57.1
10-19	10	41.7	11	28.2	18	36.7	9	25.7
20-29	9	37.5	8	20.5	7	14.3	3	8.6
30-39	1	4.2	1	2.6	1	2.1	—	—
40 and over	2	8.3	8	20.5	2	4.1	—	—
Total	24	100.0	39	100.0	49	100.0	35	100.0
Median, percent	19.5		17.3		11.7		8.2	
Lower decile	14.0		2.1		-31.0		.9	
Upper decile	36.0		50.5		27.3		19.3	

TABLE 4.3

Ratio of Net Profit to Invested Capital for
Large Diversified Companies 1953, 1957, 1963, and 1967

Ratio of net profit to invested capital percent	1953		1957		1963		1967	
	No. of firms	Per-cent	No. of firms	Per-cent	No. of firms	Per-cent	No. of firms	Per-cent
Deficit	–	–	–	–	5	20.0	1	4.8
0 – 9	1	4.3	5	20.0	8	32.0	12	57.1
10–19	9	39.1	10	40.0	7	28.0	6	28.6
20–29	8	34.8	6	24.0	3	12.0	2	9.5
30–39	2	8.7	3	12.0	1	4.0	–	–
40 and over	3	13.1	1	4.0	1	4.0	–	–
Total	25	100.0	25	100.0	25	100.0	21	100.0
Median, percent	21.3		17.0		8.8		9.1	
Lower decile	11.4		5.0		-35.0		4.4	
Upper decile	47.7		35.0		28.3		17.7	

TABLE 4.4

Ratio of Net Profit to Invested Capital for
All Firms in Sample 1953, 1957, 1963, and 1967

Ratio of net profit to invested capital percent	1953 No. of firms	1953 Per-cent	1957 No. of firms	1957 Per-cent	1963 No. of firms	1963 Per-cent	1967 No. of firms	1967 Per-cent
Deficit	1	1.4	9	8.8	28	22.2	8	8.8
0 – 9	8	10.9	21	20.6	27	21.4	50	54.3
10–19	31	42.5	39	38.2	47	37.3	26	28.2
20–29	23	31.5	16	15.7	15	11.9	8	8.7
30–39	4	5.5	4	4.0	3	2.4	–	–
40 and over	6	8.2	13	12.7	6	4.8	–	–
Total	73	100.0	102	100.0	126	100.0	92	100.0
Median, percent	18.1		15.0		8.1		8.2	
Lower decile	3.1		.5		DEF.		1.2	
Upper decile	37.5		47.3		27.4		18.2	

The sample of firms considered has also shrunk from its 1963 level. The difference in firms in each case is in part due to the fact that not every one had published a fiscal year 1967 financial statement at the time this revision was made. However, an even more significant aspect of the matter is the fact that 13 out of the 52 firms listed in 1963 in the components group have since been merged into another, and 9 systems firms have had the same experience. The diversified firms have largely remained independent. This raises the interesting speculation that perhaps component firms are considered more desirable merger partners than systems firms, but without further study one would be reluctant to make such a statement categorically.

The industry has, of course, continued to see an influx of new firms, some of them quite successful, though many of these are not publicly owned at this time. In general, however, it is undeniable that the industry is showing symptoms of maturity, and this, in turn, may tend to make it rather less flexible in responding to the challenge of conversion than would be the case in a more uniformly new industry that is still at its pioneering and extensively risk-taking stage.

PART **|** **|** NEW MARKETS

CHAPTER **5** OFFICE
AUTOMATION

by Earl J. Stresing

INTRODUCTION

The automation of clerical functions has long
been the principal objective of the office-machine
industry, which has increasingly been joined in this
task by that part of the electronics industry specializing in computers. Within the last few years,
computers have become widely used. There are very
few large firms that do not at least have one installation, and their use is spreading continually. It
is therefore important to inquire into the nature of
these systems and the degree to which they have already established a market. In this chapter, the
basic systems and their relationships to the organization are first explored. The process of adopting
data processing systems creates operational problems
for management which must be solved. The market potential is then expressed in terms of the physical
size of the market and the needs yet to be fulfilled
in office-automation systems.

A substantial increase in paperwork during recent
years has given impetus to automation as a means of
handling the ever growing volume. In some cases, a
large volume of paper generates only a small amount
of useful information. Normally, a manufacturing
company uses 200 to 250 elements of information but
requires between 500 to 1500 forms to generate it.[1]
In 1953, it cost $1.17 to get a business letter dic-
tated, typed, and delivered to its recipient. In
1968, it cost $2.49, which is 2.1 times as much. In
spite of continual wage increases of clerical staff,
moreover, typing speed has not materially increased
in the last 20 years or so.[2]

Contrary to expectations, the paperwork growth
has not confined itself to the larger companies.
Its rate of increase is about equal for the various
sizes of industrial concerns as shown in Table 5.1.
Though the table goes back a few years, it reflects
a phenomenon that is still continuing.

TABLE 5.1

Paperwork Growth

Company size	Annual sales volume (millions)	Percentage increase of paperwork growth over sales
Small	$ 1 to 9.9	36
Medium	10 to 49.9	45
Large	50 to 99.9	39
Very large	100 and up	38

Source: Thomas Kenny, et al, "Office Productivity: New Paths of Profits," Dun's Review and
Modern Industry, vol. 76 (September, 1960), p. 46.

The ratio of clerical to other employees is
steadily growing. One person out of every twenty was
in a clerical or closely related job in 1910. By
1958, the figure had changed to one out of every
seven. As will be shown later, this trend continues.
To increase industrial production by 700 percent
during the past 50 years, 85 percent more factory
workers have been required. During this production
increase, office work also increased by 450 percent,
necessitating the addition of 46 percent more clerical workers.[3] Thus far, automation has inhibited
rather than stopped this growth, but in many cases it
has been the means of extending the work force to
meet a work load that simply could not have been met
manually.[4]

The information management uses has to be timely,
consistent and efficiently produced. Automation is
capable of meeting these requirements and has, in

many applications resulted in improved management
control based on more efficient reporting.[5] Because
automated systems handle repetitious tasks so well,
management by exception is not only possible but
practical as well.

Prior to the computer and integrated data processing, office operations were not considered an area
worthy of top-level attention. Now, achievement of
immediate cost savings in this area is frequently
given as one of the reasons for automating. Table
5.2 indicates the other classifications of cost
savings goals management anticipates from the use of
automated systems. Even though a firm ranks greater
accuracy, timesaving, and new information very highly,
it undoubtedly expects monetary results as well because of reduced data cost and a more efficient management. The results of a study by the System and
Procedures Association (SPA) indicated that of the
82 firms studied, almost all of them expected some
net cost savings.[6]

Increased clerical costs caused by inadequate
methods of handling a growing volume of paperwork
create a financial drain on businesses. It has been
claimed that as much as one-half the cost of admin-
istering a major company in this area can be charged
against the processing of information, and there
is no reason to expect that the importance of the
function will diminish in the future.[7]

TYPES OF SYSTEMS

Most office functions concern themselves with
handling information, changing it into a form suitable for managerial interpretation, and decision
making. The major clerical functions are reporting
and recording. Clerical tasks are those which are
essentially copying, information retrieval, and pattern recognition. Automation in one form or another
may be used to perform the basic functions of recording, storing information, and converting data to
organizational uses, such as inventory, production
control, payroll preparation, customer billing,
accounting, and others.

TABLE 5.2

Anticipated Savings from the Use of
Automated Equipment

Objectives	Objectives by number of companies and order of importance[a]		
	First	Second	Third
Clerical laborsaving	11	5	–
Equipment saving	4	1	1
Spacesaving	2	–	1
Timesaving	2	3	6
Greater accuracy	2	5	4
Overcoming clerical labor shortage	2	2	3
New information	–	2	4

[a]Some of the companies listed several objectives as being of equal importance to them.

Source: Leon Greenberg, et al, Adjustments to the Introduction of Office Automation, U.S. Department of Labor Bulletin No. 1276 (May, 1960), p. 10.

Achieving automation for the office is a matter
of application and of systems design, that is, of
deciding what machine or machines will take the routine and repetitive work, speed up its handling, and
do it more effectively than any other operation will.
This design and selection process has created three
types of systems. Listed in order of increasing complexity, they are storage and retrieval systems, Electronic Data Processing (EDP) and Integrated Data
Processing (IDP). Storage and retrieval is essentially a record-keeping function in which rapid access
tends to be the major operational problem. EDP concerns rather routine and repetitive operations, such
as invoicing premium bills for insurance companies,
or payrolls, which are thereby automated. IDP is the
total set of record keeping for a business, including
information for the financial, operating, marketing,
and planning activities and implying the at least
attempted optimization of business operations under
varying conditions.

The problems in adopting any of these are of two
general kinds, the development of the necessary equipment and, at least equally important, the definition
of the problem, the program, and the software in general. From the viewpoint of a diversifying electronics firm, the former set of activities is
naturally the most important and the one in which
the firm is likely to be most competent. Accordingly,
the present discussion focusses on the equipment
rather than on the systems-software aspects. This,
however, is in no way to minimize their importance.
Quite to the contrary, there has been an extraordinarily high casualty rate among firms seeking to
enter the computer field and its ancillary areas,
and some of these casualties have been among the
leading American corporations. Much of this sorry
record can be traced to an inability on the part of
the manufacturer to devote adequate resources to enable their potential customers to use the equipment
efficiently and integrate it with their operations.

The simplest systems are those concerned with
storage and retrieval. In general, these must deal
with large numbers of individual items that are in
part required only infrequently, such as major file
records. The problem thus resembles at times that of
the library, which also has its automation problems,
considered in a subsequent chapter. As a result,

there are several design alternatives for the actual
storage medium which may range from microfiche and
microfilm to ordinary computer tape and, indeed, to
microfilmed tape, so as to minimize tape storage
space. Tape systems are generally meant for situations in which a voluminous set of data must be
scanned fairly often, as, for example, active inventory records. Tape readers and tape units are expensive, and thus it is usually not practical to have
many of these units working simultaneously without
each having a fair amount of work to do.

Microfiche, on the other hand, fulfill the requirements of giving extensive information; for consisting as they do of sets of microfilmed pages
mounted on a card, they can be stored at low cost
and retrieved by several electromechanical systems.
For example, land-title records for Nassau County,
New York are now placed on microfiche and can be retrieved merely by entering the section, block, and
lot numbers on a keyboard, whereupon the microfiche
is delivered to the operator or requestor who may
then peruse it in a document viewer. The Mosler
Selectriever, which is the core of the system, can
retrieve any of the 200,000 records stored and present it to an operator, display it on a TV screen,
create a duplicate card, or prepare a regular copy
of the information. A controlled flow of air sorts
out the documents which are housed in specially constructed files. In line with the first requirement
of such storage and retrieval systems, i.e. that
they save space so as to help pay for themselves,
this unit saved 90 percent of the previously required space.[8] (Parenthetically, one wonders if such
systems could not be used to end the expensive practice of repeated title searches whenever property
changes hands rather than of accepting the records
up to the last purchase.)

Tape does not store anything in facsimile but
rather in digital form. This is no drawback because
it is possible to reconvert the information into
plotted curves, alphanumeric text, tables, and even
engineering drawings. The digital storage has its
greatest application in situations in which some
work has to be done on the data, e.g. adjusting an
inventory balance without necessarily looking at each
item in detail. Thus, for example, in an inventory-
control system, it is possible to have the tape
changed daily or, indeed, after every transaction,

but to retrieve only the information or incipient
shortages, spoilage, or other conditions requiring
action.

Finally, of course, we must on no account neglect the value of the well-established punched card.
It has many of the advantages of the microfiche in
that it can be stored and retrieved at relatively
low cost, as well as of tape, in that it can be used
as a direct input to computation, which can generate
new cards as an output if needed. A major disadvantage is the relatively slow input and output rate of
card information--a matter of some concern when very
large numbers are involved--and, perhaps even more
importantly, that the information capacity of each
card is relatively small so that many cards are required for even a limited program of information
storage.

Microfilm seems sure to play an important part
in EDP and IDP as well. A variety of systems have
now been developed for entering a computer output
directly onto microfilm. Some systems such as that
of Datagraphics (a subsidiary of General Dynamics
Corp.) use a camera, obtaining its information from
a cathode ray tube, which in turn presents the computer output. A development of the 3M Company now
uses an electronic beam recorder which operates
directly on microfilm and is then developed by heat
instead of chemicals. The purpose of such systems
is to eliminate the line printer which, although
greatly speeded up over the years is still very slow
compared with the output capabilities of the computer.[9]

One problem remaining is the useful application
of all the information that is gathered and processed
in this way. Certainly, little is gained by rapid
processing of information which is afterwards stored
in a data bank, never to be used again. It is thus
essential for users to be sure that the information
is actually required for decisions and for operational reasons. Obviously, rapidly produced payrolls, premium notices, and similar documentation
are ends in themselves and are acted on by many different recipients. The matter is different when the
output relates to decision making by the firm, for
then the physical volume of information cannot extend beyond the capacity of human beings to compre-
hend and act upon it. This is, and remains, a problem

in the implementation of IDP, to which the answer
lies in the automation of simple decisions, such
that only exceptional situations are actually recorded and brought to the attention of management.

Two other subsystems are of interest here, because they have often enabled firms to enter the
market with a good idea without necessarily or immediately running up against competition from the
giant corporations that have fought over the computer market itself. One such set of systems concerns
remote terminals and computer-to-computer communications. Another is data scanning directly so as
to eliminate punched cards or other specialized inputs; of course, it is also possible to generate
cards or punched tape as a byproduct of conventional
typing, as in the Friden-Flexowriter invoice machines
which even small firms use. Dataphones are based on
several approaches, and, as will be shown in the
next chapter, there is even some problem about their
use in conjunction with the telephone system. A
reported extension of the concept actually uses a
computer which again makes use of a touch-tone phone
and performs many of the identification and input
needs; apart from this however, the AUDREY (for AUDio
REplY) system answers with a human voice derived
from a photographic memory tape.[10] In summary, then,
the new computer subsystems rely not only on purely
electronic technology, but on its integration with
optical, chemical, and mechanical concepts; frequently such multidisciplinary approaches are potentially within the resources of firms now in the
military-electronics industry.

THE SIZE OF THE MARKET

The impetus for the installation of equipment
for office automation comes largely from the availability of systems that make an effective contribution
toward stemming the rise of administrative overhead,
which has been a pervasive feature of American industrial development throughout this century. Melman
has drawn attention to the role of this phenomenon
as a counterpoise to the much more spectacular productivity improvements of production workers.[11] It
is clear that if systems can be made available to
potential customers at costs justifiable by savings,
substantial extra business would result.

This section primarily concerns itself with the
physical extent of present installations and the market for future ones, based on the number of large
offices now in existence. In this manner it is then
possible to estimate the extent to which markets have
already been penetrated.

As shown in Table 5.3, there were 59,400 installed computers in 1967 in the United States, triple
the number of five years previously. Of these, 63,4
percent were IBM units. The group with rentals up
to $5,000 a month is the largest, accounting for
about half of all units. Indeed, about 80 percent
of the units rent for $10,000 or less. Thus, there
is still impressive evidence of the central position
in the market which IBM continues to hold, and it
also seems that computers can be obtained for modest
amounts. Still, the rental data have important implications for the computer market.

The question is: What relationship does this
large number of computers have to the number of offices potentially able to use them? Even though the
price has come down, it is still true that only
larger office operations can typically make good use
of computers, since they alone have the capacity of
getting the benefit of its analytic output. Even a
relatively low computer rental of $6,000 per month
would be the equivalent of about a dozen office
workers. Certainly, at present the market of computers is small for offices with fewer than 100 employees. It is possible that smaller offices can
become markets if present efforts to make computers
suitable for small operations are successful, whether
by time-sharing or small, cheap, individual units.
Accordingly, size categories from 25 office workers
up were investigated.

There are no published data that give employment by size class of office alone. The surveys that
exist, notably the Census and County Business Patterns
do, however, classify all relevant establishments
by size class of total employment. In Table 5.4,
the number of establishments in the larger size
classes in manufacturing, transportation and public
utilities, wholesale trade, retail trade and finance,
insurance, and real estate are given. It is clear
in all of them that the number of establishments
drops rapidly with increase in size class and follows
the familiar reverse-J distribution of such data.

TABLE 5.3

Number of Computers Installed in USA, by
Manufacturer and Average Monthly Rental, 1967

Manufacturer	Total[a]	AVERAGE MONTHLY RENTAL $(000)					
		0-5	5-10	10-15	15-30	30-60	over 60
Autonetics	36	36					
Bailey Meter Co.	14						14
Bunker Ramo Corp.	297	278	19				
Burroughs	1,370	73	1,170	129	20	59	
Control Data[b]	2,107	957		29	10		
Digital Electronics Inc.	10						
Digital Equipment Corp.[b]	2,186	2,073	23	21			
Electronic Assoc. Inc.	36	15		20			
EMR Computer Div.	94	59	26	9			
General Electric	1,600						
Hewlett-Packard	93	93					
Honeywell	2,740	1,241	1,250	90	89	21	
IBM[b,c]	37,700	16,500	13,650	1,400	3,000		
Interdata	33	33					
NCR	2,893	2,164	625	104			
Pacific Data Systems	135	135					
Philco	44	16				28	
RCA	1,190	160	720	148		8	
Raytheon	234	222					
Scientific Control Corp.	38	38					
Scientific Data[b,c]	980	825			155		
Standard Computer Corp.	7						
Systems Eng. Labs	79	78					
Univac Div. of Sperry-Rand	5,340	4,300	507	131	90	232	82
Varian Data Machines	143	143					
Total	59,400	29,439	17,990	2,081	3,364	348	96

[a] Includes installations where rentals straddle several class intervals or are not known.

[b] Data incomplete or unavilable.

[c] Data estimated by Computers and Automation.

Source: Computers and Automation (March, 1968), pp. 62-64.

TABLE 5.4

Establishments and Employees by Industry Group and
Selected Size Classes, First Quarter 1966

Industry group	No. of employees (000)	Number of reporting units	Number of reporting units by employment size class				
			50-99	100-249	250-499	500+	
Manufacturing	18,722	299,541	25,259	19,614	7,736	5,886	
Transportation and public utilities	3,365	129,359	5,113	3,008	892	756	
Wholesale trade	3,593	302,016	7,738	3,044	495	182	
Retail trade	9,449	1,071,618	14,273	5,586	1,444	998	
Finance, insurance, and real estate	3,110	326,437	4,810	2,682	729	500	

Source: U.S. Department of Commerce, Bureau of the Census, County Business
Patterns, 1966, U.S. Summary, CBP-66-1 (Washington, D.C.: U.S. Government Printing
Office, 1967).

83

To convert this information into numbers of establishments by size class based on office employment, the first task is to determine the proportion
of clerical and kindred workers in each major industry group. This is done in Table 5.5. The proportions range from 13.6 percent in retail trade and
12.0 percent in manufacturing up to 45.7 percent in
finance, insurance, and real estate. These percentages are then applied to the class intervals used in
Table 5.4. This, of course, produces unequal class
intervals for each line in the table. However, it
is possible to rearrange the groups proportionately
in each class interval and to arrive at a new common
distribution by office size.

The final results are shown in Table 5.6. There
are an estimated 22,490 offices with 25 to 49 employees and 19,092 offices with 50 or more. A finer
breakdown of the latter can only be estimated. If
one takes the 100 and over group of the total as the
same proportion as that in transportation and public
utilities, wholesale trade and finance, insurance
and real estate combined, one can plausibly estimate
the number of offices with 50 to 99 employees as
13,000 and the rest, or 6,092, as having 100 employees or more.

These numbers are not large compared with the
number of computers already installed, and it is evident from the above results and the number of installations that much of the potential has already
been tapped, at least to the extent of first installations.

The future market will therefore have two major
determinants. The first is uptrading, in which simple systems with limited tasks are traded in for more
elaborate ones able to interpret data for an ever
wider range of jobs, including systems which are
able to assemble and process information from many
locations and treat many business problems simultaneously. A second influence in the market is likely
to be a continual decline in price in much the same
way as it has happened in many electronic-consumer
products, such as radios and television sets. There
is some evidence that this is occurring in connection
with new systems that try to bridge the gap between
the electronic desk calculator and the computer.
There is no doubt that price competition has entered
this field, but it remains to be seen to what extent

TABLE 5.5

Percentage of Clerical and Kindred Workers
in Selected Industry Groups, 1965

Industry group	Clerical and kindred workers as a percent of group totals
Manufacturing	12.0
Transportation and public utilities	24.2
Wholesale trade	21.7
Retail trade	13.6
Finance, insurance and real estate	45.7

Source: U.S. Department of Labor, Bureau of Labor Statistics, "Special Labor Force Report No. 69," Monthly Labor Review (July, 1965), p. A-23.

TABLE 5.6

Number of Offices by Industry Group
and Selected Size Classes, 1966

Industry group	Number of reporting units by approximate size class of office employment		
	25-49	50-99	100 and over
Manufacturing	10,306	9,514	
Transportation and public utilities	2,076	1,439	1,066
Wholesale trade	2,335	819	262
Retail trade	3,143	1,760	
Finance, insurance and real estate	4,630	3,072	1,160
Total	22,490	19,092	

Source: Tables 5.4 and 5.5.

these smaller computers can furnish all of the useful
information which a management requires.[12]   As in
all data processing, the benefit which certain kinds
of information can confer upon a business must be
carefully evaluated and judged against the cost of
obtaining that information. Obviously, cheaper computers make such evaluations much more favorable to
the eventual acquisition of the machine.

One problem which will have to be solved is
that of making peripheral equipment cheaper than it
is at present. Much of the price decline in computers has been due to the miniaturized solid-state
circuits which, once manufacturing quality control
problems have been solved, can be produced at rather
low cost. Such advantages, however, do not arise
in equipment which must physically handle reports,
such as printers, or which must read cards or other
forms of input. Some of these subsystems involving
microfilm or other media discussed earlier in this
chapter may prove highly useful in making the price
decline among computer systems rather more uniform.

The most important issue, however, still remains that of successful systems design. Suitable
mathematical models must be devised for a good many
functions which are not now easily handled by means
of computer systems. The industry has had an impressive growth, but it cannot stake its future on
the excessive elaboration of administrative tasks
and on the further rise of administrative overhead.

NOTES

1.   Thomas Kenny, et al., "Office Productivity:
New Paths to Profits," Dun's Review and Modern Industry, vol. 76 (September, 1960), p. 46.

2.   IBM Corp., Advertisement, Business Week
(March, 1968).

3.   Thomas Kenny, op. cit. p. 46.

4.   George M. Muschamp, "Tomorrow's Integrated
Offices and Plants," Automation, vol. 8 (May, 1961),
p. 47.

5. B. F. Ells, "Automation for the Small Business," _Office Executive_, vol. 35 (June, 1960), p. 22.

6. _Ibid._, p. 21.

7. L. E. Bermont, "New Frontiers in Office Technology," _Credit and Financial Management_, vol. 63 (November, 1961), p. 9.

8. "Land-Title Records Microfilmed for Automatic Retrieval," _Data Systems News_ (November, 1967), p. 23.

9. "Computer Gets Fast Running Mate," _Business Week_ (June 8, 1968), p. 84.

10. "GE Develops AUDREY - a Talking Computer," _Computers and Automation_ (January, 1967), p. 58.

11. S. Melman, _Dynamic Factors in Industrial Productivity_ (New York: Wiley, 1956), pp. 69-94.

12. "Tiny Computers Lead a Price Decline," _Business Week_ (May 11, 1968), p. 108.

CHAPTER **6** AUTOMATION
OF DISTRIBUTION

by Lawrence J. Wackerman

INTRODUCTION

The area of greatest potential sales of electronic equipment in the area of distribution is that of accessory equipment for major computer systems, for the acquisition, transmission, and display of data. The trend is towards complete EDP integration of manufacturer, transporter, distributor, retailer, buyer, and bank. This chapter deals, primarily, with examples and projections of this trend and offers suggestions for the diversifying company wishing to capitalize on it.

The biggest need in business today is information to assist management decision making. Many companies are seeking improved information systems. New computers are being installed at a rate of 500 per month. The aim is complete integration of information from all company functions through a central computer: the automation of information. Electronic equipment to make these systems more efficient and economical offers a large market.

One author predicts the direct and immediate relation between profit accounting for an individual product and its production. When the computer determines that a product is unprofitable, it shuts down the production line.[1] Another author predicts complete integration of all functions of a major oil company: production, transportation, refining, distribution, and marketing. He says:

> What is needed are powerful management decision making tools and methods that will help to keep track of what is happening, as it

> happens, throughout the total organ-
> ization. . . . These requirements
> for timeliness suggest the need for
> frequent or continuous acquisition
> of data on primary operational re-
> sponses and the processing of infor-
> mation by an automatic means on a
> centralized basis.[2]

In the automation of distribution, two areas of
need will be considered: (1) types of systems for
the functions of choosing of products; ordering; recording, billing, and reporting; shipping and transportation; payment; and (2) specialized components
associated with these functions, mainly for input to
EDP systems. Several of these are, in turn, keys to
major markets in their own right.

TYPES OF SYSTEMS

Choosing of Products

The first step in distribution is informing the
potential customer about the product being offered.
Today this is done through advertising, publicity,
door-to-door selling, retail stores, shows and exhibitions, displays, direct mail, and catalogs. In
predicting the future, it has been suggested that
some day consumers will shop at home viewing products
on color television and placing orders by dataphone.
But on the basis of cost, color television could never replace a cheaply printed, excellent quality, full
color catalog, and it would take too many six-cent
postage stamps to amortize a dataphone.

Sears, Roebuck & Co. and others are finding
catalog sales are increasing and profitable. Sears'
catalog sales increased 50 percent between 1955 and
1962 to $1,150 million. Sixty-two percent of these
orders, or $713 million, are received by phone or
mail. Sears puts a catalog into its customer's hands
for $1.80. Total cost of its 50 million copies is
$90 million, or about 12.6 percent of catalog sales.[3]
At these costs, it would be more realistic to develop
electronic equipment to help the seller handle orders
and speed information than it would be to try to put
electronics in the home for shopping.

At present the technical work associated with
the dataphone centers mainly on being able to use
conventional telephone circuitry for the purpose.
For example, the Computer Telephone Corporation has
a system which permits alphanumeric phone-to-key-
punch translation, using any standard ten- or twelve-
button touch tone telephone. A template is placed
on the telephone keyboard, and without further change
to the equipment the instrument is in effect converted to a miniature control console or special
purpose keyboard for the data entry job being done.
The system is claimed to be effective for order entry, credit checking, and banking transactions as
well as shopping by phone.[4]

Another automated approach to giving the consumer the opportunity to choose a product is the
vending machine. In some applications it has proven
an economical method of selling, and the operation
of these machines offers possible new markets, for
example, electronic heating and cooling of foods and
ultrasonic cleaning of food-handling parts, two currently recognized needs.[5] Automatic computation of
receipts and inventory, transmitted to a central
control, is a potential sophistication.

Coin-operated devices were dispensing tobacco
in English pubs and American taverns in the 1700's.
In 1930, a major breakthrough came in this field
with the invention of a slug ejector.[6] In 1962,
sales in this country through four million vending
machines reached $3 billion, twice the 1958 volume.[7]
Of all sales, 40 percent are cigarettes, followed
by beverages, cookies, and candy.

The vending machine has thus not revolutionized
retail selling and automated merchandising has not
always worked well. Wilbur B. England reports on a
1950 test in marketing such items as low-priced
leather goods and jewelry in vending machines in a
public location. In commenting on the failure of
this test, England states, "People did not want to
buy higher priced items ($1 or above), nor did they
seem to want to buy style goods in a vending machine. . . ." He also felt that the test was too
short; that the public needs to be educated to the
purchase of goods in vending machines for at least
two years.[8] A. R. Andreasen comments on a more recent test: grocery marketing in vending machines
placed in a shopping center. This test was labeled
"unsuccessful" by the management of the store that

conducted it. Andreasen feels that more promotional
effort, higher prices, and more shopper conveniences
could have made this venture profitable.[9]

Louis Stein, President of Food Fair Stores, Inc.,
feels that one quality which has made the small Food
Fair Groceries a success is friendly, courteous services. Speaking of the housewife, he says, "Above
all, she likes personal service and we make sure our
services stay personal, too, no matter how big the
store is."[10] With self-service generally adopted,
however, such service may lose its appeal in time
particularly if the elimination of such service helps
keep prices down.

The vending machine has not revolutionized retailing. The feasibility of its doing so is still
open to question. It can work well in a captive situation, such as feeding of plant personnel since they
have little choice but to use machines or bring their
own food. But in selling the public, limited tests
have failed. Is it because people like to deal with
people? Do they like to compare competitive products
side by side on the shelf, handle them, read labels?
Or is it because investors have not been willing to
gamble on large-scale, long-term tests?

For the present a principal market deterrent of
vending is the lack of an adequate and fully reliable
banknote-recognition device. Such units are available, both as changemakers and direct inputs to vending systems; for example, in some Western states,
there are self-service gas stations with vending
units that accept dollar bills. The gasoline is
sharply discounted and, one would think, this is a
potent argument. However, in most localities, there
may be considerations of safety that would argue
against wide adoption of this merchandising method.
Some other self-service stations have nothing more
than a remote reading gasoline pump, with the customer paying at a nearby store, after having served
himself.

The issue of automated choice of product for the
consumer has its industrial counterpart. Many firms
with a product line that must serve many different
conditions but is still standardized enough to cover
most conditions without requiring special components
have tried certain set methods to satisfy their customers. One of the more elaborate systems is that

of the A.O. Smith Corporation of Milwaukee. The company offers its customers for oil field casings a
computerized program which uses data on drilling
pressures, the physical properties of drill casings,
geological characteristics, etc., to specify the
cheapest grade of casing that will do the job.[11]

Ordering

In the automation of the seller's internal procedures, order processing is a logical place to start
because it triggers all other functions. Order processing includes editing of orders, preparation of
shipping orders, preparation of bills of lading, invoicing of customers, and control on the accuracy of
these steps. M. C. Rue has given details of an extensive system used by Johnson and Johnson in New
Brunswick, N. J. Among other purposes, EDP is used
for relief of finished goods inventory-by item, preparation of sales statistics--by product, group,
sales area, salesman, customer, cost of sales reporting, information for forecasting purchasing needs,
production planning and scheduling, finished goods
inventory, accounts receivable, traffic analysis,
and customer mailing list.

The justification for such a system is not merely the efficiency with which it performs the function
of order processing but in the other benefits it produces in the eyes of the management which pays the
bill. The existence of valid justification of this
type is an important consideration in anticipating
market demand for new improved equipment.

Chrysler Corp. had for years been plagued with
problems in inventory control. Improved methods were
needed in the updating of inventory records, the
continuous screening of these records to detect trouble areas, and the reporting of these trouble areas
so that corrective actions could be taken. The company therefore established what is referred to as a
"computer subsystem, centered at headquarters including random access files and a network of on-line
terminals." The system is composed of an IBM 360,
model 40. On line with the computer is a bank of 14
IBM 2311 magnetic disc units, with over 100 million
characters of storage. IBM 1050 data terminals at
assembly plants, supplier's warehouses, etc., give
direct access to the disc files for data input or
retrieval purposes. An IBM 2702 transmission control

unit directs the data flow between terminals and the
computer. A typical working of the system is as follows: When demand is heavy for a particular part and
stocks are reduced to the reorder point, the computer
automatically sends advance notice to a supplier who
can contact the computer through a terminal device.
If the computer gives an "OK," the supplier can ship
the product while the computer has recorded that the
parts are on the way. The system has built-in accuracy and validity checks to ensure reliability. The
outflow of reports is kept to a minimum as the computer reports only those things which have gone awry.
Because of the high degree of accuracy, management
by exception has become a workable reality at
Chrysler.[12]

Direct Order Recording and Invoicing System
(DORIS) is another example of beginning distribution
automation with the customer orders but under different conditions. This system was developed in England
by Creed and Co., Division of International Telephone
and Telegraph Company. It uses standard machines
and components.

The Shell-Mex and British Petroleum Ltd. depot,
where DORIS is being tested, delivers 6 million gal-
lons of assorted petroleum products a month. Eighty-
five percent of orders are received by telephone.
DORIS permits processing of all orders with just one
clerk. He operates a console, pressing buttons for
input to the system: customers' names (up to 3,000
in memory), type of product, quantity, delivery date,
package, transportation method, and " . . . special
instructions, "which prints an asterisk on an output
ticket on which he writes instructions. If any essential input is omitted, DORIS notifies the clerk.
When input is complete, clerk presses "End of Order"
button, then, calling on punched tape memory, the
system prints invoice and sales tickets which go to
a routing clerk, and it records the order on punched
tape. Daily shipments are tallied after delivery.
Detail and summary tapes are sent daily to a central
office for processing.[13]

A system like DORIS or Chrysler's could be adapted to any distribution point which receives a large
percentage of orders directly from customers. A central office receiving machine-readable input from
numerous distribution points could then accumulate

data and quickly produce the reports described by
Rue. Also, inventory at various points could be re-
plenished more efficiently.

A recent development in the automation of ordering is a significant step toward total integration.
It is the use of dataphone communications between
buyer and seller which is proving advantageous for
repeated orders of low value, high-volume items. In
Los Angeles, seventy suppliers are using or planning
to use telephone-ordering devices with necessary back-
up equipment.[14]

Recording, Billing and Reporting

Ordering, of course, is only one input to a
larger central system. Information must be processed
for useful output. The processing needs and the money available for this service vary greatly, from
small scale purchases of service to large investments in computer installations.

For the smaller users who cannot justify the
expense of automation equipment, the growth of data
processing service centers and the packaged programs
they offer indicate the demand and the nature of automation needs. Input tapes are usually prepared as
by-products of other functions performed by the customer: purchase order preparation, posting of inventory, invoicing customers, and posting of accounts
receivable. Typical analysis available are sales by
customer, salesman, and product.[15]

The continuing increase in speed and capacity
of computer systems increases their salability for
high volume functions. The Bell Telephone Company
of Pennsylvania installation at Conshohocken, Pa.
illustrates this point.

This office maintains the accounts of 300,000
telephone subscribers. During an average day, it
handles 300,000 calls, issues 15,000 bills, receives
15,000 payments, reviews and updates all 300,000 accounts and reports data. Magnetic tape units store
names and addresses, telephone equipment items, coin
telephone information, directory delivery address
and credit data. The system produces reminder notices on unpaid accounts, issues collection notices,
reviews credit ratings, analyzes deposit records,
and prepares refund checks. It has excess capacity
which is used for internal functions, such as payroll.

Such a system, of course, requires expensive
equipment. When installed, it used two IBM 1401's
for input-output conversion, with an IBM 7070 for
central processing. The 7070 can read 62,500 magnetic tape characters per second, and has in-process
magnetic core storage of 100,000 decimal digits.[16]

Shipping and Transportation

In the automation of distribution, the integration of the physical handling of goods with the foregoing record-keeping functions. For example, the new
parts warehouse at the Fisher Body Plant in Euclid,
Ohio has been elaborately automated to eliminate hundreds of manual materials handling and record-keeping
operations. The warehouse receives, stores and keeps
over 4,000 different supplier parts used in GM assembly plants across the U.S. and Canada. Because of
this, its efficiency is central to the entire GM complex. The end product includes: an automated, computer controlled, high density warehouse that takes
advantage of height, cuts down on labor costs, increases the speed of storing and retrieving, and provides the warehouse with an up-to-the-minute daily
inventory, which is coordinated with production needs.
The system works like this:

1. Parts arrive by truck and are sorted manually.

2. Sorted cartons are put into standard carts
which double as storage bins.

3. Cart contents are recorded on punch-cards
which accompany the cart.

4. A "train of carts" is pulled by a driverless
tractor which follows a buried cable to the storage
area.

5. In the storage area, carts are placed automatically near any one of 15 cranes depending on cart
size.

6. When in position, the punch-card is inserted
into a special reading device that activates the computer which selects the nearest empty bin and directs
the crane to move the cart to that bin.

7. The computer remembers the location of the
parts, and when a punch card order is received, the

computer knows where to find it and automatically
takes the steps necessary to deliver the parts to
the order assembly area.

The unique thing is that this is the first fully
integrated computer controlled automatic warehouse,
and it will no doubt serve as a model for many warehouses to come.[17]

Payment

A necessary part of buying is paying, or transfer of credit. In business this involves the banks,
which must therefore be considered in anticipating
total integration of distribution information. Banks
could be easily integrated, for example, through adoption of an automated version of the British Credit
Transfer system.

This system is simple in concept. A debtor does
not write checks to each creditor in payment of bills.
He writes one check in the amount of total bills for
the day and sends it to his own bank. He also sends
credit transfers instructing his bank to credit the
accounts of his creditors at their banks. His bank
processes the check and returns it with copies of the
transfers. No check clearing is necessary. The creditor receives the processed transfer as notification
that the bill has been paid and his account has been
credited.[18]

Using an ordinary typewriter to prepare input
to an optical scanner, this system could be highly
automated:

1. The seller prepares an invoice showing,
along with other information, the amount due, buyer's
purchase order number, and the bank and account number to which he wants payment credited. This is done
during automated order processing. Amount is posted
to accounts receivable.

2. The buyer places the invoice in the optical
scanner. The invoice is read, checked against purchase order and receiving department report stored
on tape. If these do not match, invoice is rejected
with discrepancies noted. If they do match, information is typed on a continuous, daily credit transfer form and posted to accounts payable. At the end

of the day, transfers are totalled, and a check is
printed for signature and the amount debited to cash.

3. The buyer's bank places the check and daily
credit transfer form in its optical scanner. The
check is compared with the buyer's account to see if
sufficient funds are available. If so, the amount
of the check is deducted from the account, and each
seller's account is credited at his own bank via
Telex transmission.

4. The seller's bank receives the Telex trans-
missions as input to its system. Seller's account
is automatically credited and a confirmation of credit transfer printed for the seller.

5. Finally, the seller places this confirmation
in his optical scanner, and the system automatically
credits accounts receivable and debits cash.

This scheme would largely supersede the only recently installed system of check accounting by banks,
based on Magnetic Ink Character Recognition (MICR).
As discussed in more detail in the next section, this
was a major development in its own right from the
viewpoint of subsystem development. However, its
actual use by banks varies. Though nearly all have
it now, some only use it for routing the checks between banks rather than posting to accounts. In any
event, the real automation issue here is the elimination of physical clearing of many checks and of
their distribution to the original issuer.

Such schemes would eventually involve instant
payment, perhaps by means of telephone codes punched
in by "touch-tone" instruments. Problems of confi-
dentiality and security arise here, of course. Besides, one of the objectives of such a system, from
the banks' viewpoint, would be the reduction of
"float," i.e. delays within the present payment process and the ability to charge interest on even short
delays in payment, as if they were revolving credit
accounts. In part, such a system would be expected
to offset recent more insistent demands by consumer
groups for interest payments on demand deposits, a
practice which has not existed in the U.S. for some
forty years. A nationwide cashless, checkless system, quite apart from its technical complexities,
thus raises social and political issues as well.
Such a system seems far off, therefore, but its potential subsystems may be expected to engage the

careful attention of major computer manufacturers
as well as innovating manufacturers of peripheral
equipment and subsystems.[19]

SPECIAL SUBSYSTEMS

In putting into effect systems such as those
described in the last section and extending them to
further areas of distribution, major problems remain
in the translation of information into a form that
the machines can use and in the conversion of machine
output back into human terms. Although some progress
has been made, the available solutions either are
still too expensive or have practical drawbacks. For
example, in anticipating the use of electronics in
retailing, the concept of an electronic cash register
transmitting data directly to a computer is as appeal-
ing as the idea of shopping at home with color television. But again cost makes the difference, at
least in the near future.

There are more practical systems now in operation. For example, a retail price tag can be made
much like punched tape, which then serves as direct
input to a computer. The tags are generated on receipt of goods. When a sale is made, the tag becomes
direct input for cash and inventory accounting. Also,
mechanical accounting machines are available which
produce punched tapes, to be processed internally or
by an outside service. When these systems were first
proposed, it was believed that they would be associated with point-of-sale inputs with significant
electronic content. However, what eventually happened was either simple mechanical devices that im-
pale the tags on clips suitable for the processor or,
even less costly, ballot boxes. Thus, even widely
adopted systems may sometimes fall considerably short
of the market potential envisaged.

Other systems are much like the sense-marking
methods long employed by IBM and other punched card
systems, in which a carbon deposit on paper made by
a soft pencil is sensed by two electrodes side by
side which then transmit the signal. A variant of
this system uses a code of long and short dashes to
read all information required for the processing of
gasoline credit cards. Such a system is not directly
readable but the information is also printed in regular numbers.

The most successful automatic input form is
MICR, referred to before. It represents a method
whereby computer inputs are directly readable by man,
rather than adapting a computer to interpret human
speech, writing, or the ordinary printed word.

In 1965, it was estimated that Americans wrote
some fifteen billion checks. This huge volume is
expected to increase by another billion each year.
In 1956, the American Banker's Association recognized the problem of handling such volumes of checks
and recommended the use of magnetic ink as the best
solution. The MICR system was worked out in detail
during 1957. The system was recommended for national standardization after its successful use during
1958 by the Bank of America, using a General Electric accounting machine. By August, 1962, according to a Federal Reserve System survey, 97 percent
of all commercial banks were issuing encoded checks--
six years from inception to saturation.

MICR uses a special type font called "E 13B,"
designed by Stanford Research Institute. It is
printed on magnetic ink containing iron oxide, making it optically readable by humans and magnetically
readable by machines. Checks are issued with the
bank's ABA and transit routing numbers and the account number of the customer already printed in MICR
numerals. When the check is received, the dollar
amount is added in magnetic ink along with identification of the check-processing method to be used.
With all necessary information in machine-readable
form, checks can be processed at speed limited only
by the capabilities of the equipment. Checks can
be sorted today at a rate of 1,600 per minute.

But MICR is not very readable, and it only can
function with numbers. The ideal input is the printe
word. It can be easily read and prepared without
special skills and equipment. An optical scanner is
a device that can read printing into a computer. Its
development is still open to competition, since no
manufacturer has introduced a dominant product, that
is one that answers most of today's input requirements. But optical scanning is proving its usefulness: An oil company reads customer account numbers
from credit card invoices; a large company reads
stockholder numbers, geographic area codes, and
dollar amounts on dividend checks; a telephone company reads customer telephone numbers, billing cycle

number, credit symbol, and amount from cash stubs
returned with bill payments; a food company reads
salesman number, customer number, and dollar
amount from sales journals of 250 field offices; the
Air Force converts typed messages to teletype tape
for transmission.[20]

Optical scanners, as input devices to electronic automation systems, offer a replacement market for present systems and new markets for the
automation of functions now requiring the human eye
and mind. The human process of converting input information into machine-readable form would be eliminated. Most documents could be prepared on an
ordinary typewriter and used both to inform humans
and as machine input. Input could be prepared at
locations remote from processing centers where special equipment is now required to prepare punched
cards and punched or magnetic tapes; fewer and less
skilled operators would be required.

The first practical scanner was developed in
1952. Now virtually every major business machine
company markets an optical scanner, and the machines
are becoming more sophisticated and versatile. Rates
exceeding 1,500 characters a second are now possible;
this output corresponds to that of 150 keypunch machines. At present most readable information must
be printed in certain fonts determined by the requirements of the individual scanner, but typewriters and similar machines can be easily equipped
with these. In order to make different kinds of optical scanners compatible with each other, the U.S.A.
Standards Institution has established a subcommittee
on character recognition, which is supposed to establish a single alphanumeric and symbol type font
that can be used by all machines. Optical scanners
are still quite expensive machines, and so they find
their principal use in firms such as the oil companies mentioned above, public utilities and insurance companies which traditionally have very heavy
loads of paper work of a fairly uniform character.
Another major application is, of course, in the
field of credit card accounting by banks and specialized firms in which return stubs, invoices, etc.
are read, and the data are fed into the computer
with accounts automatically prepared and adjusted.

As to specific machines, one recent item is the
IBM 1287 optical reader, which has extended its

capabilities into the much more difficult hand-
printed realm by recognizing the ten digits and the
letters c,s,p,x and z. Designed for use with the
IBM System/360, the 1287 reads machine printed and
credit card imprinted numbers as well as handwritten
numbers in any combination from paper forms and cash
register or adding machine journal rolls. Data
transmitted directly from source documents eliminates
the need to convert pencil written or printed numerical data into punched card machine language before
processing. IBM solved the problem of variations
in handwritten numbers by a technique called "curve
following." Projected by the 1287's optical sensing unit, a tiny flying spot of light scans lines
of fields of numbers on the document. When the flying spot crosses any part of a handwritten or printed
number, it traces the outline of the number before
moving cn. The values of the numbers traced are
interpreted by the logic components of the machine
and are automatically transmitted through cable connections to a System/360 for processing.[21]

The high-speed output of modern computers presents the problem of producing printed information
fast enough to permit computers to operate at capacity. Fast equipment can print 1,000 lines per minute. A recent development of Benson-Lehner Co. can
print 29,000 lines per minute on microfilm from magnetic tape. Basic price is $79,900. However, hard
copy can be produced at only 900 lines per minute,
using an added optical camera. The first commercial
model of this computer is being built for a bank.
All branches will send data to a central computer at
the end of the day; next morning, each branch will
have an updated, microfilm record of all accounts.[22]

High-speed print-out devices, then, are yet another example of potential areas of development for
new entrants to the market. The reversal of the
optical scanning process suggests the use of cathode-
ray tubes for printing information on photo-sensitive
paper at line speeds equal to their scanning rate.

COST CONSIDERATIONS

The decision to invest in equipment to automate
production is based primarily on the effect on unit
production cost, with the number and kind of units

specified by marketers. The decision to automate
distribution, however, is based on the effect of
less predictable, interacting variables. The mar-
keter, the man to whom this equipment must be sold,
is assigned the task of maximizing the product "profit per unit" times "number of units sold." Profit
per unit is affected by the cost of sales, administrative, clerical and physical distribution labor,
and by real estate, delivery, customer services,
warehousing, packaging, and other direct cost. Price
affects both the profit per unit and the number of
units sold. The number of units sold depends also
on quality of sales personnel, design, advertising,
promotion, timeliness, number of outlets, reputation,
and quality of service.

To sell successfully to the market, therefore,
the electronics manufacturer must first determine
what devices can contribute to profit by affecting
these variables. The amount of increase of anticipated profit would then determine the price at which
such devices could be sold.

Anticipating profit increases is extremely difficult for the marketer-customer. One cannot accurately predict in advance, for example, the increase in
sales that will result from institution of a new
customer service. Marketers may often make decisions
based only on judgment, incomplete market research,
limited tests, and even intuition; seldom on demon-
strable fact. To the extent that this is true, it
has two implications:

1. The manufacturer entering this market must
take special pains to displace engineering-oriented
marketing department with experienced consumer and
industrial marketers,

2. The very nature of the customer's problem
offers a market for devices which can add to his
information, giving him more useful facts at the
time he needs them. This is why ADP equipment is
now being used in distribution and why it offers a
large potential market there. The examples of current automation cited earlier in this chapter depend heavily on ADP for increased information flow.

In game theory, there is Expected Value of Perfect Information (EVPI). The quest for perfect information continues as a recurrent trend in distribution today. The first example is a new system

which, besides cost savings, brought new information
for management, such as profit or loss on individual
sales, product cost variances from standard reduced
inventory investment, and improved customer service.

James H. Hawarth, Jr. reports on pay-out justification for installation of an IBM 305 RAMAC system, to replace the existing punched card system,
for the integration of accounting production, inventory, and customer-service programs. Management
approved the recommendation on the assurance that
after thirty months, accumulated savings would exceed accumulated operating costs and that after sixty
months, accumulated savings would exceed accumulated
operating cost plus pre-installation cost.

Pre-installation cost.

Programming activity	$13,800.
Preparation of site	13,400.
Miscellaneous (panels,	
wires, transportation,	
forms, revision, etc.)	2,410.
	$29,610.

Monthly operating cost.

Rental of equipment	$ 4,422.
Personnel	522.
	$ 4,954.

After five years, total accumulated cost will be
$326,850, which should then be equalled by total
accumulated savings.

A look at conditions after ten months indicates
this assignment will be met. At this point, the
monthly savings rate had reached $2,840; accumulated
savings were $16,024. Savings resulted from (1) re-
duced rental of equipment used in previous system:
407 accounting machine, 519 reproducing punch, 085
collator; (2) reduced labor cost: release of one
clerk and two operators and transfer of one operator.
Hawarth states: "We now predict that the payout
point may be reached in about three and a half years.

The second example is of a computer used primarily for production control at Symington Wayne
Corp., Depew, N.Y. Among other justifications for
this system, one is relevant to this chapter:

> Business volume is up. At the pre-
> sent rate, it may mean the firm can
> handle an additional $1 million
> worth of business by the end of the
> year(1963). Reason: The computer
> system enables the company to meet
> promised delivery dates via im-
> proved scheduling and production.[24]

Here production automation has given marketing an
opportunity to sell more units.

The third example is of an electronic switching
system to improve communications, at reduced cost,
between headquarters, sales offices, plants, and
parts warehouses of Chrysler Corporation. This digital computer system, built by General Electric,
will handle three times as many messages as their
old "torn-tape" system, having an 18.8-million char-
acter-memory capacity. Renting for less than $12,000
a month, at executive insistence, it cost 12 percent
less than mechanical equipment formerly rented from
American Telephone and Telegraph Co. (AT&T). Beside
the lower rental, Chrysler expects to save $100,000 a
year in Western Union telegram cost. In the future,
Chrysler also plans to save another $100,000 in
leased Teletype circuits by transmitting over already
leased telephone lines. Chrysler also plans to provide added information for marketers by means of a
new memory capacity to store all service information
on cars under its five-year or 50,000-mile warranty
and to give all sales offices immediate, complete
histories.[25]

The last example of justification in the broad
information area is the management-information system, now being installed by Lockheed. By the end
of 1964 it had 850 input stations, wiring five division managers into one network of Automatic Data
Acquisition(ADA). By 1964, savings in administrative
costs were expected to have paid for development and
engineering costs. Additional savings of 4 million
dollars are expected in reduced clerical work. Sig-
nificantly it is stated that the " . . . real pay
off is in the speed and accuracy of the information
the system will flash to management."[26]

It is essential to note here that EDP systems
which have justified their cost are in the minority.
A recent survey of 27 companies using EDP for four

years or more revealed that two-thirds of these systems have yet to show net savings, even in the current year.[27] This would seem to indicate that many
users are still far from convinced of the usefulness
of the information which they receive or of the actual value of the speedup in its presentation.

MARKET POTENTIALS

In spite of the remaining problems standing in
the way of successful application, there is little
doubt that purely on the grounds of productivity lag,
there is reason for automating distribution if it
can be done economically. Distribution has been
lagging behind many other fields. For example, total
selling expense was shown to have increased from 6.7
percent of sales in 1954 to 10 percent in 1961. This
represents an increase of 50 percent in the share of
selling expense of total sales. Of this substantial
change, moreover, most (88 percent) was due to increases in nonadvertising expense.[28]

Another demonstration of the relatively poor
productivity of distribution is obtained by comparing the number of manufacturing employees to those
in retail and wholesale trade. As shown in Table
6.1, the number of employees in those fields per employee in manufacturing has increased steadily since
1920. From 1930 to 1950 the proportion remained
fairly stable, in the first decade no doubt due to
generally depressed conditions and the second due to
the growth of self-service outlets.

Since 1960 there has been very little change in
the ratio of wholesale and retail employees to manufacturing employees, and the same may be said of the
relationship between nonsupervisory wholesale and
retail employees and production workers. Since 1962,
moreover, there has been a sizeable increase in the
number of employees in wholesale and retailing, on
the order of 450,000 a year since 1963. This is a
considerable number. If half of this increment could
be avoided by the expenditure of $2,000 per worker
involved, a market of about $450 million would result.
This is a very large amount, although it will be recalled that there was an increase of $500 million in
the total data-processing market between 1965 and
1966. On a more modest estimate, an electronics expenditure of only ten dollars per employee applied

TABLE 6.1

Number of Manufacturing, Wholesale and Retail Employees and
Inter-group ratios, Selected Years 1920-1966

Year	Total employees (000) Manu-facturing	Total employees (000) Wholesale & retail	Wholesale & retail employees per manu-facturing employee	Number of production workers in manu-facturing (000)	Number of non-supervisory wholesale & retail employees (000)	Non-supervisory wholesale and retail employees per production workers
1920	10,658	4,467	0.418	N.A.	N.A.	N.A.
1930	9,562	5,797	0.606	N.A.	N.A.	N.A.
1940	10,985	6,750	0.614	N.A.	N.A.	N.A.
1950	15,241	9,386	0.615	12,523	8,742	0.697
1960	16,796	11,391	0.678	12,586	10,315	0.822
1962	16,853	11,566	0.687	12,488	10,400	0.834
1963	16,995	11,778	0.693	12,555	10,560	0.840
1964	17,274	12,160	0.704	12,781	10,869	0.851
1965	18,062	12,716	0.706	13,434	11,358	0.845
1966	19,186	13,211	0.690	14,273	11,786	0.826

Source: U.S. Dept. of Labor, Bureau of Labor Statistics, Employment and Earnings Statistics for the United States, 1909-1967, Bulletin No. 1312-5, Sec. I (Washington, D.C.: U.S. Government Printing Office, 1967), pp. 45, 686.

to the 1966 figures would reflect an electronic investment of almost $132 million. In short, the
record keeping and distribution functions of business offer substantial prospects for new equipment.
Particularly in the peripheral areas of input and
output there is still a possibility of substantial
involvement of new firms, since even the major manufacturers are often content to put their own labels
on equipment manufactured for them by specialist
firms. The technical and economic problems in this
field at any rate have not been solved yet to an
extent sufficient to foreclose market entry of new
firms by way of the ordinary processes of technical
innovation and commercial development.

NOTES

1. G. M. Muschamp, "Tomorrow's Integrated
Offices and Plants," Automation, (May, 1961),
pp. 35-50.

2. George M. Stankiewicz, "Integrating
Corporate Functions for Optimum Performance,"
Automation, (November, 1963), pp. 63-65.

3. "Putting Out the 'Wish Book' is a Complex
All-Year Production at Sears", New York Times,
(May 19, 1963), sec. 3, pp. 1F and 14F.

4. Advertisement, Computer Telephone
Corporation, (Washington, D.C., 1968).

5. "Quarters, Dimes and Lots of Nickels
Count Up to Profits for Suppliers, "Steel, (cf.
England, H.B.R., passim, November 11, 1963),
pp. 51-55.

6. Wilbur B. England, "Automatic Merchandizing,"
Harvard Business Review, XXXI, (November-December,
1953), pp. 86-94.

7. "Quarters, Dimes . . . ", Steel, op. cit.

8. England, op. cit.

9. A. R. Andreasen, "Automated Grocery
Shopping," Journal of Marketing, XXVI, (October,
1962), pp. 64-66.

10. "You Have to Change to Grow," Business Week (March 2, 1963), pp. 48-52.

11. "Computer Helps Firm Clinch Sales," Steel (Oct. 12, 1966), p. 44.

12. "For Your Inventory Management: Superb Control over Changing Variety," Modern Materials Handling (October, 1967), p. 43.

13. "Project DORIS--Direct Order Recording and Invoicing System," Automation (May, 1961), p. 39.

14. "How Automated Phone Order Systems Cut Costs on MRO Purchases," Purchasing Week (Dec. 2, 1963), pp. 20-21.

15. "Computers Service Cards, Tape, by Mail," Purchasing (May 22, 1961), p. 115.

16. "Computers Begin Telephone Billing Operation," Automation (May, 1961), p. 16.

17. "The Stackers and Computer Are Really One Machine," Modern Materials Handling (August, 1967), p. 46.

18. Westminster Bank Ltd., Credit Transfers (ca. 1962).

19. "Money Goes Electronic in the 1970's," Business Week (Jan. 13, 1968), p. 54 ff.

20. Joseph B. Mahony, "Optical System Reads Printed Data," Automation (September, 1963), pp. 82-83.

21. "IBM Shows Optical Reader to Interpret Handwritten Figures," Management Services (January-February, 1967), p. 11.

22. "Speeding Up Computer Output," Business Week (April 13, 1963), p. 103.

23. James H. Hawarth, Jr., "We Are Keeping Track of Our Computer's Pay-out," N.A.A. Bulletin, XLIII (April, 1962), pp. 78-84.

24. "Computer Plots Foundry Profit Moves," Steel (Nov. 4, 1963), pp. 94-95.

25. "Chrysler's Computer Does the Talking
Faster and Cheaper," Business Week (Aug. 24, 1963),
pp. 52-53.

26. "Millenium for Decision Makers," (editorial), Business Week (Aug. 10, 1963), pp. 54-56.

27. John T. Garrity and John P. McNerney,
"EDP: How to Ride the Tiger," Financial Executive
(September, 1963), pp. 19-26.

28. McGraw-Hill Publishing Company, How Advertising Affects the Cost of Selling (New York, 1963),
p. 22. Note: 1954 figures were calculated by
McGraw-Hill from results of a survey of 99 companies,
made by the National Industrial Conference Board.
Figures for 1961 were calculated by McGraw-Hill from
their survey of 893 companies. Results were rear-
ranged by the author to illustrate "Nonadvertising
Increase" in selling expense as a percent of sales.

CHAPTER 7 AUTOMATION OF
PROCESS INDUSTRIES

by Jon Blauner

BASIC CONCEPTS

In this chapter, the new markets for electronic
equipment related to the process industries are examined. Process industries are taken here to include
the chemical process industries, which in turn include
petroleum, food and paper, the primary metals industries, and the production of electricity. All of them
are characterized by the continuous transformation of
streams of material or energy. By their nature, they
require the continuous flow from one unit operation
to the next, that is, materials handling is automatic.

The industries concerned have long made use of
automatic controls. Many of their unit operations
could not be controlled by man acting alone. Thermo-
stats and pressure and flow controls have long existed, largely operating pneumatically and electrically. The introduction of electronic components has
mainly been a factor in an evolution toward a "closed-
loop" system of control encompassing the entire process. Under a closed-loop system, the intermediate
or final process streams are monitored according to
their composition or other characteristics, and the
process controls are set by the computer.

Physically, such a system requires sensors
which act as inputs to a computer. The computer in
turn makes adjustments to process controls, which
then assure the proper balance of temperatures, pressures, and flow. The sensors and computers contain
the bulk of the electronic applications that have
been proposed. Although there have been successful
closed-loop applications, they are relatively difficult systems to design and develop. Examples of them
are still relatively few compared, say, to the use of
computers in offices.

111

This chapter first presents a description of some
of the systems that have been used, discusses some of
the problems of their economic justification, and
lastly discusses the market in terms of the physical
limitations set by the number of units for which the
electronic controls could be used.

The market for this type of industrial-control
system is characterized by a need for a variety of
specialized components which still permit considerable scope for the imaginations and enterprise of new
firms. In sensors, controllers, actuators, and recorders, as well as other industrial aids, market
growth as indicated earlier in Chapter 2 has been most
impressive, rising from $250 million in 1963 to $416
million in 1966. It is not easy to estimate what part
of this total properly pertains to process controls
alone, but is probably not less than $280 million,
which makes it by far the biggest component of the
controls market.

TYPES OF SYSTEMS

The most costly element in an electronic-control
system is the special computer which forms a part of
it. There are two major types, the analog and the
digital. Although it still has its place, the analog
computer is now considered to be largely on its way
out, though it is still found, especially in open-loop
systems in which human intervention occurs at one
point or another. As Stout puts it:

> Data loggers (analog computers)
> cost $50,000 to $100,000 or more,
> depending on the number of variables
> involved. Justification for such
> expenditures was to be found in
> better data, for both accounting
> and engineering use; elimination
> of some standard recorders; and
> reduction in clerical labor needed
> to get routine accounting data from
> process records. In general, bene-
> fits proved less than adequate to
> justify the investments, and data
> loggers never became popular. Their
> functions are now performed in a
> growing number of plants by digi-
> tal computers.[1]

One of the disappointments concerned the process of getting the better data. The control system was not automatic enough to permit any substantial reduction in operating staff, and the provision of automatic loggers often mainly produced idle time for operators who could not in any event be dispensed with. Indeed, in some cases, this led to a significant increase in boredom on the part of operators and an undesirable feature in processes where dangers of fire, explosion, or expensive loss of material and plant may occur.

From a functional viewpoint, moreover, the analog computer is limited by not having a memory, and this restricts its ability to react to process conditions. By contrast, the digital computer operates as a counting device and is able to interpret a variety of mathematical formulations of the underlying process by using its memory. There are two major types used in industrial processes. Special purpose computers are only able to deal with a limited range of tasks. In effect, they have a fixed program, able to respond only to one general type of process. The general purpose computers resemble the ones used for clerical automation, inventory control, and scientific calculations and are programmed in the usual manner to deal with a variety of processes. Computers of this type may be used on a shared-time basis for a variety of operations, perhaps merely to determine set-points of controls rather than continuous monitoring. In either case, there is a need for correct programming, allowing for a proper response to a wide variety of process conditions.

Here is one of the main functional inadequacies of many of the currently proposed systems. Not enough is known of the relationship between the process variables to devise a scientifically rigorous model which, given variations in raw materials, can operate the plant at optimum levels of efficiency in order to produce a specified output. In some instances, it is even a matter of not knowing what the crucial variables are or of inability to measure them fast enough to service a continuously operating control system. This, for example, is still the case in the high-speed measurement of the moisture content of paper. To solve such problems, the producers of control equipment have resorted to empirical methods, for example, gradient analysis, in which it is determined by experiment what happens when each variable is changed within a practical range. Precise knowledge of the physical phenomena is then unnecessary.

The computer systems used are now of several types, depending on the extent of automation, that is, of "loop closure." Increasingly, the more advanced systems are the ones adopted. In general, automatic plants use controls to regulate temperatures, pressures, and flows. An operator relays data to a computer that calculates the best combination of settings; then operators regulate the instruments accordingly. This is termed an "off-line computation and control unit."

By relaying the instrument readings directly to the computer and letting it receive the material electronically, an "on-line, open-loop computer control" is established.

In "closed-loop computer control," both the instruments and the control settings of the controls are connected directly to the computer.

In advanced systems now in use, called "supervisory closed-loop control," the computer sets thermostat-type controls. The computer does the same job as a human supervisor. The most advanced system is "dynamic closed loop control." In this, the computer reads the characteristics of output and process variables from the sensors, analyzes them, and adjusts valves and motor controls, based on process optimization.[2]

EXAMPLES OF SYSTEMS

The most notable installations of advanced process computers are heavily concentrated in four areas, electric utilities, petroleum, the chemical industry proper, and steel. The characteristics of representative systems and some of their operating problems will now be described.

Electric Utility Industry

Financially, it is easier for utilities than for many other industries to justify the cost of computer control. An average power plant has a useful life of thirty years, and equipment costs are spread proportionately. By contrast, the chemical

industry often requires equipment to pay for itself
in two years or less, making it harder to justify
the cost of a computer system.

Power-station design is more standardized, and
that makes it easier to apply computer-control procedures to one plant after another. In refineries
and chemical plants, every process is likely to be
radically different. Because of the essentially
noncompetitive nature of their industry, executives
of electric utilities tend to share their knowledge
with their opposite numbers in other firms. With
little secrecy about the technical features of power
plants, the industry's advance in technology is
cumulative, with relatively little duplication of
effort.

Power-plant engineers must look for even small
gains in efficiency and reliability. Power stations
are already at a high level of productivity; utilities
work on a rather narrow profit margin on a large
volume of output, and therefore improvements in
efficiency make a big difference in overall plant
function.

An argument in favor of computer control is the
attitude of leading power-plant engineers and de-
signers:

> Ebasco Services, Inc., and Bechtel
> Corporation are enthusiastic about
> the computer technique. Ebasco de-
> signed Louisiana Power & Light
> Company's Little Gypsy station,
> fifteen miles north of New Orleans,
> and Bechtel Corporation designed
> Southern California Edison Company's
> four stations, including the two
> Huntington Beach plants. The
> Louisiana station, which started
> up in March of 1961, was the first
> fully automated, closed-loop plant
> designed by Ebasco, using a compu-
> ter supplied by Daystrom Control
> Systems Division.[3]

Those projects had a forerunner that gave them
a basis of experience. Several years ago, Louisiana
Power and Light Company added a generator to its

Sterlington station in upstate Louisiana. It decided
then to install a computer to monitor but not run
the plant.

Daystrom Control Systems Division guaranteed
that the computer would operate more reliably than
any other commercial machine. Specifically, they
promised that the computer system would operate for
six months at better than 99 percent availability.
Daystrom pointed out that they "didn't mean reliability but availability--counting time for preventive
maintenance as non-available time."[4]

The computer performed better than its guarantee
and was accepted by Louisiana Power and Light Company
in March of 1960. Among its achievements was the
ability to make an efficiency calculation in 2
seconds, which used to take 24 hours. It ran continuously for the period March, 1962-December, 1962 at
99.992 percent availability, having been shut down
for only 30 minutes.

The cost for the closed-loop system at Little
Gypsy added $1.1 million to the cost of the plant,
a figure that checks closely with the incremental
cost of automating the Huntington Beach (Calif.)
unit for Southern Edison Company, which was designed
by Bechtel Corporation.[5]

Of the extra $1 million spent at Little Gypsy,
it is estimated that $630,000 is the difference
between the closed-loop control system and the lesser
instrumentation for automatic data-logging and computing.

The investment is justified on the basis of the
following expected savings: $1.5 million in reduc-
tion of major mishaps; $175,000 in fuel economy;
$500,000 reduction in manpower as soon as two more
computer-controlled units are installed at Little
Gypsy (construction was planned for completion in
1966); and $100,000 in reduction of routine main-
tenance.[6]

Paralleling the above, the following are the
benefits expected from the use of the computer
supervisory system at Southern California Edisons'
Huntington Beach operation:

1. Increased safety for personnel and equipment from major accidents.

The probability of a major accident should
be materially reduced under the precise direction of
the supervisory system, especially during start-up
and shutdown operations. The cost of one avoidable
four-month interruption plus the consequent cost of
replacement power during the operating history of a
2-Mw unit is estimated at $3,500,000.

2.   Improvement in continuity of service.

It is anticipated that the supervisory
system will reduce the number of unit outages because
of prompt corrective actions during emergencies.
When outages do occur, faster returns to service will
result than is possible under conventional control.

3.   Reduction in fuel costs.

A saving equivalent to 1/2 percent increase
in plant efficiency is expected because of continual
monitoring of plant performance and more precise
control.

4.   Reduction in operating costs (manpower).

It will be possible to operate the two new
units with eight fewer employees than conventionally
with a consequent capitalized saving of $738,000.

5.   Reduction in maintenance costs.

Although there will be some increase in
cost of instrument maintenance, a significant overall
saving will be realized in maintenance of major
operating equipment because of better temperature
control.

The estimated aggregate value of tangible
savings over the life of the equipment is $1,116,000
more than the initial cost.[7] Electric generating
power plants have always feared a breakdown in plant
function. Computer control provides a means of fore-
stalling breakdowns in the plant. With more accurate
supervision of critical operations and faster reaction, the computer system cuts mechanical breakdowns
to a minimum.

The electric utility industry has progressed
very far in its utilization of computers. Present
new installations, however, stress system-wide
applications. It is possible to integrate all power

plants in the system, to cut in various generators
according to criteria of overall optimizations, and
to centralize efficiency controls for each station.
One such system is currently being installed by the
American Electric Power system.[8]

Petroleum Industry

The first computer-controlled plant to turn
out a commercial product was built by the petroleum
industry. Texaco's automated polymerization unit
at Port Arthur, Texas has been operating for more
than three years. The petroleum industry also had
the first large computers to make calculations
directly from remote instruments, in the operation
of a fluid catalytic cracker of Standard Oil Co. of
California and a crude still of Standard Oil Co. of
Indiana and pioneered in the use of simulation techniques in the planning of production and distribution.[9]

At Standard Oil Co. of Indiana, the pipe still
processes 140,000 barrels of crude per day, yielding
ten product streams. For Standard Oil Co. of California, the fluid catalytic cracker takes 40,000
barrels a day; aviation and auto gasoline are its
primary products, with a secondary yield of light
gases-propane, butane, and ethylene. Both plants
are on line, "open loop," retaining operators to
set the controls, although instrument readings are
telephoned directly to computers without human intervention. Operating instructions from the computer
are interpreted and printed out on an automatic
typewriter in the control room.

Originally, both these projects used computers
on a limited basis, instead of devoting a medium-size
computer to the job full time. The larger units can
control much larger and more complex programs than
smaller control computers that now run "closed loop"
plants.

Standard Oil Co. of Indiana began to study
computer control at Whiting, Indiana, in 1959, at a
small operation for processing crude oil. The conclusion was that the output of a new, larger pipe
still could be increased substantially by improved
instrumentation, including the rapid analysis made
possible by a large computer. One point revealed
by the first study was that normally a human operator

would not feel justified in changing control settings
on the basis of a single instrument reading. Manually
operated stills would be unlikely ever to reach peak
capacity.[10]

The large still began operations in May, 1959,
and International Business Machines Corporation and
Standard Oil Co. of Indiana decided to install a
complete on-line operation. There were some 100
controllable variables affecting the yield of the
still, but only nineteen of these were considered
important enough to be included in the computer program. These nineteen had to be related to a set of
160 other considerations reflecting the physical
limits of the plant. The final computer program
consisted of 75,000 unit instructions.

The automatic recording equipment obtains
readings from 196 instruments. The scans, which
last about five minutes, are made almost continuously
and are sent by telephone to the computer center.
When it has three scans, the computer averages the
values and subjects them to logic tests. Then the
computer compiles any changes in settings that
would improve performance in the still and transmits
them to the human operators, allowing several controls
to be reset at once rather than one at a time.

Results of the system have not been made public,
but it is estimated that Standard Oil Co. of Indiana
will be able to reduce the programming by half to
three-quarters; a reduction that would put the cost
within the range of a smaller computer.

The company is planning computer control for
its Ultraformer, which upgrades the octane of gaso-
lines and should have the plant operational within
the year. There are also proposals for automatic
catalytic cracking and alkylation units.

The control project at the catalytic cracker
of Standard Oil Co. of California is more complex
than the one at Standard Oil Co. of Indiana. The
refinery is preprogrammed, via telephone line, by a
computer in San Francisco. By installing an "on-line,
open loop" control system with its own small on-site
computer the bigger computer operation in San
Francisco remains available for major problems.

Another well-known installation, however, shows
a possible limitation of this market. Phillips

Petroleum Company maintains computers for improving
processes and has bought units from several manufacturers. Phillips Petroleum maintains that no
manufacturer constructs a special purpose digital
computer as a standard item and has had to make up
eighty of its own special purpose computers from
modular components.

In 1960, Phillips Petroleum Company revealed a
detailed breakdown of a 16 percent increase in
ethylene production that a computer had helped secure.[11] The gain in efficiency paid for the experimental work and the computer in a single year, but
the breakdown showed that only six of the sixteen
percentage points came from the on-line use of the
computer. The other 10 percent were a permanent
gain, obtained through a revised schedule of set
points produced by the computer. The other 6 percent
of yield were no longer sufficient to justify the
computer, and therefore its use was discontinued.
It has since been used for other purposes. This
demonstrates, much to the disadvantage of potential
computer suppliers, that even the machine may at
times do its job too well.

At present, there are 27 computer units on
stream, formally announced or being initiated. Of
them, 11 are for catalytic crackers or similar processes, 3 in crude units or similar primary processes
and 3 in alkylation, polymerization, and reforming.
The remaining 10 units are used for pilot plants,
refinery optimization, blending or they are "mobile,"
that is, they can be converted to the solution of a
variety of production problems in different refinery
units.[12] This indicates that 37 percent of the units
now existing or shortly in prospect are not connected
to a single process. This possibility of duplication
cannot fail to reduce the ultimate market potential
of computer installations.

The Chemical Process Industries

Most of the present installations of computers
in chemical process plants are to be found in the
petrochemical industries. Among the earliest
installations were two units of the B. F. Goodrich
Chemical Company, producing vinyl monomer and
acrylonitrile and an ammonia plant of Monsanto
Chemical Company in Luling, Louisiana. Even these
early plants showed the possibilities of sharing

computer time. Both the Goodrich plants are run by
a single computer. Monsanto Chemical Company chose
the Luling plant for their initial control by a
digital computer because it was new and already
highly instrumented. It uses computers to adjust
set points on conventional pneumatic remote controls
with the objective of obtaining the highest potential
production from their Barton plant, which runs continuously. Capacity depends on the volume of gas
that its compressors can pass through the reaction
vessels, and this in turn is largely dependent on
the weather. A compressor is less efficient on hot,
dry days than on cool, damp ones. Humidity is also
a variable in the process, since the air pumped in
from outside enters the product stream and its water
content must be controlled. In adjusting the plant
so quickly to temperature changes, the computer can
produce a more efficient manufacturing operation by
maintaining peak production.

    Monsanto Chemical Company has indicated that
the instrumentation and controls that had to be
added to complete the closed-loop operation came
close to costing as much as the computer. Since the
computer costs in the neighborhood of $100,000, it
is likely that the whole installation of computer
control cost more than $250,000. Monsanto is also
presently using an $85,000 trailer-mounted analysis
complex. This should provide data to guide decisions
on installing computers.[13]

    At present, there are 45 computer installations
on stream, formally announced, or being initiated,
with the computer furnished by American firms. Seven
of these are abroad. Functionally, there is again a
large group able to do several tasks, with 12 units
listed as mobile or having general plant duties. A
further 12 units are for plants making ethylene and
other basic petrochemical inputs, 6 for the more
complex plastic monomers and plasticizers, 7 for
complete plastics and rubbers, and 3 are for other
processes, including two for inorganics.[14]

                    Steel Industry

    The first production unit involving digital
equipment, but not computers, was simply routine.
Punch cards were prepared that would, through reading
devices, automatically adjust the rolling mill for
each pass as a metal piece is run back and forth to

press it into sheet or plate. There are many suppliers of card-programmed rolling-mill controls.
Westinghouse Electric Corporation has installed
twenty-five since producing its first program in
1957 for Jones and Laughlin Steel Corporation. Many
have been installed by the General Electric Company
and the Square D Company.

The first card programs were compiled on the
basis of experience, a certain series of passes, for
a certain size of ingot, at a certain temperature.
But each alloy and size of ingot requires a different program, so the program cards kept multiplying
until some industry libraries now contain 25,000 or
so "routines."[15]

The company's next step was to use an on-line
computer to recalculate the number of passes and the
roll pressures according to changes in temperature
that may occur in the process. Presently, two rolling mills are almost completely controlled by computers. These processes begin when an ingot reaches
the roughing mill from the holding furnace. Its
temperature, weight, and measurements are taken automatically and sent to the computer. The computer
estimates the roll settings and the number of passes
through the rolls. All the computer requires is the
composition of the alloy and the size and gauge of
the coil or sheet that is to be manufactured. As the
metal passes through the rolls, its temperature is
measured continuously and the rolling pressure also
recorded. If this information does not agree with
the prearranged program, the computer automatically
recalculates the whole program and automatically
regulates the mill's controlling devices.

In the summer of 1960, Linde Company, Division
of Union Carbide Corporation, made public the results
of a simulation, on a large computer, of a blast
furnace operation. The variables were few, consisting of blast temperature and the oxygen and fuel
content of the blast, but they were the basis for a
complex mathematical model of the operation. The
computer performed the mathematics of the model,
largely the calculations of the heat balances. It
was estimated that this part of the study would have
taken fifteen years with manual calculations.

These simulations showed that production could
be boosted by as much as 30 percent by the best
possible combination of oxygen and fuel mixes,

pressures, and coke rates. Results of these simulations were questioned as to accuracy. Spot checks
were made in a blast furnace, and the tests found
few errors of more than 2 percent, none over 3 percent.[16]

It is estimated that there are twenty-seven
computers presently utilized in the steel industry.
As computer technology advances, it is possible that
one computer can do the work that several did before
and that shared time on a single supercomputer will
mean fewer though more complex units in steel-
making.[17]

The automation of the steel industry has been
beset by an additional problem which frequently occurs
in process automation, i.e., the design of suitable
sensors. Although thermistors for sensing heat and
transducers for pressure are well developed, they
have to be especially rugged and yet precise if they
are to be used successfully in a steady industrial
environment. Further, there is still no effective
method for measuring certain variables, such as, for
example, the temperature in the middle of a blast
furnace. The task of developing such sensors is
handicapped by the high cost of such work and by the
suspicion in some cases that even if a sensor were
developed, the variable which it measures would turn
out to be either insignificant or more easily inferred
from other data.

Other Process Industries

Two other applications of process control are
noted here briefly--those for the cement and paper
industries. The former are essentially controls for
the flow of material through the kilns which also
involve the sensing of temperatures and composition.
An important element of this task is a spectrogra-
phic analysis. There have been a number of experimental installations which have proved to be fairly
successful.

In the paper industry, the major task would be
to find a suitable control system for the Fourdrinier
machines. The objective here is to sense variables
such as moisture content, web width, and thickness,
and adjust the speed of the machine accordingly.

Just as in steel and in cement, the installation of
such equipment is still in part handicapped by sensor problems.

ECONOMIC FACTORS

The economic justification of electronic process
control systems today must rely on many factors beyond the labor saving which has been the traditional
justification for automated equipment. This is
because many of the industries which are now considered ripe for computerization are already heavily
automated by electro-mechanical and simpler electronic
devices. Reliance must, therefore, be placed in more
output from given raw materials or from a given
plant, improvement of quality of product in cases
where this can command a price premium, reduced fuel
consumption, and overall optimal allocation of company resources.

It is not readily possible to derive general
data on these factors and from them, to judge whether
the electronics industry has succeeded in solving
its technical and economic problems. Thus far,
results have been found to vary considerably among
installations. Even the cost of making a study for
a given firm may, in fact, be very costly, and
therefore the results are kept confidential. There
is no doubt, however, that the cost of a computer
includes substantial expenditures over and above the
basic equipment. As shown in Table 7.1, the required
application engineering matches and may substantially
exceed the cost of the computer itself. The costs
also show a substantial range of variation.

An additional factor concerns the problem of
economy of scale. In many cases, the application of
a computer to an existing plant can just produce
the modest increase in output which the firm requires
rather than compel it to install a new production
unit, which, following the trend in equipment size,
would necessarily have to be very much larger.

Under these conditions, the total economics of
a computer instrumentation must take into account
the computer installation cost (including application engineering), the total investment in the
plant, and the proposition of return on a total investment, which is attributable directly to the

TABLE 7.1

Required Application Engineering Costs of
Control Components for Advanced Control Systems Are
Usually More Expensive Than the Basic Computer Equipment

	Basic equipment		Required application engineering	
Conventional controls (per loop)	$ 750 –	1,250	$ 450 –	1,250
Stream analyzer or other special sensor	1,000 –	65,000	2,400 –	160,000
Integrated control (per loop, no digital computer)	1,200 –	1,500	2,000 –	3,000
Added costs for digital computer control	175,000 – 1,100,000		200,000 – 1,100,000	

Source: R. E. Finnigan, "Modern Process Control," International Science &
Technology (May, 1963), p. 38.

continuing work of the digital-control computer. The
latter point is important because of the previously
mentioned possibility of realizing substantial
economies merely through a single recomputation of
process set points. In his analysis based on these
concepts, Williams makes the following points:

1. An increased return on total plant investment of at least 0.5 percent per year is probably
possible on any process due entirely to the monitoring and long-term economic optimizing abilities of
the computer.

2. If a plant system shows that a return of
greater than about 6 percent per year is possible, a
serious engineering study should be made on the
possibilities of process improvement work in the
plant. After this, the plant should be restudied
to determine the remaining return on investment which
can still be credited to the computer.[18]

Figure 7.1, which is based on his study, shows
the allowable computer cost in relation to plant
investment if only monitoring ability is considered
in the justification. That is, there is an additional
0.5 percent return on total plant investment. Given
a value for the latter, it is clear that the justifiable installed cost of the computer goes up in
direct proportion to the payout time for the computer
itself. A two-year payout, for example, on a computer costing $57,000 could be justified for a plant
worth $10 million.

In Figure 7.2, the relationship between total
plant investment and justifiable computer cost is
plotted for various increased returns on total plant
investment, assuming a three year payout for the
computer itself. This decline indicates an area to
the right in which the monitoring ability alone
justifies the computer and an area to the left in
which further studies of the process are indicated.

There are two major conclusions to be drawn
from these graphs: First, computer control favors
large plants. This is due to the close relationship
between allowable computer investment and total
plant investment and to the fact that the cost of
computers for the same process is virtually independent of the capacity of the production unit. It
is also clear that, in spite of a declining trend
in computer prices, the units are not likely to drop

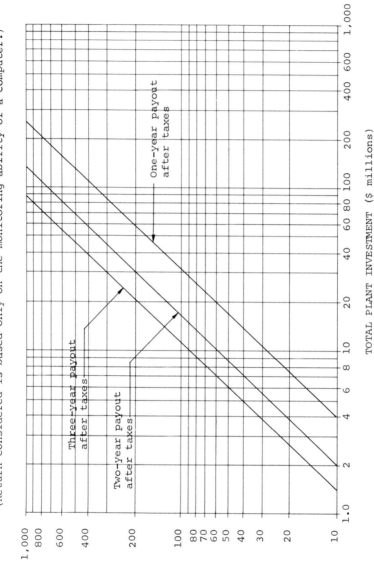

FIGURE 7.1

Justified Cost of a Computer Assuming an Annual 0.5 Percent Additional Return on Total Plant Investment

(Return considered is based only on the monitoring ability of a computer.)

Source: T. J. Williams, "Considerations In Applying Digital Computers In Process Control," Automation (March, 1962), p. 56.

127

FIGURE 7.2

Justifiable Computer Costs and Total Plant Investment for Various
Increased Returns on Investments
(Plot is based on a three-year payout of the computer.)

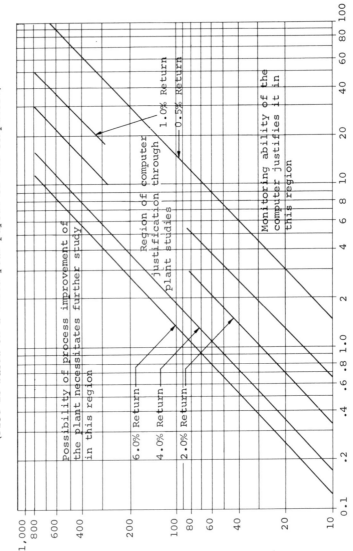

JUSTIFIABLE INSTALLED COST OF COMPUTER ($ Thousands)

TOTAL PLANT INVESTMENT ($ Millions)

Source: T. J. Williams, "Considerations In Applying Digital Computers In
Process Control," Automation (March, 1962), p. 57.

in cost below fairly substantial levels. Consider,
for example, a simple computer-control unit which
costs about $50,000 installed, ($20,000 for hardware). According to Figure 7.1, such a computer
could not be considered for its monitoring ability
in a plant costing less than $6 million for a
three-year payout period and $18 million for a one-
year period. The second conclusion is that new
plants are likely to justify computer controls more
easily than old ones, because the existence of
modern instrumentation makes the installation of the
computer less costly.

MARKET SIZE

     The market for process controls is circumscribed
by the number of units to which it can be applied.
In Table 7.2, the numbers of selected processing
establishments and items of equipment are given. It
is, unfortunately, not possible to obtain the numbers of suitable processing units in all cases,
but, actually, in view of the possibilities of shared
time it may well happen that there may ultimately
be single large computers running fairly substantial
plants and alternating between the control of different units.

     It is therefore not readily possible to trans-
late the results of Table 7.2 into the number of
process computers that may ultimately be required.
There can be no doubt that the number of units thus
far installed, as described previously in this chapter, is very small compared with the potential--pro-
bably less than 10 percent of what could be realized.
Nevertheless, there has to be a realistic estimate
regarding the ultimate dollar volume.

     Certainly, the table suggests that an annual
increase of 100 installations would be quite substantial. Yet, at an average expenditure of
$100,000 per unit for the electronics hardware alone,
(perhaps optimistic in light of the Westinghouse
unit) this represents a market of only about $10
million. These figures would have to be increased
by whatever share of application engineering has to
be borne by the electronics manufacturer. These
amounts are not large but would be additional to
the industrial-controls field as a whole, which has
had, and will no doubt continue to have, a high level

TABLE 7.2

Numbers of Selected Processing Establishments and Items of Equipment

Item		Number
Petroleum refineries		427[a]
Blast furnaces		236[b]
Open hearths		
Rolling mills:		
Copper rolling	112	
Aluminum rolling	212	449[a]
Rolling and drawing n.e.c.	125	
Fourdrinier machines in paper mills:		
No. of paper mills	820	
No. of pulp mills whether		1189[c]
connected with paper or not	369	
Cement mills:		
Capacity under 2 million bbl/year		71[d]
Capacity from 2 to 4 million bbl/year		86[d]
Capacity over 4 million bbl/year		127[d]
Basic chemical plants		
Alkalies & chlorine	38	
Industrial gases	456	
Cyclical coal tar crudes	36	
Intermediate coal tar prod.	141	
Inorganic pigments	96	2570[a]
Organic chemicals n.e.c.	464	
Part I inorganic chem. n.e.c.	674	
Privately owned & operated		
establishments	665	

Sources:

[a] U.S. Bureau of the Census, U.S. Census of Manufactures: 1963, vol. 1 (Washington, D.C.: U.S. Government Printing Office).

[b] U.S. Bureau of the Census, Statistical Abstract 1967 (Washington, D.C.: U.S. Government Printing Office), p. 771.

[c] R. E. Theummes (ed.), Lockwood's Directory of Paper and Allied Trades (New York: Lockwood Trade Journal Co., 1967).

[d] U.S. Bureau of Mines, Minerals Yearbook, 1966, vol. I (Washington, D.C.: U.S. Government Printing Office, 1965).

of activity based on nonmilitary electronic equipment. Between 1961 and 1966, the total controls
market more than doubled. Making an allowance for
other control fields in the piece parts and public
sectors yields a probable increment within five
years of $120 million over the present volume.

NOTES

1. Thomas M. Stout, "Process Control: Past,
Present and Future," The Annals of the American
Academy of Political and Social Science, vol. 340
(March, 1962), p. 37.

2. "Computers Start Running Plants," Business
Week (November 5, 1960), p. 37.

3. Ibid. p. 39.

4. Ibid. p. 40.

5. Ibid.

6. Ibid.

7. W. L. Chadwick, "Computers to Automate
Huntington Beach Units," Electrical World (January 18,
1960), p. 46.

8. "Computer Industry Chalks Up a Big Day,"
New York Times (April 30, 1963), p. 8.

9. "Computers Start Running Plants," op. cit.,
p. 41.

10. Ibid. p. 42.

11. G. L. Farrar, "Computer Control Comes of
Age," The Oil and Gas Journal (October 28, 1963),
p. 83.

12. Ibid.

13. "Computers Start Running Plants," op. cit.,
p. 44.

14. G. L. Farrar op. cit. p. 90.

15. "Computers Start Running Plants," op. cit.
p. 45.

16. Ibid.

17. "Computers Cut Steel Costs; Market Seen for
4,000 Units," Steel: The Metal Working Weekly
February 11, 1963), p. 98.

18. T. J. Williams, "Considerations in Applying
Digital Computers in Process Control," Automation
(March, 1962), p. 56.

CHAPTER **8** THE AUTOMATION
OF PIECE PARTS
MANUFACTURE

by David L. Dallob

INTRODUCTION

In the last decade, a sustained effort has been made to extend to piece parts manufacture some of the benefits of automation. The machines used in the manufacture of fabricated metal products, machinery, instruments, etc., have long included automatic features, beginning with the century-old back gear of the lathe. The more recent automatic machines, however, have generally required very large production lots in order to justify the elaborate tooling and setups required. For small lots, manual or semi-manual machines still retained a strong competitive advantage relative to the automatic machines, but only at a greatly increased unit cost when small lots were made. In solving this problem, it was realized that the answer did not lie in the very large specialized unit used, for example, in automobile and appliance manufacture. Rather, methods for producing small quantities economically were a principal objective in developing the new methods, in addition to such traditional aims as increasing the scope of the machining process to shapes and materials not hitherto successfully dealt with.

The numerically controlled machine tool has emerged as the principal answer to the above problems. In a short period, it has become a major product of its industry. Its importance requires a thorough study of its growth potential. In this chapter, the systems used are first described. This is followed by an analysis of the economic factors which have

133

proved to be a major market impetus. Lastly, the
market potential itself is critically examined, with
special reference to the prospects of reducing further the presently declining, but still high, cost
of the new controls.

USES OF NUMERICALLY CONTROLLED EQUIPMENT

In its broadest sense, the term numerical control can be applied to any system in which a physical process is controlled by means of discrete
numerical (digital) data and instructions. Although
the use of numerical control to operate machine
tools and other metalworking equipment represents
only one application of this new concept, it is
here that numerical control has attained its highest
development to date.

Numerical control can be divided into two types
by definition: numerical-contouring control, where
the path of the tool is controlled continuously, and
numerical-positioning control for point-to-point
positioning, where the path between two points is not
controlled.[1] The latter is far more numerous.

Numerical-Positioning Control

There are approximately 2,000 machines in use
and about 900 new machines equipped with numerical-
positioning control that were put in service in
1964.[2] They range from a simple single spindle
drilling machine with two controlled motions up to
a fifteen motion specially designed milling machine.
Whatever the capacity, in each case the work-head is
positioned automatically over the work-piece, and
the actual machining and tool feed are also programmed by the machine. In general, such machines
can use a variety of standard and special tools.
However, this type of numerical control is unsuitable for most turning and grinding operations.

The reports of savings realized from these machines range from mediocre to fantastic. One user
saved enough money on his drilling machine to pay
it off in four months.[3] Typical users of these machines are paying them off in approximately two to
three years.[4]

Numerical-positioning controls find an ideal
application on machines, such as the six-spindle
drilling machine. One user reports that this particular machine eliminated the need for 124 different drill jigs at an average cost of $1,500 each.[5]
This machine eliminated the need for special tooling
costing six times the machine and control investment.
Similar results are reported by the Reliance Electric
and Engineering Company. They installed a program
controlled machine that drills and taps holes in
field poles and interpoles for direct current motors.
K. H. Meyer, Reliance's manager of computer services,
estimates a $120,000 net saving over the fifteen-year
life of the machine. The machine, complete with
tooling and installation, costs about $62,000.[6]

Another good application for numerical control
is the layout drilling machine, which can be programmed for working dies, jigs, fixtures, molds, and
other tools to an accuracy of $\pm$ 0.001 inch. Installation of such a machine at Foster Wheeler Corporation reduced machining time by 48 percent on dies
and jigs.[7]

Some numerical control machines are so versatile
that they will mill, drill, bore, counterbore, and
tap with practically no unproductive time in the machine cycle.[8] On one group of six different parts,
manufactured by the Bryant Chucking Grinder Company,
tooling savings ranged from a low of $870 to a high
of $2,800. Quantities varied from 30 to 120 parts
with production time savings ranging from 54 to 375
hours. The greatest savings were made on the short-
est runs.[9]

Numerical-Contouring Control

Contouring control is primarily being used on
large milling machines and lathes. The control system provides for simultaneous full control of the
speed and position of all the axes of the machine.
The user is thus able to undertake any combination
of continuous-path machining without any restrictions on the size or shape of theworkpiece, apart
from those imposed by the limitations of machining
itself and the size and power of the machine tool.

The system usually permits the manufacture of
parts which could not have been manufactured by utilizing conventional machine tools. Boeing claims to
have cut over 1,000 hours from tool design and fabrication at the sacrifice of 19 hours in production
planning time by using a contoured-controlled milling
machine on its large wing skins.[10]

Future Trends and Developments

Improvements and advances in the existing numerical-control technology will probably be made in
the following three areas: mechanical design of the
machine tools, design of the machine-control units,
and improved computer software.

The next generation of numerical control machine
tools will probably be based on the concept of the
self-contained machining center--a machine tool or
family of machine tools able to perform all of the
machining operations required to complete a part.
More sophisticated engineering approaches to machine
design and systems development will lead to improved
machine reliability through the introduction of hard-
ened, anti-friction ways, preloaded ball screws,
automatic lubrication, and the adaptation of transistorized and static-electronic circuits. In addition, more efficient means for stabilizing the heat
created by the machine tool will be designed to ensure accuracy and maintain machine alignment. Feedback will come from the control element rather than
the driving element, and built-in tool length measuring devices may make presetting of the cutting
tool unnecessary.

Machine control units will probably all have a
block number counter and display which will facilitate dimensional verification of machine performance
at any point during the machining cycle. Manual
data insertion into the machine control units will
permit the machinist to incorporate engineering
changes without delaying manufacture. Machine control units will be designed to have full range zero
shift of command. This eliminates the problem of
machine differences and permits blending cuts to be
made with minimum setup changes. Substitution of
photoelectric tape readers in place of the slower
magnetic tape readers will permit the machine control units to lead rather than lag the machine tool

on small incremental cuts. Air conditioners will be
incorporated into the design of the control systems
in order to stabilize circuit parameters. Increased
modulization will aid trouble-shooting and reduce
downtime. Incorporation of fail safe circuitry into the machine control units will eliminate part
scrappage resulting from line transients and power-
line fluctuations. Test equipment used to maintain
the control units will be simplified and be universally applicable. Punched tape, because of its
larger storage capacity, will be generally used in
place of magnetic tape for input. Further design
advances will permit incorporation of substantial
digital logic in the machine control units, which
could lead to operation directly from the programmer's
input tape, bypassing the general-purpose computing
step entirely.

There will probably be a strong trend to con-
solidate and simplify programming systems. The APT
system, a technique of programming shorthand, will
continue to grow in usefulness and in users. Concentration will be on debugging, documentation, and
language simplification.

A potentially even more important development
appears likely to be introduced into piece-parts
manufacture. It is a similar kind of centralized
control as is now encountered in some of the more
sophisticated automation systems of chemical and
similar processing. Basically, it involves the use
of time sharing in the computers used for the control of NC machine tools. Several companies, including the Boeing Company and Bunker-Ramo
Corporation, have been working on such a central
control system. Boeing's plan is to have from ten
to twenty-five NC tools connected directly to a computer memory that holds NC programs as well as programs for ordinary accounting. This again is a
similar development to that encountered earlier in
process automation. The manufacturers of equipment
have also participated in this development. For example, the Sunstrand Corporation has now developed
the Omnicontrol System which eliminates the need for
putting program data on magnetic tapes. As many as
sixteen metalworking tools, such as milling machines
and lathes can be tied in to the same computer that
performs routine data processing jobs.[11]

ECONOMICS OF OPERATION

One of the basic problems in dealing with numerical control is justifying its relatively high cost. All areas of potential savings (or increased costs) must be looked at closely. These are direct labor, indirect labor, overhead, setup time, scrap, spoilage, tooling, inspection, maintenance, down time, inventory, and floor space. This is an imposing list, but all are factors to be considered.

Initial Investment

The major economic disadvantage of numerical control is its high initial cost. When numerical control is applied to machine tools or other production equipment, the basic machine must be made more rigid and have heavier lead screws, bearings, and other actuating mechanisms than conventional machines. This allows a machine to obtain the high accelerations required for accurate servo response without at the same time losing accuracy due to component deflections.

Normally, such requirements would encourage a systems approach, that is, a unified design procedure leading to controls and machines designed especially for each other. While some progress has been made along these lines, much of the equipment still looks quite conventional, with the controls tacked on almost as an afterthought. For example, the need for effective chip removal is great in these high-output machines. Yet few of them either put the tables upside down or at an incline to assure clean operation.

This makes the basic numerical control machine more expensive than a conventional unit. To this cost must be added the cost of the tape or punched card electronic control system, the servo control unit, and the measuring system, which typically all total to a sum at least as great as the basic machine. The net result, as shown at the end of this chapter, is a capital expenditure ranging from about $7,500 for a small two axis point-to-point drilling and boring machine to $500,000 or more for a five axis machine capable of continuous path contouring in three dimensions.

These difficulties might be alleviated if existing machine tools could be adapted to take numerical controls. Such "retrofit kits" have not thus
far been developed, and the comments above suggest
some of the technical obstacles. If such systems
could be developed, of course, a very important new
product in the field would come into being.

Setup Cost

Since most setups for numerically controlled
machines only require simple fixtures or perhaps only
standard clamps, a major time saving is realized on
the setup of all parts and particularly the more complex ones. The simpler jigs and fixtures, the presetting of cutting tools in the tool crib, the
replacement of often time-consuming setting of machine
controls by a quickly installed tape can all make
this factor an important cost-reduction item. It is
particularly so when lot sizes are small and when
setup time is proportionately large in comparison
to machining time.

Cummins Engine Company reports a 65 percent
saving in setup time for its flywheel assemblies,
due to the adoption of a numerically controlled
drilling machine. This reduced setup time has a big
financial importance at Cummins where, because of
the large variety of flywheel configurations, the
typical lot size is five.[12]

This is of considerable importance in machine
manufacturing in general. Large production lots,
of course, readily make it possible to assure economies of scale by nonelectronic automation and high
output machinery. While the machine industry in
general has failed to adopt the sort of standardization, simplification, and modulization that would
tend to increase production lots, there are sure
to be limits to this procedure. In a sense, therefore, the efficient use of numerical controls gives
the production of small quantities a new lease on
economic life.

Jigs and Fixtures

A published comparative cost study on a representative sampling of the 20 jobs run on all types of the numerical control machines, reveals that fixture costs average 70 percent lower and machining time 54 percent less than on conventional machines.[13] On three typical jobs comparative fixture costs totalled $1,676 versus $5,707, and setup and machining costs $5,500 versus $12,266. Overall savings on these parts from numerical-control processing amounted to $8,974, even allowing for the substantial extra cost of programming.[14]

Fixture savings can be traced to two main sources. First, fewer setups are needed. Jobs that normally require two to four machines are now done in one setup. Because of this, one fixture replaces individual fixtures formerly needed for each operation.

Also, the tooling that is required tends to be much simpler and less expensive. A report on 20 parts run thus far at Sundstrand, revealed that less than half required special tooling. Four of the jobs were run on one general purpose tool block valued at about $200. The only special fixtures for these parts were inexpensive adapter plates. The study showed that the greatest savings were earned on parts where several sides must be machined, and parallelism and squareness are critical; a series of operations must be performed (e.g. milling, drilling, boring, tapping, etc.); and many tool changes are required. Programming costs for these twenty jobs ranged between $70 and $800.[15]

As more and more operations are assigned to numerically controlled machines and fewer jigs and fixtures need to be stored between jobs, less plant space is needed for tool storage and repair. For example, at least 75 percent of the shop area now given over to tool storage at Sundstrand is planned to be released for production operations.[16]

Cutting Tools

Another major source of time saving in using numerical-control equipment is its ability to utilize cutting tools to their maximum capacity. Speeds

and feeds can be programmed for optimum performance,
and because no time is lost checking measurements,
maximum chip production per unit of time can be
achieved. Also, automatic tool changing provides
a boost to production efficiency by increasing time-
in-spindle and by eliminating the human error factor.
Labor savings over comparable conventional manufacture have been reported as high as 90 percent.[17]

Also, fewer tools are needed, for the work
usually is done on fewer machines. This reduction
in the number of cutting tools that must be stocked
is particularly evident in shops where, as at Sundstrand, spare tools are stored at each machine so
that the machine operator does not have to make numerous trips to the tool crib to exchange dulled
tools for sharp ones. Sundstrand claims it has been
able to show a 30 percent reduction in the number of
tools required when operations have been shifted to
numerically controlled machines.[18]

Machine Operating Costs

Cost reduction is the primary reason for buying
numerically controlled machine tools.[19] Direct reduction in machining time may amount, in some cases,
to 90 percent or more; although the average would
be considerably lower. Along with the reduction
in machining time and the correspondingly lower
direct-labor cost, additional manpower savings may
include the operation of two or more machines or the
performance of other operations by one operator, the
possibility of using semiskilled workers on some
machines, and the need for less supervision.

The operator on the numerical control machine
is primarily a monitor. In addition to this function he is called on to make some machine adjustments
as the process is started and continues to operate.
The product or part is simply loaded and unloaded
by the operator, who has no control over the choice
of tools and the sequence of operations. Machine
speeds and feeds are also a part of program but can
be modified to some extent on some numerical control
machines. Consequently, it is difficult for the operator to speed up or slow down the process by any
significant amount.

There is currently some diversity of opinion as
to the skill required or desired for the operator of
a numerically controlled machine. In theory the
machine does all the work that formerly required
skill and experience. Therefore, it should be possible to train anyone to clamp parts in the appropriate fixture and push the start button on the machine.
In practice it has been found that due to the influence of unions and because of managements' concern
for these very expensive machines, it has been the
practice to use well-trained machinists or toolmakers
to operate these machines.[20] Consequently, a direct
labor hour for a numerically controlled machine costs
5 to 20 percent more than that for a conventional
type.

Quality Control

The principle of numerical control is bringing
about interesting changes in quality control. The
very consistent performance of numerical control
machines in terms of accuracy and repeatability has
drastically cut down the amount of inspection needed
and the number of parts rejected. The effects of
operator skill, fatigue, and human reliability have
been reduced to a minimum. More complex parts can
be produced with much lower rejection rates than on
conventional equipment.

Because of the inherent accuracy and repeatability of the numerical control machine, it is reasonable to expect very low scrap losses due to faulty
machining. With rigid clamping, locating fixtures,
and well sharpened tools there is little cutter
breakage and accompanying part spoilage. The elimination of human direction also accounts to a considerable extent for the low loss of parts due to
errors.

A survey of 37 major users of numerically
controlled machines revealed that the reject rate
runs well under 1/2 of 1 percent compared to 4 to 5
percent on comparable work done on conventional
machines.[21] Good quality control and a low reject
rate also result in considerable saving of the time
normally consumed by supervisory personnel in discussing inspection data. These discussions are often
lengthy, disturbing, and interrupt the normal work

schedule. By using good numerical control equipment,
properly maintained and operated, product quality
is high, and a minimum of personnel hours are involved
in quality discussions.

Work Handling

Another area of direct savings in the shop is
in work handling, moving the work to and from several
machines as in conventional manufacture, loading and
unloading the machine, handling the work from operator to operator. All these can be reduced or eliminated with the trend in numerical control toward
the performance of more operations in one machine and
elimination of secondary operations. However, this
can be done only on the more versatile units.

Lead Time

Numerical control contracts lead time to a
fraction of that required with conventional machining.
The delays inherent in tool design and fabrication,
in engineering changes, in planning for conventional
manufacture, in material handling, in layout, and in
inspection can cause costly traffic jams in the
manufacturing process but are minimized by utilizing
numerical control.

With the numerical control machine, a new part
can be put into production within three to six weeks
after receipt of the order, depending on the complexity of fixturing required. A minimum of ten weeks
is needed to get into production with conventional
machines because more fixtures and more elaborate
design are usually involved.[22]

For example, the basic reason for the choice of
numerical control at Graflex was to allow the
engineering division a high degree of latitude in
making design improvements.[23] If a projector casting
had been routed to conventional equipment, using
jigs and fixtures, major engineering changes would
have been extremely expensive. Minor changes that
improved the final product only slightly could not
have been afforded. With the numerical control
equipment, Graflex made more than a hundred changes.
Many of them are very minor; some were quite drastic.
All were made for the purpose of improving the

work-piece to the utmost before it was tooled for a
line operation. Graflex estimates that by using
numerical control machines, they have saved $5,200
on tooling changes for that part alone.[24]

Lodge and Shipley even made a substantial saving
by going to numerical control after drill jigs had
been designed for its Superturn lathe headstock.
Discarding the tooling drawings and taping the job
saved about $10,000 and cut lead time from eleven to
five weeks.[25]

At Numac Incorporated, components, such as
gimbal blocks, reflector mounting brackets, separator
racks, and electrical-equipment chassis lend themselves to machining on tape-controlled equipment.
These parts have many revisions made during their
development. Numerical control makes such changes
practical and economical.[26]

Several electrical-equipment chassis, machined
on Kearney and Trecker Milwaukee-Matic and a Brown
and Sharpe numerical control turret drill, were
recently involved in such revisions. Each chassis
has more than 240 holes and a 10-foot long 1/8 inch
end-milled slot.

One chassis had 28 hole location changes requiring 87 changes to the tape. It took about 3 hours
to locate all 87 changes on the tape and repunch.
The actual machining of the chassis, which has a
2-hour cycle, together with the program and tape
changes was completed within one 8-hour shift.
Savings on this job were estimated at $1,300.[27]

MAINTENANCE

Maintenance and repair costs for numerical-control equipment are averaging two to four times greater
than for comparable conventional equipment.[28] The
primary reason for this is the complexity of the
equipment and the lack of shop experience in trouble-
shooting it. A secondary reason could be the much
higher machine utilization rate for the numerical-
control equipment. Most conventional machines are
"up" an average of only 30 percent, while most
numerical-control tooling is in use 70 percent of
the time.[29]

A survey was made of thirty-two users of two-
motion controls with over six months operating experience.[30] Although seven indicated start up
problems, follow up showed that four were machine
problems, and of the remaining three only one could
be considered a real problem.

The average operating time was 64 hours per
week and the average down time per week was less
than four hours. Most users had an average of eight
preventive-maintenance checks per year.[31]

OVERALL EFFECTS

When the foregoing cost components are considered jointly, some formidable arguments in favor of
numerical controls emerge. The main result is an
enhanced ability to deal economically with small
manufacturing lot sizes. In an analysis of total
costs of operating manual, automatic and numerically
controlled lathes, Panzeca has shown that the numerically controlled machines can produce small lots at
the lowest cost of all three types of machines.[32]
Without a numerically controlled machine, the manufacturer must resort to manual lathes when making
small lots, and even this fails to prevent a very
sharp cost rise at the lowest quantities. However,
in most products there comes a lot size above which
the automatic lathe is the cheapest. Clearly, the
numerically controlled machine has an overwhelming
superiority only at low rates of production. However, this still leaves it a wide market in the
many areas in which production quantities are limited.

Impressive as they are, the savings must still
pay for the initial investment in a short enough time
to realize an adequate rate of return. Here the
evidence is less persuasive. Clearly, the savings
must be really substantial in order to justify a
first cost which may be five or six times as great
as that for a machine without numerical controls.
In a replacement study of turret drills, Panzeca
arrived at a payout period of 2.4 years based on
initial gross earnings and 4.9 years after taxes,
both results including an allowance for debugging.[33]
This is rather high in the usual industrial context
in which any payout greater than two years appears
to operate under an increasing competitive handicap.

The market must therefore depend on the ability of
the industry to cut prices of the machines. The
evidence of at least one manufacturer indicates that
this results in strong market demand. The characteristics of installations and the future of the
industry will now be reviewed.

THE MARKET

    Numerically controlled machines have witnessed
an extraordinarily rapid growth in number of installations, although they are still a minute fraction
(less than a quarter of one percent) of America's
2.5 million machine tools. Nevertheless, Table 8.1
indicates an extraordinarily rapid rate of growth,
at an average rate of 40 percent per year from
1959 to 1967. The backlog as of the end of 1967
appears to indicate something of a slowdown, but
this may actually not be reflected in the actual performance of the field in 1968. The table also gives
average unit values of the control systems of these
machines. Here it is clear that there has been a
fair degree of stability in prices in the point-to-
point and continuous part units. Although there
have been some fluctuations, they have not reflected
the rise in machine prices that have been a characteristic of the machine-tool industry in general.
The dial- or plug-board types, once expected to be an
answer for cheap units, have increased in price to
more than the level of point-to-point controls. In
the early years they were a fraction of the cost,
as little as 26 percent. What has happened then has
been a trend towards approximate equality for these
two categories of controls. While the higher prices
may reflect greater versatility, ease of programming,
and reliability, the fact remains that this puts a
considerable burden on the economic justification of
these controls by the users.

    This is done in Table 8.2, which gives the
results for 1959, 1962, and 1967. There is considerable variation in electronic value relative to the
machine within machine types, but the cost of the
electronic package has either remained roughly steady
as in boring machines or tended to decline in the
other categories. Of course, within each group
there are considerable differences depending, for
example, on the number of axes controlled and other

TABLE 8.1

Total Shipments and Unfilled Orders of Numerically Controlled Machine
Tools and Average Unit Values of Controls, by Type of Control
1954-June 30, 1962

| | Total | | Type of control | | | | | |
| | | | Point-to-point | | Continuous Path | | Dial of Plugboard | |
	No. of units	Avg. unit value of controls (dollars)	No. of units	Avg. unit value of controls (dollars)	No. of units	Avg. unit value of controls (dollars)	No. of units	Avg. unit value of controls (dollars)
1954-1958 (Total)	193	36,500	85	17,130	71	73,300	37	7,700
1959	203	22,750	122	20,050	39	50,250	42	5,070
1960	402	23,400	278	24,150	34	54,900	90	6,500
1961	518	22,950	308	24,450	64	49,700	146	8,080
1967	2,957	23,458	2,050	17,602	621	43,958	286	20,913
Unfilled orders Dec. 31, 1967	2,054	35,103	1,033	23,267	782	52,949	239	27,866

Source: U.S. Department of Commerce, Bureau of the Census, "Metal Working Machinery,"
Current Industrial Reports, Series M35 W (67)-1, 2 & 3 (Oct. 6 and Dec. 21, 1967, Mar. 28,
1968); Series BDSAF-630-1 (Nov. 19, 1963).

147

TABLE 8.2

Unit Costs of Controls and Machines, Relative Cost
Proportions and Ratios, 1959 and 1962

	1959 Unit Costs (dollars)		Cost of controls as per-cent of machine costs	1962 Unit Costs (dollars)		Cost of controls as per-cent of machine costs	Ratio of 1962 prices to 1959 prices	
	Machines only	Controls only		Machines only	Controls only		Machines only	Controls only
Boring machines	63,100	23,400	37.1	81,000	30,900	38.1	1.28	1.32
Drills	25,150	12,300	48.9	12,100	10,550	87.2	0.48	0.85
Milling machines	90,200	41,700	46.3	86,800	50,700	53.4	0.96	1.22
All others[a]	111,600	7,700	6.8	61,500	19,300	31.4	0.55	2.51

	1967 Unit Costs (dollars)		Cost of controls as per-cent of machine costs				Ratio of 1967 prices to 1962 prices	
	Machines only	Controls only					Machines only	Controls only
Boring machines	95,736	38,166	39.9				1.18	1.24
Drills	39,578	15,056	38.1				3.27	1.43
Milling machines	148,031	46,775	31.6				1.71	0.92
All others[a]	62,491	15,054	24.1				0.98	0.75

[a]Includes lathes, presses, grinders and all other metal forming and cutting machines.

Source: Computed from U.S. Department of Commerce, Bureau of the Census and Business and Defense Services Administration, "Machine Tools with Numerical and Prerecorded Motion Program Controls," Current Industrial Reports, Series BDSAF-630-1 (November 19, 1963); and "Metal Working Machinery," Series M35 W (67), 1, 2 & 3 (Oct. 6 and Dec. 21, 1967, March 28, 1968).

148

characteristics and capacities of the machine. The
price ratios present a rather mixed picture. From
1962 to 1967, however, the electronic package has
generally had a smaller price rise than the machine
itself. Unfortunately, there is no adequate price
index for machine tools as such (mainly because of
the technical difficulty in allowing for design
changes). However, as an approximate indication,
the ratio of the price index of durable manufactures
in 1967 to that of 1962 is 1.06, which is exceeded
by five out of the eight ratios shown in the table.[34]

Finally, it must be realized that some of the
numerically controlled machines are closely defense
related. As late as 1963 government purchases
accounted for some 40 percent of the highly expensive
continuous path machines,[35] and thus a curtailment
of defense spending would cut at least into their
near-term markets.

It is clear then that the numerical-controls
industry has still not made the market breakthrough
which the more copious employment of standardized
units, modulization, etc., could bring about. With
an electronic content of upwards of $20,000 per
machine, a market of $55 million (cf. Chapter 2) is
certainly nowhere near the potential for this field.
The machine-tool industry maintains that technical
progress in its industry suggests a replacement
frequency of ten years, which would mean about 250,000
new units a year. The number bought in 1967 would
only be about 1.2 percent of such a desirable replacement rate. Even assuming a 20 year replacement
cycle, the market penetration would only be 2.4 percent. Of course, most machine tools bought for
industrial purposes do have some automation features
based on electrical and mechanical designs that have
been known for decades, but in view of the fact
that the job shop is still the most common form of
manufacture and that the NC tools are most useful
there, the market record thus far is certainly
not encouraging in spite of the impressive growth
rate in NC machines themselves. Even a 5 percent
replacement rate with a $20,000 electronic content
would mean a market of $2.5 billion. This certainly
does not appear to be in the cards. However, we
may certainly anticipate a market of about $250
million a year for these devices within three to
five years, especially if computer-based economies
can be realized and if the machine tool industry

puts its own technological house in order. This
would reflect an increase of about $200 million a
year above present sales of NC controls.

NOTES

1. "Role of Numerical Control," American
Machinist (Dec. 9, 1963), p. 82.

2. "U.S. Takes Census of Numerically Controlled
Machine Tool," American Machinist (Dec. 9, 1961),
p. 92.

3. "Producing Holes in Structural Steel,"
American Machinist & Metalworking Manufacturing
(Mar. 6, 1961), pp. 105-114.

4. "Tape Pays Off," Iron Age (Aug. 31, 1961)
pp. 85-87.

5. "Tape Controlled Turret Drills," Automation
(December, 1960), pp. 91-92.

6. "Boring Mill Designed for Tape Control,"
Machinery (January, 1961), p. 172.

7. "Punch, Nibble, Notch, and Prepare Tape,"
Machinery (July 23, 1962), p. 105.

8. "Burgmaster Corporation Tape Controlled
Turret Drilling Machine," Machinery (April, 1962),
pp. 158-159.

9. "Numerical Control Pays Off in Small Jobbing
Shops," Iron Age (Feb. 1, 1962), pp. 84-85.

10. "Milling Machine Has Continuous Path Tape
Control," Steel (Apr. 3, 1961), pp. 103-105.

11. Business Week (Mar. 16, 1968), p. 158.

12. "Shop Application," Mechanical Engineer
(September, 1962), pp. 66-67.

13. "Job Shop Save Up to 50% With Numerical
Control," Steel (Oct. 8, 1962), pp. 65-67.

14. _Ibid._

15. "Making a Numerical Control Department Pay,"
American Machinist (Dec. 10, 1962), pp. 115-122.

16. _Ibid._

17. "Making a Numerical Control Department Pay,"
Op. Cit., pp. 115-122.

18. _Ibid._

19. "1961 Numerical Control Survey," _Control
Engineering_ (June, 1961), p. 81.

20. "Economic Efficiency of Automation,"
Automation (August, 1963), pp. 65-70.

21. "Numerical Control Clips Costs, Guarantees
Quality," _Mill & Factory_ (September, 1962), p. 105.

22. "Job Shop Save Up to 50% With Numerical
Control," _Op. Cit._, pp. 65-67.

23. "Tape Pays Off," _Op. Cit._, p. 123.

24. _Ibid._

25. "Tape Controlled Machine Developed for Job
Lot Production," _Machinery_ (November, 1960), p. 161.

26. "Complex, Short Run Parts, a Natural for
Tape Control," _Machinery_ (August, 1961), pp. 138-139.

27. _Ibid._

28. "Impact of Numerical Control Goes Beyond
Cost Savings," _S.A.E. Journal_ (November, 1961),
p. 90.

29. "How to Prove the Profit in Numerical
Control," _Machinery_ (Oct. 30, 1961), pp. 77-120.

30. "Numerical Control Earns Its Keep,"
American Machinist (Jan. 8, 1962).

31. _Ibid._

32. P. Panzeca, "Numerically Controlled Machines as a Competitive Aid to the Job Shop," (M.B.A. Thesis, Hofstra University, 1964), Chapter IX.

33. Ibid.

34. U.S. Bureau of Labor Statistics, Wholesale Prices and Price Indexes, 1963 Cumulative Number (January, 1968).

35. "Numerical Control Shows Record Growth," American Machinist & Metalworking Manufacturing (July 22, 1963), pp. 71-77.

CHAPTER **9** ELECTRONIC CONTROLS
FOR ROAD TRAFFIC

by Gary Mauser

INTRODUCTION

Fifty years ago the total number of registered
motor vehicles on American roads was less than one
million. By the end of World War II it had increased
to thirty million. Today, there are approximately
seventy-five million highway vehicles. This growth
rate is much faster than that of facilities to
handle the situation. This lack is felt mostly in
cities and heavily populated suburbs where, during
rush hours, streets and roadways become oversaturated
with traffic. The result is extreme congestion and
delay.[1]

The inadequacy of the present traffic signal
control system stems from its complete lack of
flexibility.[2] There is no variable response to
changing traffic patterns during the day. The green,
red, and amber lights for each avenue or street go
on and off at regular intervals, irrespective of
whether the roadway is congested or not. A system
which controls traffic flow on a continuous basis
can alleviate the congestion problem and prevent
excessive delay. For such a system, data on traffic
flow from all streets are obtained on a continuous
basis. The data are analyzed and results translated
into a form which permits comparison to known traffic
patterns. This procedure determines the action
necessary to control the traffic flow. Ultimately,
this knowledge is translated into action through a
system of flexible traffic lights designed to respond
in the required manner.

Such controls are mainly based on electronic
equipment and thus represent a major potential business opportunity. The system requires a digital or
analogue computer to record and store traffic movements as sensed by intersection detectors. Programs

stored in the computer are determined from extensive
field analysis on the behavior and characteristics of
traffic flow for a particular area. The computer
continually reviews current results from the traffic
detectors. Then in accordance with the stored
master-control program, the computer determines the
timing of the lights and switches them accordingly.

In this chapter, the systems proposed are first
described, and their markets are then evaluated on
the basis of economic justification in relation to
traffic density and size of community.

PRESENT INSTALLATIONS

Computer controlled traffic-signal systems are
presently being used in test areas of some large
cities in this country and abroad.[3] Attempts have
also been made to control highway traffic flow using
electronic equipment.

In Toronto, the electronic system is currently
controlling five hundred traffic signals in the major
traffic areas.[4] The heart of the system is a single
digital computer which acts on information fed to
it from vehicle detectors buried in the pavement.
They continuously report the volume, speed, headway,
lane placement, and distance of vehicles approaching
each intersection in each lane. The computer decides
which direction of traffic needs the longer green
light at an intersection and adjusts the timing instantly. It changes the lights as governed by flow
of traffic, giving main street and intersecting
traffic the best possible break. The Toronto installation is of particular interest in that it is
used specifically for ordinary streets and intersections rather than freeways. The success of this
system indicates that installations, scaled to
appropriate size, can effectively serve other cities.
It is estimated that the system in Toronto decreases
congestion by approximately 28 percent. This is
equivalent to adding an additional lane to a five-lane
street. Toronto expects a reduction in total traffic
delay of more than 9,000 vehicle-hours daily.[5] It
saves motorists approximately two million dollars a
year in vehicle operating expense, not counting the
value of personal time saved. In addition, it saves
some $20 to $40 million otherwise spent for widening

existing streets or building new ones. The computer
installation costs $3.5 million; operating expenses
are about $200,000 a year.

In 1966 the City of New York contracted with
the Sperry Rand Corp. for a system for the control
of 2,700 intersections in four of the city's boroughs.
The contract was for $6 million and included the
computers and sensors. Unfortunately, the company
was unable to supply suitable equipment, and eventually the contract was cancelled after considerable
losses in development costs were incurred. The
City of New York has since decided to purchase an
IBM 1800 computer with a special traffic-control
program, which will be used to operate 500 intersections in Queens.

Altogether there are about 100 systems in the
continental United States, most of them of the
analogue type. The one in Baltimore, for example,
has been in operation for some ten years and controls
some 800 intersections. There are also two digital
systems which were recently installed in San Jose,
California and Wichita Falls, Texas. In addition,
the prospects are highly favorable for a substantial
overseas market. Many foreign cities have a combination of rapidly increasing motor traffic and narrow
streets which, because of their architectural dis-
tinction, cannot be radically changed. For example,
the British firm of Elliott Computers is now developing a traffic-control system for Madrid. With a
volume of $25 million in electronic equipment in
1966, vehicular traffic controls must be regarded as
a beginning but already significant field.

Additional electronic systems have been
installed to optimize highway traffic flow.[6] On
one major expressway, a battery of analogue computers
receives and records coded electronic data on the
volume, density, and speed of traffic.[7] Ultrasonic
detectors mounted above each lane produce information stored in the electronic-memory circuit so that
individual programs can be put into operation automatically without the use of human guidance. The
computer controls successive warning lights or signs
which tell motorists at what speeds to travel to
ensure a smooth progression of vehicular traffic.

In addition to the computer controlled traffic-
signal systems, electronic devices are being applied

in other areas of traffic control. A pacer system
has been demonstrated by General Motors Corp. Its
purpose is to instruct motorists how fast to drive
in order to keep up with the green lights in a
series of signals set progressively.[8] A group of
changing overhead speed signals (electronically
controlled) tell the motorist how fast to drive for
through-speed between intersections. The indicated
speed varies from twenty-five to forty-five miles
an hour, depending upon the distance of the vehicle
from the next intersection stop light and the time
when that light will turn red. With this system,
leading cars are slowed down and trailing cars
speeded up. This system could increase intersection
capacity by 20 percent.

Radar-sensing units are further examples of
electronic equipment used in a traffic control network. Installed over the lanes of a freeway, the
device in conjunction with a computer aids in the
reduction of traffic congestion. When one lane
becomes jammed, the radar-sensing unit reports conditions to the control computer. The latter triggers
traffic lights farther back to shunt traffic to less
congested lanes. Radar-sensing units have also
been used in a system for cars that sound a horn when
a driver closes in too fast on another car or if
cross traffic threatens a collision.

Recent developments in transistorized circuitry
have produced a communication system which transmits
messages from a roadside radio unit to the radios in
moving cars, telling drivers of traffic conditions
ahead or advising changes in speed.[9] Successful
experiments have also been concluded with a photoelectric cell and a small special purpose computer
to make night driving safer. When a car approaches
fast from the rear, as detected by the photo cell,
the computer automatically flashes the brake lights
of its own car to alert the oncoming driver.

AVAILABLE SYSTEMS AND TECHNOLOGY

With nonelectronic equipment, traffic signals
are operated by a fixed-time method.[10] Traffic
surveys are taken in advance and the results used as
input programs for setting up optimized time-variable
schedules for phasing of the lights. With electronic

equipment, traffic signals are actuated by the movement of the traffic itself. Three basic functions
must be integrated. These are detection, computation,
and instruction. The systems provide information
regarding the number of vehicles in motion in a
particular area, how to move them at optimum speeds,
and how to arrange traffic signals to accomplish
these tasks.

   Three possible computer-controlled systems are
currently available. Two of the systems employ digital techniques, while the third employs an analogue
computer as its master control unit. They are designated as follows:

   TRA digital (traffic response average)
   TRA analogue (traffic response average)
   TRD digital (traffic response detailed)

   The latter system uses a computer with a large
capacity and program storage, suitable only to large
scale traffic-control projects. A box diagram of a
typical electronic traffic control system is shown
in Figure 9.1.

   Three basic vehicle-detection devices are used
in the electronic system. They are pressure plates,
located in the intersection roadbed; induction loops,
buried under the surface, and radar detectors. All
are forms of detection devices which function by
measuring volume and density of traffic. The first
device employs a numerical-counting system. It
simply records digital response to the passing
traffic. The latter two devices produce electronic
pulses of specific intensity and amplitude, which
are relayed in coded form to a computer for assimila-
tion and analysis. Induction-loop wiring buried in
the pavement is very effective when analogue equipment is used as the master controller. Radar detection has valid economic merit in that installation
costs when compared to other systems are small due
to the fact that radar detectors require no digging
or repaving when installed.

   Transmittal of data is accomplished by either
radio or by leased telephone-line connections. Use
of radio in relaying traffic data is quite popular
with analogue-computer techniques. On the other
hand, the cable relay system is favored with standard
digital computers.[11]

FIGURE 9.1

Typical Electronic Traffic Control System,
Computer Controlled

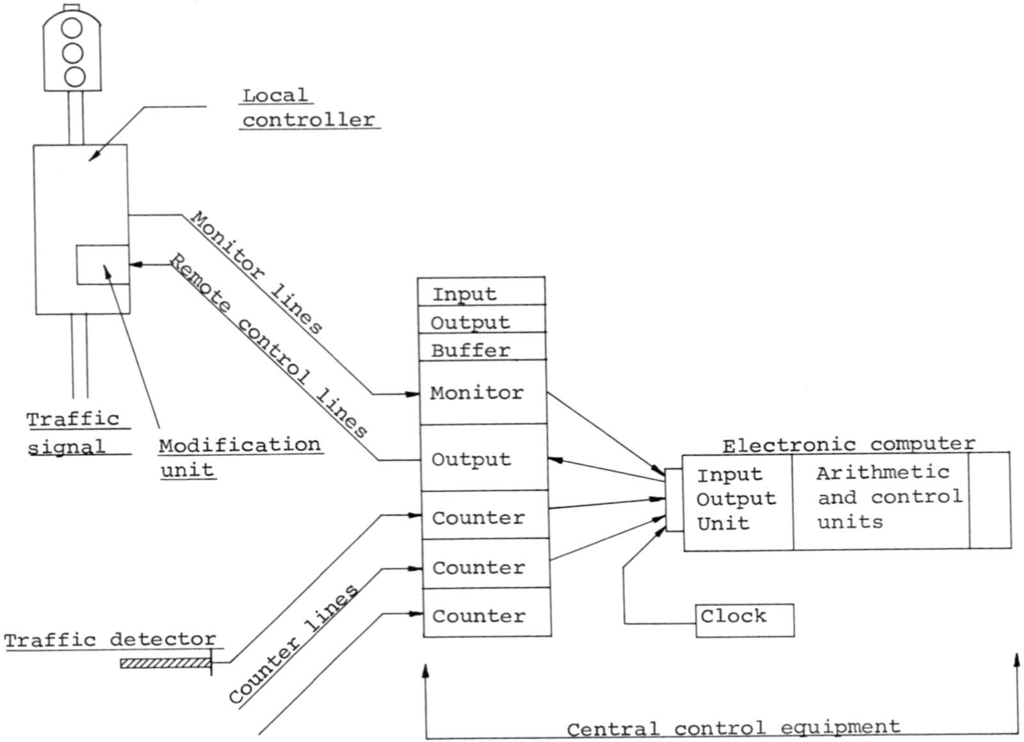

Source: "Computer Control to Untie Toronto Traffic," Canadian Controls and Instrumentation (November-December, 1962).

Program selection is made by the electronic computer from an analysis of traffic density and volume as recorded by the vehicle detector. For a typical analogue installation, pulses from the detectors are fed to a cycle computer that analyzes traffic-flow information continuously.[12] Based on input data, the computer determines which of the stored control cycles produces the most efficient movement of traffic. Information from the cycle computer is then fed to a system selector, which specifies the portion of green, red, and yellow time for the traffic lights being controlled. This cycle length is next processed through a cycle generator. The information is then converted into an electrical output and with the aid of a generator-translator circuit sent to amplifier channels for broadcast to intersection control boxes.[13]

Digital computers require additional components for converting pulses from the input circuits to coded numerical form.[14] They are thus made suitable for computer input. This so-called input buffer acts as a coupling between the computer and the cable or telephone line connections. Another of its functions is to convert coded-computer output into direct current pulses to remotely actuate the traffic controllers.

To accommodate the electronic traffic-control equipment, local signal controllers require modification.[15] When telephone circuits are used for transmission, the modification unit consists of two relays or solid state transistorized devices to hold the present traffic cycle pattern or actuate a new pattern by remote operation of the controller. Local units employing radio equipment have transistorized circuitry. The signal pole houses the radio receiver, decoder, and traffic intersection controller. The partially transistorized decoder performs the logic operations in the intersection unit. Its prime function is to break down the coded radio signal into a form suitable for mechanical operation of the traffic signal.

COST ANALYSIS

Costs

To determine the optimum traffic signal-control
system, an analysis of the capital and operating
costs of each system is necessary. The time variable optimized system (nonelectronic) consists
chiefly of changing the timing pattern of the existing lights to allow for variation in vehicular traffic load during the day. In a typical system,
programs are employed to accommodate peak rush hour
traffic, daytime slack traffic, and evening traffic.
For this type of system road detectors, local controllers, and central equipment are not required.
Total capital expenditure to initiate such a system
is basically the set-up cost involved in revamping
existing local-control boxes to receive the multi-
cycle light-phasing equipment. Here cost figures
are based on a fixed capital expenditure plus a
variable cost, which is directly proportional to the
number of signalized intersections being considered
for a particular area. The fixed portion is essentially an outlay for revision of existing equipment,
while the variable part is a charge for installation
and labor based on the number of intersections
serviced. Total capital cost is reduced to an annual
capital charge, which is derived from an amortized
schedule based on a ten-year period. An annual operating and maintenance cost of $25 is required per
intersection. The sum of annual capital charges
and annual operating and maintenance costs are the
total annual costs to effectively invoke an optimized
time variable traffic-control system.

Cost figures employed in the analysis were either
estimated or determined empirically from actual case
studies performed by Traffic Research Corporation.
Table 9.1 presents a summary of the costs for this
system as a linear function of the number of signalized intersections.

The three electronic traffic signal control systems employ counters or detectors, local controllers,
and central computer equipment as the core units of
their operating network. Installation of traffic-
detection devices in the traffic response-average
system is assumed to be at the rate of one detector

TABLE 9.1

Traffic Control System Annual Costs as a Function of
Number of Signalized Intersections (n)

Component	Nonelectronic system — Time variable optimized	Electronic system		
		TRA digital	(Average) TRA analog	(Detailed) TRD digital
Detectors	0	$500/detector = $(50n)	$500/detector = $(50n)	$500/detector = $(1,000n)
Local controllers	0	$(500n)	$(1500n)	$(500n)
Central equipment	0	$(100,000 + 200n)	$(20,000 + 200n)	$(100,000 + 2,000n)
Set-Up costs	$(2,000 + 40n)	$(250n)	$(250n)	$(500n)
Total capital costs, C	$(2,000 + 40n)	$(100,000 + 1,000n)	$(20,000 + 2,000n)	$(1,000,000 + 4,000n)
Annual capital charges amortized over 10 years at 4%, C_a	$(250 + 5n)	$(12,500 + 125n)	$(2,500 + 250n)	$(125,000 + 500n)
Annual operating and maintenance costs, M_a	$(25n)	$(100n)	$(120n)	$(250n)
Total annual costs, A	$(250 + 30n)	$(12,500 + 225n)	$(2,500 + 370n)	$(125,000 + 750n)

Sources:
1. "Signalized Intersection Studies," Traffic Research Corporation (January-July 1962).
2. "Breaking Traffic Jam," National Civic Review, vol. 51, (October, 1962), pp. 482-485.
3. "Computer to Direct Traffic," Business Week (Feb. 3, 1962), p. 50.

for every ten intersections, while for the traffic
response detailed system the estimate is two sensors
for each signalized intersection. Cost per detector
in the TRA system and in the TRD system is $500.
Local signal controller charges are figured on an
intersection basis as well as all estup costs involved in installing the various components. Analogue and digital computers are used in the TRA
average system, while only digital equipment is used
in the Complex TRD System. The cost of computer
equipment consists of a direct capital equipment outlay plus a variable charge covering the number of
intersections controlled.[16]

The cost for the TRD digital system is much
higher than that of the other two systems, due to the
complexity of the computer. For 500 controlled inter
sections the capital cost of the system is $3 million
This is approximately the figure given for the Toront
installation. Annual operating and maintenance costs
are again higher for the TRD system being $250 per
intersection. This amounts to $125,000, as compared
to the Toronto figure of $200,000. The total annual
costs for each system (shown in Table 9.1) are the
annual capital charges based on an amortized 10-year
schedule, plus the annual operating and maintenance
costs.

From the total cost figures in Table 9.1 it follows that the total annual cost of the time variable
optimized system is lower than that of any of the
three electronically controlled systems. Although
cost savings are evident with the nonelectronic system, it is necessary to measure and evaluate the
cumulative benefits derived from each of the systems
considered, in order to make the correct choice between them. Incremental costs of each system must
be compared to the beneficial attributes (measured
in dollars saved per annum) in order to determine
the optimum network.

Benefits

The principal benefits of a redesigned traffic-
signal system are a reduction in time delay and a
reduction in equivalent roadbuilding costs. Other
benefits, not as easily measured, are reductions in
personal time wasted, accidents and breakdowns, air
pollution, and business losses affecting shopping,
dining, and entertainment.

Time delay is a direct result of the improper
phasing of traffic lights to meet particular peak
traffic loads and varying road-traffic situations.
It is a function of extreme importance to motorists,
mainly due to the monetary loss associated with
delay.[17] Congestion results in increased fuel consumption and general wear and tear on the vehicle.
It is important to note here that when either of
the three fully electronic systems are operating,
cost savings are achieved only on a so-called optimized scalar basis. That is, a reduction in delay
cost is a direct function of the number of signalized
intersections operating within a system. Applying a
computerized system with a large controlling capacity to a large city may result in a sizeable reduction in costs due to delay. On the other hand,
using the same system to control lights in a smaller
city may provide no savings or may result in increased motorist-delay costs. Size and capacity of
the computer system is very important and must be
taken into account when a specific number of traffic
lights or intersections are to be controlled. Estimated percentage reduction in delay for the traffic
signal control systems considered are as follows:[18]

```
                                         Percent
      Time variable optimized. . . . 10
      Traffic response average (analogue
      or digital). . . . . . . . . 20
      Traffic response detailed
      (digital). . . . . . . . . . 30
```

Associated with delay, a formula has been derived
using empirical data from various studies made by the
Traffic Research Corporation to determine factors
contributing to delay costs. The relationship is a
function of the number of signalized intersections
controlled and is based on a cost per hour of delay.

Cost of delay = $(0.10 + 0.001n)$
per hour of delay.

Total annual delay for all vehicles is based on
average traffic-flow figures. On an intersection
basis it is approximately 10,000 hours per year or
expressed in slightly different form:

Total annual delay = $(10,000n)$ hours
per year.

Annual cost of delay is determined by multiplying cost of delay by total annual delay.

Annual cost of delay = $(100n + 10n^2)$ per year.

The annual savings in dollars due to delay reduction is determined by applying the percentage reductions in delay for each system to the relationship for annual cost of delay. The results are as follows

Time variable optimized = $(100n + n^2)$ per year.
Traffic response average = $(200n + 2n^2)$ per year.
Traffic response detailed = $(300n + 3n^2)$ per year.

The second measurable benefit of a new or revised traffic signal control system lies in the area of reducing the number of additional roads necessary to handle any expected increase in flow of traffic. The complete cost of the system must be compared to the cost of building equivalent new roads to handle the increased traffic load. Estimated percentage increases in road capacity resulting from installation of each of the traffic signal control systems are as follows:[19]

Time variable optimized. .   7 percent
Traffic response average
(analogue or digital). . . 14 percent
Traffic response detailed. 21 percent

For each 1 percent improvement in a systems capacity, the costs to build new roads are $10 times the square of the number of signalized intersections. The resulting relationship $(10n^2)$ is substantiated by semiempirical results from studies made by the Traffic Research Corporation. The resulting dollar benefits through savings in equivalent roadbuilding costs are found by multiplying the percentage increases in capacity for the systems, considered by the roadbuilding costs to produce each 1 percent improvement in system capacity. The resulting formulas are:

Time variable optimized = $70n^2$.
Traffic response average = $140n^2$.
Traffic response detailed = $210n^2$.

Annual dollar savings in equivalent roadbuilding costs are expressed, for each Traffic signal control system, on the basis of a standard amortization schedule over a 40-year period at 4 percent interest. The resulting equations yield savings on a yearly basis.

Time variable optimized = $3n^2$
Traffic response average = $7n^2$
Traffic response detailed = $10n^2$

The total annual costs as well as annual user benefits through delay reductions and annual roadbuilding savings are plotted in graphical form in Figures 9.2 and 9.3 for the various traffic signal control systems under investigation. In all cases, cost is plotted versus number of signalized intersections. The intersection of an annual cost curve for a particular system with an annual delay reduction curve determines the minimum number of signalized intersections necessary for cost savings to be realized. For more than this number, user benefits will exceed system costs. An analogous situation exists between annual systems cost and annual roadbuilding savings. The designated breakeven number of intersections required for savings due to delay reduction and reduced roadbuilding are as follows:

System	Breakeven number of intersections for savings due to delay reduction	Breakeven number of intersections for savings due to reduced roadbuilding
Time variable optimized	4	15
TRA digital	86	61
TRA analogue	98	59
TRD digital	290	155

From the above it is evident that for the time variable optimized system it is easy to produce savings due to delay reduction and reduced roadbuilding from the control of only a few signalized intersections. For electronically operated systems, economies of scale are evident. Breakeven number of

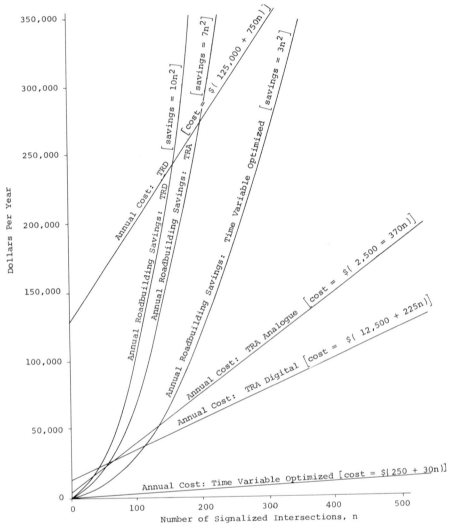

FIGURE 9.3

Traffic Signal System Cost Benefit Curves as a Function
of Number of Signalized Intersections Based on
Annual Roadbuilding Savings

Sources: 1. "Signalized Intersection Studies," Traffic Research Corporation
New York (January–July, 1962).

2. "Keeping an Eye on Tomorrow," Electrical Engineering (January,
1961), pp. 67-8.

166

FIGURE 9.2

Traffic Signal System Cost Benefit Curves as a Function of
Number of Signalized Intersections Based on Annual
User Benefits Through Delay Reduction

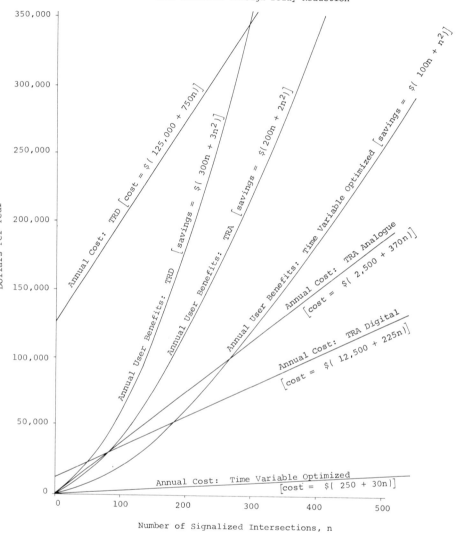

Number of Signalized Intersections, n

Sources: 1. "Signalized Intersection Studies," Traffic Research Corporation,
New York (January-July, 1962).

2. "Breaking Traffic Jam," National Civic Review, vol. 51
(October, 1962), pp. 482-5.

intersections must be controlled before cost savings are realized.[20] After this point is reached, annual benefits are derived which are considerably greater than those attained with the nonelectronic time variable optimized system. As an example, for a city requiring control of approximately 200 signalized intersections, the annual user benefits through delay reduction exceed the annual cost of a TRA-digital system by approximately $70,000. For the nonelectronic time variable optimized system the annual user benefits exceed the cost of the system by $50,000. The overall net-user saving (using the TRA digital system) is $20,000. Analogously, the annual roadbuilding saving using the electronic TRA digital is $265,000, while the annual saving under the time variable optimized system is $122,000. Employing the TRA digital system means a net saving of $143,000 in roadbuilding expenditures. For effective utilization of the more sophisticated TRD digital system it should be applied to an area which requires control of at least 290 to 300 intersections. When applied to areas with fewer intersections, annual savings due to reduced roadbuilding exist; however, no savings due to delay reduction are derived.[21]

When considering the two principal user benefits of the systems discussed, it is important to investigate the interrelationship between the two. If delay reduction is proportional to fuel savings, it follows that a reduced amount of gasoline tax dollars is available to the state government. If it is further assumed that gasoline tax dollars are used by the state for roadbuilding, then funds available for this purpose are reduced. For a system to be economical, savings due to reduced roadbuilding should increase at a faster rate than those due to delay reduction.

Figure 9.4 presents a comparison of the annual user benefits (savings) through delay reduction and annual roadbuilding savings for the traffic signal control systems. It follows from the figure that the slopes of each set of benefit curves, for each system, are approximately equal at 20 to 25 intersections. After this point, the rate of change of reduced roadbuilding is greater than that of delay reduction. This means that although a loss does occur to the roadbuilding fund, due to a reduction in fuel consumed, the requirements for additional roads decline faster. Further analysis of the cost-benefit curves of Figure 9.4 reveal the break-even number of intersections required for equal savings in delay reduction and equivalent roadbuilding for each system. These points are as follows:

System	Breakeven number of inter-sections required for equal savings in delay reduction and roadbuilding
Time variable optimized	50
TRA digital	40
TRA analogue	40
TRD digital	43

They represent the minimum number of intersections required above which savings due to reduced roadbuilding exceed savings due to delay reduction. The absolute magnitude of savings derived for a particular system can be determined from Figure 9.4 by entering the curve at the number of intersections required and reading off the incremental dollar savings in equivalent roadbuilding directly.

MARKET SIZE

The estimated market size for electronic traffic-control equipment can only be approximated, based on population data for standard metropolitan statistical areas. The choice among systems depends on the population and on an estimate of the number of inhabitants per signalized intersection. In the present study the Toronto average is used, that is, one intersection for every three thousand inhabitants.[22] With this estimate, applied to the population figures and analyzed for each system, the total number of intersections requiring electronic traffic signal control is determined. Cost equations are then applied to find capital expenditures for each electronic system.

For standard metropolitan areas with over one million people, the TRD digital system is proposed. There are 21 such areas in the United States with a

FIGURE 9.4

Traffic Signal System Benefit Curves--Annual Roadbuilding
Savings Compared to User Benefits Through
Delay Reduction

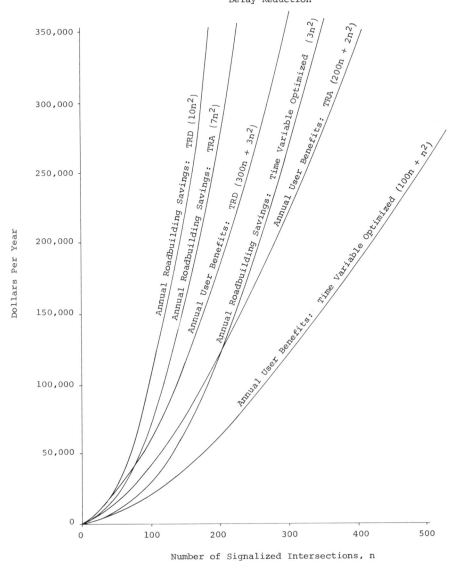

Number of Signalized Intersections, n

Source: "Signalized Intersection Studies," Traffic Research Corporation,
New York (January-July, 1962).

total of 18,250 signalized intersections.[23] The
total capital expenditure on this system is thus
$74 million approximately.

For areas (Standard Metropolitan Statistical
Areas--SMSA) with population ranging from 500,000
to one million, the TRA Analogue system is applicable. There are 29 areas of this size in the United
States.[24] They contain approximately 7,250 signalized intersections. The total capital expenditure
on this system is thus about $14.5 million.

For areas (SMSA) with population ranging from
100,000 to 500,000 the TRA digital system is proposed. There are now 133 cities of this size, with
an estimated total of 13,300 signalized intersections.[25] Expenditures on installed electronic equipment for this system amount to $13.4 million. For
areas with less than 100,00 in population the nonelectronic time variable optimized system is applicable. No market size estimate need be made here.
The total capital expenditure on electronic equipment for the three traffic signal control systems
is thus $102 million. Assuming a 5-year period of
installation would imply an annual market of about
$20 million.

This figure is based on a rather simplified
analysis, taking into account the size of standard
metropolitan statistical areas. In a more detailed
analysis, investigation of the following variables
should be made to determine the size of the system
required and its associated cost.

1. Mean traffic flow
2. Population density
3. Special congestion (near river or valleys)

Any of these variables may affect the choice of
the system to be used. Mean traffic flow may be
light in a particularly heavily populated area.
This could be due in part to the adequacy of existing roads and access routes or perhaps of public
transport. From signalized intersection requirements,
the TRD digital system would appear to be the proper
choice for such an area. However, traffic flow data
would dictate a less complex system such as the TRA
digital. Other sparsely populated areas where mean
traffic flow is heavy may require a large computerized system (TRD), whereas by the standards used

above, a smaller system (TRA digital) would be
enough.

Attention should also be focused on specially
congested areas at rivers or in narrow valleys and
hills. Here the population may be small; however,
due to the topography, congestion at strategic
points may be severe. Analysis may reveal the need
for the TRA analogue or even the TRD digital system.

In spite of these limitations of the estimate,
however, the conclusion reached regarding market
size for electronic equipment is conservative, especially since no consideration is given to the potential market for highway traffic control as an added
component of the system.

The application of electronic equipment to the
area of vehicular traffic-signal control is feasible
from the cost analysis and benefit study. It has
been demonstrated that both digital and analogue
systems can be effectively operated depending on the
size of the area. Savings due to delay reduction
and reduced roadbuilding are achieved only when capacity of the overall project is considered. For
areas where few intersections are controlled, economies of scale dictate a nonelectronic time variable optimized system.

The realization of the business opportunities
in such systems would, however, have to await a
greater diversion of public funds to the solution
of urban problems in general. In a substantial
program, electronic aids to traffic controls would
be a minor element financially but one of dispropor-
tionately high importance.

NOTES

1. Motorola Radio Traffic Light Control System,
Motorola Communications Division, Motorola Inc.
(November, 1962).

2. Arthur Daou, "The Control of Traffic Flow in
New York City," (graduate seminar paper, Department
of Industrial and Management Engineering, Columbia
University, Dec. 12, 1961).

3.   "Florida and Modern Traffic Signal Control,"
Traffic Quarterly, vol. 16 (July, 1958), p. 654.

4.   "Computer Control to Untie Toronto Traffic,"
Canadian Controls and Instrumentation (November-
December, 1962).

5.   T. Stouffis, "Breaking Traffic Jam,"
National Civic Review, vol. 51 (October, 1962), pp.
482-5.

6.   "Electronic Highway of Tomorrow," Electrical
Engineering, vol. 77 (July, 1958), p. 654.

7.   "T.V. Traffic Control System goes into Full
Operation in Detroit," Engineering News Record (May
10, 1961), pp. 51-52.

8. M. Beckman and C. B. McQuire, "Studies in the
Economics of Transportation," Rand Corporation Report, RM 1488 (May 2, 1955).

9.   E. K. Damon and R. L. Cosgriff, "Electronic
Traffic Control," Electronics Magazine (January 6,
1961), pp. 41-44.

10.   "Traffic Controller Avoids Wasted Green
Light," Public Works Magazine, vol. 92 (October,
1961), pp. 136-7.

11.   Canadian Controls and Instrumentation, op.
cit.

12.   "Electronic Controller for High-Speed Road
Traffic," Electronic Engineering, vol. 34 (August,
1962), pp. 516-520.

13.   "Computer to Direct Traffic" Business Week
(Feb, 3, 1962), p. 50.

14.   "Simplified Traffic Model for Small Cities,"
Traffic Quarterly, vol. 16 (July, 1962), pp. 336-50.

15.   "Electronic Control of Traffic Signals,"
Public Works Magazine (February, 1961), pp. 60-62.

16.   M. Beckman and C. B. McQuire, op. cit.

17. M. Beckman and C. B. McQuire, "The Determination of Traffic in a Road Network," Rand Corporation Report, RM 1088 (October 6, 1953).

18. H. R. Palmer, "The Development of Traffic Congestion," Bureau of Highway Traffic (Yale University, May, 1959).

19. Information Report by Commission on Planning and Design Policies, Road Users Benefit Analysis for Highway Improvements, American Association of State Highway Officials (Washington, D.C., National Press Building).

20. "The Application of Benefit-Cost Ratios to an Expressway System," Highway Research Board Proceedings, vol. 35, (January, 1956).

21. "A Friction Concept of Traffic Flow," Highway Research Board Proceedings, vol. 38 (June, 1959).

22. Canadian Controls and Instrumentation, op. cit.

23. "Statistical Abstract of the United States," United States Department of Commerce, 83rd Annual Edition (1962).

24. Ibid.

25. Ibid.

CHAPTER

10

ELECTRONIC CONTROLS
FOR RAILROAD OPERATION

by Gary Mauser

PRESENT INSTALLATIONS

During the past forty years, technology applied
to railroad operation has produced a number of remote control and automated systems.[1] The latter
group contains many electronically operated devices,
while the former contains relatively few of them.
The system of Centralized Traffic Control(CTC) is an
example of the most effective remote control system
used by present day railroads.[2] With the advent of
the electronic computer, the controlling function in
the CTC system is being revised, and operation is on
a self-regulatory or automated basis. An example of
an automated system is the control of freight trains
in an electronic classification yard.[3] Another example is the crewless operated shuttle train that
ran between Times Square and Grand Central Station
for a brief period during 1962.[4] The automated
train operated from each terminal at the direction
of an automatic train dispatcher. Door opening and
closing, acceleration, deceleration, and braking
were accomplished automatically. The system was not
completely successful and ultimately discontinued.[5]
Several trips resulted in control-equipment failure.
The two major sources of trouble were the automatic
dispatching unit and the inductive proximity detectors. Redesign of both components led to some improvement in system efficiency. Other applications
of automated systems exist in the mining and industrial process industries.[6] Here crewless trains perform many operations automatically and on a fail-
safe basis.[7]

It is evident that a potential market for electronic equipment exists in train operation. Automatic systems presently depend upon many electronic
devices for their basic functions. In addition,
recent developments in electronic circuitry and miniaturization have produced advanced systems which
perform such functions as detection, identification,
and communication. In this chapter the current and
prospective electronic equipment for railroads is
discussed and a cost-effectiveness analysis is performed in order to estimate the potential market.

The railroad industry, of course, has for many
years been in the doldrums and has been particularly
short of funds for capital equipment. However, a
good deal of spending has been going on, especially
for new freight rolling stock. In addition, the U.S.
Department of Transportation has now taken over the
task of providing faster and more convenient rail
transportation in some of the nation's most densely
populated areas. So far the only project of note
has been that in the Northeast corridor, in which
new rapid electric service is to be provided between
New York and Washington and fast gas turbine powered
trains between New York and Boston. As of April 1968,
all of these projects are still plagued by major
equipment problems relating to the rolling stock itself. None of these problems appear to be electronic
in nature. Since more sophisticated traffic controls
will be essential, however, it seems certain that
any resuscitation of rail service in the "megalo-
politan" areas of the country cannot fail to have
beneficial effects on this part of the electronics
industry.

EQUIPMENT AND TECHNOLOGY AVAILABLE

The system of CTC has been in operation for
many years. It is a method of train operation in
which the movements of trains are directed by signal
indications.[8] It combines block signaling and in-
terlocking together with a train-dispatching function
to form an integrated network for the protection and
control of train movement. Recently, with the advent of computer technology and advanced coding techniques, the system has been expanded to include electronic equipment. The basic operating elements in
the electronic CTC network are the computer console

and the code-control system. The former device
gathers information on all train activities in
a controlled area and maked decisions automatically
regarding dispatching, speed, and right of way.[9]
The latter device performs the function of transmitting controls to the field locations for remote
operation of the wayside signals and track switches.
In addition, provision for return indication keeps
the computer informed of field-equipment response
as well as progress of the trains over the controlled
territory. The General Railway Signal Company and
the Union Switch and Signal Company have pioneered
in the development of computer controls and circuit
coding systems.

In control of activities in a freight classification yard, electronic equipment is also in current use.[10] An analogue computer controls routing
of incoming cars and, from input information regarding destination, assembles them on outbound tracks.
The system is initiated when a tower operator detects
an entering freight car and assigns it to a classification track as determined by the computer. The
car now rolls down a hump leading to the outbound
makeup tracks, controlled solely by the computer.
The computer analyzes length of travel and determines speed requirements necessary for safe operation. It regulates the speed of the moving freight
car by activating retarders situated along the track
route. The retarders clamp in on the car wheels,
providing the required braking force.

For automatic or crewless train operation, control is maintained by a digital computer. For the
dispatching function, the computer initiates train
movements according to a predetermined schedule.
The computer performs many other functions in the
overall system. It initiates propulsion and braking by applying coded impulses to the rails for pick-
up by car-carried equipment.[11] It also closes and
opens doors automatically and holds trains for meets
with other trains.[12]

To provide safe train operation, a device which
detects hot wheel journal bearings is available.[13]
The installation of this device provides warning of
imminent bearing failure. The sleeve or journal
surrounding the axle of a train wheel generates extreme heat, resulting in failure and ultimate train
derailment. An infra-red electronic heat sensing

device positioned along the wayside focuses on the
hub of the wheel or the journal bearing box. It
detects excessive temperatures and records the output as a d.c. voltage, which is proportional to the
heat generated. The level of d.c. output is compared to a predetermined level considered safe for
ordinary operation. The information is either read
out as output (in standard trace form) or relayed
to an analogue computer for storage and subsequent
evaluation. The system is integrated with the CTC
network to maintain train safety. For this system,
transmission of output data is accomplished with
the aid of telemetering equipment and leased or private telephone lines.

A system which provides trains with individua-
lity and permits them to register their identification points has also been developed. Sylvania
Electronic Systems is the originator of the automatic railroad car identification system.[14] The
specific identity registration is used in conjunction with other equipment to provide automatic alignment of a route, automatic announcing systems, and
aid in the further development of automatic train
operation. The system consists basically of a marker
or Scotchlite label placed on the railroad car, an
electronic transducer for car counting, a wayside
scanning device, and a printer or data-transmission
device.

To detect the presence of a train, an electronic
sensing device is currently being evaluated. The inductive proximity detector is used in automatic subway operation to determine whether a car has stopped
over door control track loops.[15] The information
is relayed to the computer controlled dispatching
unit to initiate door opening and closing. Equipment for transmittal of data consists of wayside
coils connected to wayside boxes, each of which contains a printed plug-in circuit board with a filter
network and a self-contained power supply. The detection system consists of a transmitter, two receivers, two detector heads and a master receiver
sensitivity-control unit.[16] A detector head is positioned overhead at each end of a door control track
loop. Each contains an electronic transmitting and
receiving transducer.

In the field of communication, an inductive
train communication system is being marketed. Voice

communication between motormen and station-train
dispatcher is a valuable aid, particularly at times
when rerouting of trains is necessary.[17] A completely transistorized train-to-wayside and wayside-
to-train system operating from standard cell batteries is available to fill this need. Each set consists of a microphone, a transmitter-receiver unit
and a blocking unit. A voice signal is received by
the car receiver through inductive reception from
the third rail to the wheel shoe. For transmission
from car to wayside, the path is the same but in
reverse. Energy is sent to and received from the
third rail through coupling filters. Transmission
to and from the coupling filters is accomplished
with the aid of a pair of line wires.

In the area of track-circuitry design, a fully
transistorized overlay track network is available.
In the present nonelectronic system, relays initiate
grade-crossing signals as detected by the presence
of the train over a specific section of track. The
electronic system dispenses with the four insulated
joints which control the relay circuits.[18] The miniaturized device performs the function of the relay,
starting and stopping signal warning lights in both
directions of travel.

COST ANALYSIS

These systems have proved to be profitable investments for their users. A practical example of
the application of electronic equipment in a CTC
network is presented and analyzed with regard to
cost incurred and savings derived from the new system. The New York Central Railroad designed and
placed the system in operation on a 130-route mile
project between Syracuse and Schenectady, New York.[19]
The project is typical of installations which derive
cost savings through the use of integrated electronic
equipment. The network before the use of electronic
equipment consisted of four main tracks, two in each
direction. The present system consists of centralized control of only two tracks; the other two were
retired.

The net cost of the installation was $3.3 mil-
lion, arrived at as follows:

1. Labor cost of removing and retiring the old
equipment................................. $ 500,000

  2.   Labor and material necessary for installation of track changes.................   3,000,000

  3.   Labor and material cost associated with
revised signaling system.............   3,700,000

  4.   Cost of new communication equipment (computer controlled console plus associated electronic
coding equipment).....................   500,000
             Total for new work $7,700,000

             Less salvage value on two tracks taken
up....................................   4,300,000

             Net cost of new installation $3,300,000

     The annual saving from the system was shown to
be about $1 million in reduced labor charges for
track maintenance and snow removal as well as in reduced costs for the consolidated control equipment
itself. The installation would thus pay for itself
in a little over 3 years.

     Electronic equipment in railroad classification
yards has also proved profitable. In the $14 million
installation in Elkhart, Indiana, approximately $3.7
million was spent on electronic apparatus.[20] The
equipment includes nine analogue computers, grade
retarders, radar trackers, proximity detectors, and
extensive radio and closed circuit television equipment. Savings from this installation have produced
a return on incremental investment of 20 percent.
Actual saving in operating expense (as compared to
older nonelectronic yard) is $4.0 million, or a net
return on total investment of 28 percent. The additional 8 percent is credited to improvement in functional operations resulting from other than electronic innovation.[21]

     Capital cost figures on automatic dispatching
equipment vary according to the scope of the project.
A typical cost estimate for a small size digital computer console and associated tie-in-equipment is
$300,000. Savings from this system as opposed to
a nonelectronic dispatching unit are estimated to
be 15 percent.[22] This is a result of a reduction
in manpower required, decreased maintenance cost,
and efficiencies resulting from reductions in human
error and consolidation of operations.

The cost breakdown on a typical hot-box detector installation is as follows:

Detector (electronic heat-sensing
device).................$10,000
Telemetering equipment... 2,500
Installation cost........ 1,000
Total capital cost......$13,500

Savings from such a system are difficult to define because they would have to come from avoided accidents as well as from simplified bearing maintenance. However, experience indicates that costs of the system, including its own maintenance, reflect a saving of more than half the cost of the unreliable methods now often used.[23]

The capital equipment and installation cost for a complete train identification system is about $5,000.[24] This includes the price of the trackside scanner, complete with equipment to generate a teletype code. Estimated savings of 10 percent have been realized, compared with expenditures for visual identification of railroad cars.

One proximity detection unit used in an automated subway system or in a freight classification yard costs $600 including installation.[25] The device senses the presence of a train in a particular location and is used in conjunction with the dispatching unit to provide door control and general safety in train operation. In addition, the unit eliminates the need for a mechanical detection system whose maintenance and failure rate is high. Conservative estimates range from 20 to 25 percent as far as cost saving benefits are concerned.[26]

The equipment and installation cost of a completely transistorized train communication system is approximately $25,000.[27] Savings are based on a reduction in system-power requirements as compared to that of the nonelectronic teletype communication system. Reduced maintenance and labor costs are also associated with the new system. A 15 percent overall saving is expected with the new electronic system.

Total capital cost for one overlay track section is $3,000, consisting of $2,100 for equipment and $900 for installation.[28] The reduced cost of

the transistorized device as compared to the nonelectronic relay system is about 10 percent. Savings are based on a reduction in the number of insulated joints necessary with relay circuitry and a
reduction in maintenance cost.

MARKET SIZE

A large market for electronic equipment exists
in the CTC system. By replacement of present dispatching units with computer-controlled devices,
operating efficiency and economy are obtained. The
cost of electronic computer equipment is estimated
at $3,800 per route mile, based on the Schenectady-
Syracuse installation described earlier. Approximately 30,000 route miles of railroad are currently
operated by CTC.[29] The potential expenditure might,
therefore, be as much as $114 million.

Small digital computers suitable for dispatching cost about $300,000 each. There are 106 Class
I railroads in the United States, i.e., those with
revenues greater than $3 million. There are also
four cities currently with subway systems. One unit
per railroad and a total of six for the subway systems would result in an expenditure of $33.6 million.
Many of the smaller lines would not require such
equipment, but the larger ones would undoubtedly
need more than one if this equipment were fully
developed.

At present, plans have been announced for a
further 20 major railroad classification yards.[30]
At $3.7 million each on electronic equipment, this
would result in a total of $74 million.

With respect to hotbox detectors, some fully
equipped railroads, such as the New York Central,
have them every thirty miles or so on their main
lines. While there are some 220,000 route miles
of the Class I lines, it would be unrealistic to
expect more than about a third to become fully
equipped because of the low traffic density found
in many cases.[31] Even this would produce a substantial market, however. At $13,500 per instal-
lation, a total of $33 million would result.

If ten train identification units were to be
used on the average by each of the Class I lines,
a total market of $5.5 million would result, based
on a unit cost of $5,000. Inductive train commu-
nications and train proximity detectors would be
minor items, with no more than about $4 million re-
quired for a first set of equipment.[32] Overlay
track circuits may be a little more important, with
2,500 units at about $3,000 each being the prospec-
tive requirement.[33] This would be a total of $7.5
million.

The market can thus be summed up as follows:

	$ millions
Electronic CTC	114.0
Dispatching Computers and accessories	33.6
Railroad classification yards	74.0
Hotbox detectors	33.0
Train identification	5.5
Communications and proximity detectors	4.0
Overlay track circuits	7.5
Total	271.6

There is, therefore, a potential market of about
$272 million. Spread over a period of eight years
or so, it would represent annual business of about
$35 million compared with only $9.0 million in 1966.

Whether or not such a market comes to pass depends on future prosperity of the railroad industry.
In general, this is as much a function of the prowess
of managements as it is of public policy, especially
in the proposed rapid transit systems.[34] The future
of the railroads has, of course, often been viewed
pessimistically in recent years. In 1963, however,
rail equipment again began to stir extensive interest,
although more in new types of cars and other heavy
items than in new controls.[35] However, a continuation of this development is bound to affect the
controls industry as well. Though there are several
strongly entrenched firms now in the field of rail
automation and controls, the inherent suitability
of the medium (contrasted with road travel, for example) is bound to make this field technically attractive to diversifying firms within its size
limits.

NOTES

1. J. W. Hansen, "The Potential of Remote and Automatic Control for Train Operation," Financial Analysts Journal (March, 1962).

2. "Centralized Traffic Control," publication of Union Switch and Signal Division, Westinghouse Air Brake Company, (Swissvale, Pa.)

3. "Railroads Use Electronics to Cut Costs," Electronics, vol.33, (Nov. 4, 1960), p. 35.

4. "Shuttle Train Automation," Handbook 77, General Railway Signal Company, (Rochester, New York, February, 1962).

5. "Automatic Train Disappoints New York," Control Engineering, (December, 1962), p. 26.

6. B. McKnight, "First Crewless Freight Train," Railway Age, vol.153, (Sept. 3, 1962), pp. 12-15.

7. L. R. Allison, "Unmanned Helper being Tested," Railway Age, vol.151, (July 17, 1961), pp. 24-25.

8. "Centralized Traffic Control," op. cit.

9. "Discontinuous Control Stops Train Automatically," Control Engineering, vol.8, (January, 1961), pp. 90-93.

10. "Control Freight Electronically," Electronics, vol.31, (May 16, 1958), p. 19.

11. "What's Ahead for Transit Automation," Railway Age, vol.152, (May 21, 1962), p. 25.

12. G. W. Gaugham, "Step by Step Approach to the Crewless Train," Journal of Financial Analysts, vol.18, (May, 1962), p. 67.

13. "Railroad Equipment - A Long Overdue Break," Printer's Ink, vol.280, (Aug. 17, 1962), p. 29.

14. "Car Identifier Does Fast Accurate Job," Railway Age, (Mar. 25, 1963), pp. 39-41.

15. Paul Graham, "What's New in Rapid Transit Signalling," Union Switch and Signal, Division of Westinghouse Air Brake Company (Swissvale, Pa).

16. "Shuttle Train Automation," op. cit.

17. Paul Graham, op. cit.

18. W. A. Robinson, "Completely Automatic Train Operation Feasible Today," Computers and Automation, vol.9, (Apr. 1960), p. 12.

19. "CTC Project Cost Analysis," New York Central Railroad, Signal and Communications Department (New York, N. Y.).

20. "Railroad Classification Yard Cost Analysis Program," New York Central Railroad, Signal and Communications Department (New York, N. Y.).

21. "Railroads Use Electronics to Cut Costs," op. cit.

22. "Railroad Classification Yard Cost Analysis Program," op. cit.

23. "Hot-Box Detector Estimates," New York Central Railroad, Signal and Communications Department (New York, N. Y.).

24. "Car Identifier Does Fast Accurate Job," op. cit.

25. "Railroad Classification Yard Cost Analysis Program," op. cit.

26. Paul Graham, op. cit.

27. L. R. Allison, "Recent Developments in the Operation of Unmanned Locomotives and Trains," Union Switch and Signal Division of Westinghouse Air Brake Company (Swissvale, Pa.).

28. "Overlay Track System Study," Pennsylvania Railroad, Engineering Department (New York, N. Y.).

29. "Metropolitan Transportation Department Bulletin," General Electric Company (2901 East Lake Road, Erie 1, Pennsylvania, 1963).

30. "Railroad Classification Yard Cost Analysis Program," op. cit.

31. U. S. Bureau of the Census, 1963, Statistical Abstract of the United States (Washington, D. C.).

32. "Studies on Subway Installations," Institute for Rapid Transit (Chicago, Ill., 1962).

33. "Overlay Track System Study," op. cit.

34. R. D. Weeks, "Rapid Transit Automation - Why? How?," Metropolitan Transportation (Schenectady, N. Y. General Electric Company).

35. "New Life on the Tracks," Business Week (Oct. 19, 1963), p. 120.

CHAPTER **11** AVIATION
SUPPORT
EQUIPMENT

by Stephen Gideon

PRESENT SUPPORT EQUIPMENT

Despite the existence of extensive communications and control systems, the effective surveillance and management of air traffic is still an unrealized objective. It has long engaged the attention of government agencies and of firms in the electronics industry. To the former, the continued occurrence of delays and, at times, of accidents for which bad traffic controls are responsible, has been a cause of great concern. In the industry, firms with knowledge of radar systems, other aircraft instruments, data displays, and computers have looked upon the reequipment of American and other airports as a promising source of new business, outside of their usual defense-related lines. As a result, several firms appear to be firmly entrenched in the field, at least in the present preliminary stages. The FAA which has the principal task of evaluating the systems, has not, however, settled on final designs and, in part, is still waiting for acceptable systems to emerge from its own research efforts and those of the industry.

In this chapter, the present systems are first described. It is shown that they have failed to solve problems of delays, cancellations, and accidents. The economic criteria for new systems are then set forth, and from this a maximum economic price for the equipment is derived, leading to an estimate of the market. This is related to the characteristics of certain important new systems that have been proposed or exist in prototype.

Aircraft traffic-control equipment can be classified by the segment of flight which it controls: en route, terminal area, and airport surface.

Traffic in the en route segment of flight is controlled by a series of airways, which are three dimensional blocks of airspace described from point to point by one or more of the following radio facilities:

1. Low Frequency/Medium Frequency Navigational Aids

This equipment transmits in the 200- to 550-kilocycle range and is used either as a homing aid or to establish a radio range with four separate legs or beams in any desired direction.

2. VHF Ominrange (VOR)

VOR ground-based transmitters generate an omnidirectional VHF signal. VOR receivers in aircraft, when tuned to the frequency of a transmitter, have the capability of determining the magnetic bearing to and from the transmitting station.

3. Tactical Aid to Navigation (TACAN)

The TACAN equipment is similar to the VOR equipment, in that it operates at VHF frequencies, but it provides greater accuracy.

4. Distance Measuring Equipment (DME)

A unit in the aircraft transmits a signal which is received by a ground installation (transponder) and transmitted back to the aircraft at a different frequency. The airborne unit measures the time differential between transmitted and received signals and converts this to nautical miles.

In addition to the airways defined by radio equipment, the FAA has established Air Route Traffic Control Centers which are equipped with ARSR-2 surveillance radars to aid monitoring-air traffic.

Control of terminal traffic involves control of arriving flights from the time aircraft enter the airport vicinity until they are on the airport runway and vice versa for departures. The approach-control facilities at high-density terminal areas

which handle heavy IFR traffic normally include
surveillance radars and are classified as radar
approach control facilities. Sometimes neighboring
airports share a single approach-control facility.

With present equipment the radar-approach controller monitors the position of all aircraft in
his sector on a radar display on which he can see
only a plan view. He must estimate aircraft closure rates, while remembering the altitudes to
which he has cleared them.

Airports also are equipped with Instrument
Landing Systems, used to control landing aircraft
when poor visibility exists. The Instrument Landing
System presently used consists of a localizer radio
beam used to keep the aircraft aimed at center of
runway, a glide-slope radio beam used to keep the
aircraft on a sloping approach, and vertical marker
radio signals that serve as distance reference points.
These signals are all emitted from ground-based
equipment, giving the pilot an indication of his
position relative to a sloping line he should be
traveling. The pilot must be able to see the ground
from 200 feet up, because at that point he must
switch to visual control.

With only a handful of exceptions, control of
airport-surface traffic is completely manual. Controllers guide aircraft by means of instructions
transmitted to the pilot by VHF radio frequency communication, who acknowledges them by radio and performs accordingly. During minimum visibility
conditions under which aircraft can presently operate, the controller must rely completely on the pilot
to report his location and then issue instructions
based on this information. A radar set has been
developed, tested, and installed at a few airports
which provides the controller with extended visibility on the airport surface. This radar known as
Airport Surface Detection Equipment (ASDE) presents
the controller with a picture of the airport surface
so that he has the ability to exercise manual control, regardless of weather. There are presently
nine operational ASDE radars at commercial airports
in the United States.[1]

COST OF PRESENT AVIATION SUPPORT EQUIPMENT

The costs of operating the present aircraft
traffic-control equipment are the normal operating
and maintenance costs plus costs due to disturbances
of normal operation, which result from control-
equipment ineffectiveness. The disturbances to normal operation are manifested as delays, diversions,
cancellations, and accidents. These disturbances
and costs associated with them will now be discussed.
Their reduction is the principal objective of the
proposed new systems.

Delays are the most frequent category of disruption to aircraft operations and the most difficult
to define. This is because no standard exists with
which actual times can be compared. Existing data
are based on scheduled times, which themselves include an allowance for normal delays. In this study
the elapsed time between actual performance and
scheduled performance will be used as the delay time.
This result is conservative compared with using an
estimated deviation of scheduled times from ideal
times, which could result in overestimating the market. Table 11.1 presents the types of delays incurred and possible causes for these delays.

In order to determine criteria for FAA expenditures, United Research Inc., obtained flight logs
from three air carriers for the first six months of
1961. Among other information, these flight logs
gave total block-to-block and station delays.[2] They
also gave either a breakdown of delays by causes or
a cause code for the aggregate delay.[3] This sample
information was used to estimate the distribution
of delays by cause and the average delay per departure. The data were seasonally adjusted by an index
based on the monthly number of instrument approaches
by air carriers, which, of course, are related to
weather.[4] The results are presented in Table 11.2
and Table 11.3. Clearly, a major portion of the delays is now due to deficiencies in aviation support.

The cost of delays to the aircraft operator that
will be used in this study are the out-of-pocket
costs associated directly with operating an aircraft
an additional increment of time. These costs are
primarily expenditures for salaries of flight personnel, fuel, and for direct maintenance of flight
equipment.[5]

TABLE 11.1

Delay Attributable to Support System

Type of delay	Cause of delay
Departure	a. Below minimum weather at departure and/or destination airport b. En route airways saturation c. Terminal area saturation d. Airport surface congestion
Terminal area departure	a. Terminal area saturation b. En route airways saturation
Inbound	a. Below minimum weather at airport b. Arrival rate greater than airport acceptance rate
En route	a. En route airways saturation b. Terminal area saturation
Taxi	a. Ramp congestion b. Crossing active runway c. Taxiway congestion
At active runway	a. Landing aircraft traffic b. Departing aircraft traffic

Source: Gary Fromm, Economic Criteria for Federal Aviation Agency Expenditures, Prepared for Aviation Research and Development Service, Federal Aviation Agency (Washington, D.C.: Federal Aviation Agency, 1962) p. IV-3.

TABLE 11.2

Distribution of Minutes of Delay Per
Departure for Air Carriers, 1961

	Percent
Total gross delay	100.0
Block-to-block	47.4
Station	52.6
Block-to-block	100.0
Aviation support	52.9
Other	47.1
Station	100.0
Aviation support	12.7
Other	87.3
Block-to-block aviation support	100.0
Airborne	61.8
Surface	38.2
Airborne	61.8
Terminal area	53.8
En route	8.0
Surface	38.2
Departing	30.6
Inbound	7.6
Terminal area	53.8
Departing	2.8
Inbound	51.0

Source: Fromm, p. IV-3.

Hourly costs were computed by converting estimates of hours flown by aircraft type to block-to-
block hours and then dividing this number into the
applicable variable operating costs by aircraft type.
Cost for a typical aircraft was obtained by weighting
the costs by aircraft type according to the proportion of total hours flown by aircraft type. In this
way the block-to-block hourly operating cost for a
typical aircraft was estimated to be $213.00.[6]

Table 11.4 presents the data used to obtain
this estimate. These estimates are low when compared
with the results of an operating cost analysis conducted by Airborne Instruments Laboratory, and,
therefore, can be expected to lead to conservative
results.[7]

Cancellations and diversions which can be attributed to an ineffective aviation-support system
are similar to delays, differing only by degree. A
diversion is the shifting of an aircraft from its
intended destination as a result of conditions which
prevent landing at its intended destination. Diversions are usually the result of weather or heavy
traffic conditions. A cancellation is the failure
of an aircraft to leave its origin airport within a
specified time interval. As with diversions, those
cancellations which are the result of aviation
support-system performance are usually due to weather
or heavy traffic conditions at the destination.

The number of cancellations per air-carrier departure for 1961 was 0.0292, with 63 percent, or
0.0183 the result of weather.[8] The number of diversions per air-carrier departure for 1961 was .0048,
with 83 percent, or .0040 caused by weather.[9] Those
cancellations and diversions which are the result
of weather conditions are an approximate estimate
of disruptions caused by ineffective aviation-
support equipment.

Costs which result from flight diversions are
dependent on the time of diversion. When diversions
occur after entering the terminal area of the original destination, additional flying time is incurred
in holding over the original destination, flying to
the new destination, and possibly holding over the
alternate terminal. On the other hand flying time
is saved when aircraft are diverted to nearer airports before entering the terminal area of the destination airport. It was found that the net average

TABLE 11.3

Air Carrier Delay by Cause, 1961

	Average minutes per departure
Total gross delay	11.48
Block-to-block	5.44
Aviation support	2.88
Airborne	1.78
Surface	1.10
Station	6.04
Aviation support	.77

Source: Fromm, p. V-9.

TABLE 11.4

Variable Operating Cost by Aircraft Type

Aircraft type	Revenue aircraft hours: 1961[a] (in thousands)	Variable operating cost per block-to-block hour: 1961[b]
		dollars
Small piston	1232	85.50
Medium piston	1646	207.50
Small turboprop	94	124.50
Medium turboprop	437	197.50
Medium turbojet	6	323.50
Large turbojet	722	465.00

Weighted average per aircraft hour: $245
Weighted average per block-to-block hour: $213

Sources: [a]Fromm, p. VI-2.
[b]Fromm, p. VI-3.

additional operating time per diversion was 30 minutes.[10] Using the $213-per-hour cost the cost per
diversion is $106.50. Diversions also cause non-
revenue mileage to be flown in order to reposition
aircraft. The cost of this additional mileage is
estimated to be $43.50 per diversion.[11]

Cancellations result in costs for increased
passenger handling, ferrying aircraft for reposi-
tioning, and lost passenger revenue, as well as
savings of direct operating costs. Table 11.5 presents estimates of these costs.

TABLE 11.5

Breakdown of Cancellation Costs

Item	Cost per cancellation
Ferrying cost	$ 29.00
Passenger revenue loss	230.00
Duplicate handling expense	13.00
Subtotal	$272.00
less	
Direct operating savings	249.00
Net cost per cancellation	$ 23.00

Source: Fromm, p. VI-16.

It has been shown that a high correlation exists
between the reliability of air travel, measured in
terms of scheduled miles completed and the airlines'
share of the first class travel market (air and first
class rail).[12] Also, a survey conducted by Fortune
Magazine revealed that passengers rate carriers in
accordance with their reputation for safe, fast,
and on-time service.[13] Figure 11.1 shows the relationship between reliability and share of the market
for 1959 and 1960.

The effect of unreliability resulting from the
aircraft traffic-control system on revenues can be
determined as follows:

1. Determine the demand for air and first class rail service.

2. Determine the increase in reliability obtainable from an improved aircraft traffic-control system.

3. Calculate the increased share of market obtained by increased reliability.

4. Calculate increased revenue by multiplying additional passenger miles by yield per passenger mile.[14]

Revenue passenger miles for 1960 were 30.6 billion. First class rail passenger miles equaled 3.1 billion in 1960.[15]

Reliability for the 1957-1959 period averaged 97.4 percent. Although this figure decreased in 1960 with the increased usage of jet aircraft, it can be expected to return to this figure as more experience with them is acquired, if the present level of support equipment is maintained.[16] Since 63 percent of the cancellations are attributed to the support system, 63 percent of 2.6 percent, or 1.6 percent of the scheduled mileage could be completed with an improved support system. Results of the calculations outlined above are presented in Table 11.6. The total loss of revenue of $23.8 million is equivalent to $7.12 per departure.

Accidents are the most serious and costly result of the ineffectiveness of air traffic-control systems. Accident figures as advertized by the airlines are very deceiving, since they present data expressed in accidents per mile. With the trend towards increased miles per trip this figure tends to give a very optimistic picture. Since most accidents occur in or around the terminal area and are associated with take-off or landing, the number of accidents per departure is a more realistic indicator of aircraft safety.

A study of accidents between 1946 and 1958 by the Flight Safety Foundation revealed that 94 percent of all accidents in the U.S. occur under instrument flight-rule conditions.[17] This figure will be used as the estimate of accidents which can be eliminated by an improved support system.

TABLE 11.6

Summary of Effects of Reliability on Demand

Revenue passenger miles (billions)			Aircraft share of air plus first class rail market		Additional air carrier demand with perfect system		
Domestic air carrier	First class rail	Total air plus rail	With present support system (%)	With perfect support system	Increased share of market (%)	Increased revenue passenger miles (mill)	Increased revenue (\$-millions)
30.6	3.1	33.7	90.8	92.0	1.16	390.9	23.8

Source: Fromm, p. VII-6.

197

FIGURE 11.1

Variations in Reliability and Air Carriers' Share of the Market

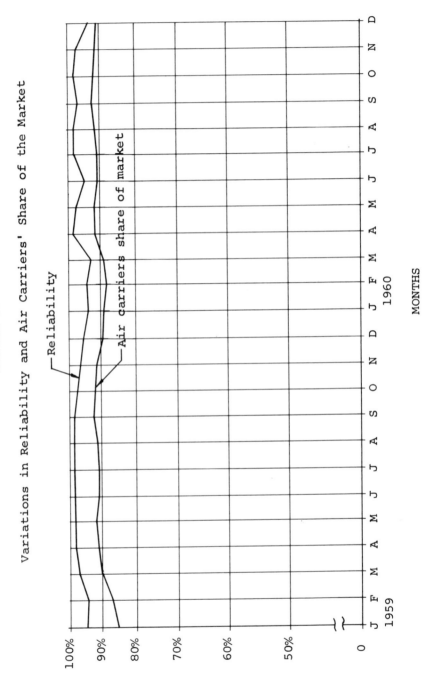

198

TABLE 11.7

Breakdown of Accident Costs

	Total[a]	Due to support system	Cost per accident[b] $(000)
Fatalities per million departures	150	141	$345
Severe injuries per million departures	17.4	16.3	48
Aircraft destroyed per million departures	5.4	5.0	770
Aircraft severely damaged per million departures	18.5	17.4	385

Sources: [a]Federal Aviation Agency, Statistical Handbook of Aviation, 1961.

[b]Fromm, p. VII-7.

TABLE 11.8

Total Accident Costs

	Cost[a] $(000)	Cost per million departures due to support system $(millions)
Fatality	$345	$48.6
Severe injury	48	0.8
Destroyed aircraft	770	3.9
Severely damaged aircraft	385	6.7
Total		$60.0

Source: [a]Fromm, p. VII-7. (See also Table 11.7, last column.)

Tables 11.7 and 11.8 present a breakdown of accidents and their costs for 1960.

OPERATING COST AT AIRPORTS

The previous analysis, as well as a study of delays conducted by the FAA indicate that the disruptions en route are relatively insignificant when compared to the total disruptions of normal aircraft activity.[18] Since virtually all disruptions do take place in the vicinity of airports or on the airport surface and most aircraft traffic control equipment is installed at airports, the comparative costs of new and present equipment are best examined separately for each airport. Ineffectiveness costs associated with present equipment, summarized in Table 11.9, have been expressed in terms of costs per departure so that knowing departures at a given airport, costs can be determined.

These costs are a measure of possible savings. Normal maintenance and operating costs need not be considered; they also exist for new equipment, and the assumption is made that these costs do not change. This assumption is conservative because increased maintenance costs of more complex equipment will tend to be more than balanced by decreased operating costs of more automatic equipment.

Table 11.9 indicates that of the $81.10 ineffectiveness costs per departure, 75 percent are attributable to accident costs. Since, as aforesaid, almost all accidents occur under instrument flight-rule conditions, it appears that accident costs could be reduced by placing further restrictions on the weather conditions required for flights. However, this would lead to increased costs for the other categories of disruptions, especially delays and lost share of the market, and would soon result in a net increase of total ineffectiveness costs. It, therefore, appears that in order to reduce these costs, more efficient air traffic-control equipment must be developed.

In order to determine the value of a new piece of equipment, savings for not only one year but for the useful life of the equipment must be determined.

It was found by the FAA that aviation-support equipment has a useful life of well over ten years, but
considering the increased complexity of new equipment and in keeping with the procedure of using conservative estimates, a useful life for new equipment
of ten years will be used for this study.[19]

TABLE 11.9

Summary of Ineffectiveness Costs

Cause	Cost per departure
Delay	$12.96
Cancellation	0.42
Diversion	0.60
Lost share of market	7.12
Accidents	60.00
Total	$81.10

If it is assumed that present effectiveness of
the aviation-support system is maintained, the
savings resulting from more effective equipment can
be predicted on the basis of estimated departures
over the next ten years. If the trends of the past
twelve years continue, these are expected to remain
approximately constant. This is because the expected
increase in passenger miles is likely to come more
from the use of larger aircraft than from more frequent departures. If this prediction should prove
pessimistic, it is still on the side of under rather
than overestimating the market.

On the basis of a constant level of departures
and a constant effectiveness level disruption costs
for the next ten years can be expected to remain
constant.

Using an interest rate of 10 percent, the present value of $81.08 per year for ten years is
$495.62.

Table 11.10 lists the present value of ineffectiveness costs, by airport, for all airports reporting over 9,000 departures in fiscal year 1961.

In 1961, 1,750 aircraft comprised the air carrier fleet.[20] Since some new equipment would be installed in the aircraft, and new equipment costs are compared to savings separately for each airport, the air carrier fleet must be allocated to the airports for purposes of the cost comparison. In column 3 of Table 11.10 the aircraft are allocated to airports on the basis of percentage of total departures at the airport.

NEW EQUIPMENT

New equipment now exists, or is well within the present state of the art, for reducing the ineffectiveness costs. As noted before, terminal and airport-surface equipment are the most important potential products.

An effective terminal area-control system requires continual knowledge of aircraft position in three dimensions, which does not depend on voice communication. This can be accomplished by means of a transponder in the aircraft, which upon interrogation transmits a reply containing altitude and identity information. The interrogator, as well as the receiver for detecting aircraft replies, can be built into present surveillance radars. This type of equipment is well within the present state of the art and has already been recommended for use by the System Design Team formed within the FAA for the purpose of preparing a long-range plan for efficient, safe control of air traffic within the United States. In addition to the transponder for determining aircraft altitudes, effective terminal-area control requires automation of the routine tasks normally performed by the controller. This can be accomplished through use of a data processor which receives inputs from the radar equipment and performs the following functions:

1. It performs the normal clerical tasks associated with the control function.

TABLE 11.10

Ineffectiveness Costs by Airport

Airport	Departures 1961[a] (thous.)	Present value of ineffectiveness cost ($millions)	Allocated aircraft
New York, Kennedy	68.7	$34.0	37
Chicago, O'Hare	70.2	34.8	38
Los Angeles	67.4	33.4	36
Washington, National	104.4	51.7	56
Chicago, Midway	88.7	44.0	47
Atlanta	71.8	35.6	38
Miami	42.8	21.2	23
New York, La Guardia	57.6	28.5	31
Newark	55.1	27.3	29
San Francisco	52.0	25.8	28
Dallas, Love	58.9	29.2	32
Boston	51.8	25.6	28
Cleveland	51.4	25.5	28
Philadelphia	47.4	23.5	25
Pittsburgh	48.6	24.1	26
Denver	33.6	16.7	18
St. Louis	42.7	21.2	23
Cincinnati	34.2	17.0	18
Kansas City, Municipal	34.9	17.3	19
Detroit, Willow Run	34.8	17.2	19
Minneapolis	32.9	16.3	18
New Orleans	29.1	14.4	16
Louisville	26.1	12.9	14
Baltimore, International	21.6	10.7	12
Indianapolis	27.1	13.4	14
Houston	27.5	13.6	15
Tampa	24.5	12.1	13
Milwaukee	30.3	15.0	16
Columbus	25.6	12.7	14
Portland	25.1	12.4	13
Detroit, Wayne	23.9	11.8	13
Charlotte	24.8	12.3	13
Jacksonville	25.2	12.5	14
Memphis	25.1	12.5	13
Buffalo	25.2	12.5	13
Phoenix	18.6	9.2	10
Seattle-Tacoma	20.1	10.0	11
Dayton	23.3	11.6	12

(continued)

TABLE 11.10 (continued)

Airport	Departures 1961[a] (thous.)	Present value of ineffectiveness cost ($millions)	Allocated aircraft
Rochester	19.6	$ 9.7	10
Oakland	11.1	5.5	6
Syracuse	19.6	9.7	10
Ft. Worth, Carter	22.4	11.1	12
Birmingham	18.4	9.1	10
Tulsa	17.2	8.6	9
Nashville	18.0	8.9	10
Salt Lake City	17.4	8.6	9
Oklahoma City	18.1	9.0	10
Knoxville	12.9	6.4	7
San Diego	13.5	6.7	7
San Antonio	12.9	6.4	7
Las Vegas	14.4	7.2	8
Toledo	13.3	6.6	7
Charleston	15.9	7.9	8
Omaha	16.8	8.3	9
Albany	14.8	7.4	8
Chattanooga	10.4	5.1	6
Roanoke	12.7	6.3	7
West Palm Beach	10.3	5.1	5
Albuquerque	10.3	5.1	6
Providence	12.4	6.1	7
Greensboro	11.8	5.9	6
Sacramento	12.2	6.1	6
Raleigh	11.3	5.6	6
Tucson	9.0	4.5	5
Shreveport	12.4	6.1	7
Binghamton	10.8	5.4	6
Orlando	12.1	6.0	6
Grand Rapids	11.4	5.7	6
El Paso	10.5	5.2	6
Akron-Canton	9.8	4.8	5
Richmond	10.9	5.4	6
Jackson	10.0	5.0	5
Des Moines	11.7	5.8	6
Hartford	18.2	9.0	10
Little Rock	10.5	5.2	6
South Bend	10.1	5.0	5
Wichita	10.6	5.3	6
Austin	9.9	4.9	5
Lexington-Frankfort	9.3	4.6	5
Madison	9.4	4.6	5
Wilkes-Barre	9.7	4.8	5
TOTALS	2,137.0	1,059.2	1,144

Source: [a]Federal Aviation Agency, Air Commerce Traffic Pattern--Fiscal Year 1961 (Washington, D.C.: FAA, 1961), pp. 5-11.

2. It acts as an accurate and readily available storehouse for all information required to efficiently control the aircraft.

3. It organizes, processes, filters, and distributes all necessary data.

4. It predicts flight paths of all aircraft under control and warns of potential conflicts.

The data processor can generate a display which contains alphanumeric identity plus altitude and control information. Three-dimensional displays are being considered for this purpose.

The cost of the aircraft transponder can be estimated on the basis of similar equipment to be $5,000, and the estimated cost of modifying existing terminal-area radars for radar-beacon operation is $185,000.[21] The data processor would vary in complexity from airport to airport, according to capacity. There are presently no available cost data on such a unit.

Delays, cancellations, diversions, and accidents can be reduced through use of more effective terminal-area control, as described above, plus an all-weather landing system. Such systems are presently being developed and tested, although the question of system philosophy is still being argued. One all-weather landing system which is under evaluation is Flarescan, developed by the Airborne Instruments Laboratory Division of Cutler-Hammer, Inc. This system takes over where the present glide-path beam ends, and the pilot now must switch to visual control. It transmits a narrow radio beam from a "nodding" antenna, which is picked up by a receiver in the plane. The received signal is fed to a small computer, which continuously calculates the plane's altitude and distance from the runway and displays this information for the pilot's use. Estimated cost of this system is about $10,000 per plane for the airborne equipment and $100,000 per runway for the ground based equipment.[22] Data are not available on the landing rate per runway, which is possible through use of this system.

Increased effectiveness of airport-surface control also requires automation. An automated ground
traffic-control system requires development of a device capable of detecting aircraft position and transmitting this information to a data processor. The
data processor with all necessary inputs can then
determine optimum control procedures and control
movement on the airport by means of transmitted instructions or traffic lights. A radio doppler-
detection system which would observe aircraft as
they approach the runway and as they travel on it
seems to be the most promising detection technique.
Another possible detection technique utilizes a magnetic induction loop buried in the runway to detect
aircraft positions. There is no cost data available
for these systems as yet. The ASDE equipment discussed earlier, which has thus far been installed
at only nine locations and provides improved although
limited effectiveness, costs $410,000 installed.[23]

ESTIMATED MARKET

The goal for new equipment is elimination of all
disruptions due to the aviation-support system. Procurement of equipment which fulfills this goal is
desirable if equipment costs per airport are less
than the present value of ineffectiveness costs,
shown in Table 11.10. Equipment which does not eliminate all disruptions can be evaluated by comparing
the cost savings per airport which result from the
decreased disruptions with the equipment cost.

An example of the calculation is afforded by
examining New York International Airport, which has
ten runways in operation and was allocated 37 aircraft in Table 11.10. A Flarescan landing system
is estimated to cost $10,000 per plane, or $370,000,
plus $100,000 per runway, or $1 million. The ASDE
installation is estimated to cost $410,000, but no
data are available on the cost of a fully automated
ground traffic-control system. Addition of a transponder to present terminal-area radars is estimated
to cost $185,000 plus $5,000 per plane, or $185,000
for the planes allocated to New York International
Airport. The total cost of all the above equipment
is $2,150,000, and the present value of the ineffec-
tiveness costs for the aircraft is $34 million.
Therefore, a data processor and automated ground

traffic-control system could cost $32 million if they
could eliminate all the present costs of poor controls. Such a system is probably beyond the immediately foreseeable technical capability. Nevertheless, it is clear that even with a less than perfect
system, there is a substantial cost range within
which a suitable automated ground traffic control
and data processor could be developed. At 60 percent
efficiency, for example, a system would breakeven
at $(.060 x 34 - 2.15) million or $18.25 million.

Such estimates, of course, fall short of what
could be done if systems of the kind required were
already available. It would then be possible to
judge the extent to which each piece of equipment
is actually able to eliminate various components
of ineffectiveness costs and to perform this analysis for each airport.

With the present data, an assumption of 100 percent efficiency for a future system may at first
appear as an unattainable maximum. However, the
principal purchaser of this equipment is the FAA,
and since accident costs are a large part of total
ineffectiveness costs, the FAA might consider more
efficient equipment socially desirable. Although
the possibility does exist that the FAA will buy
equipment that it feels will increase the public welfare even if not economically justified, the FAA
must justify its expenditures on the basis that they
yield benefits which are sufficiently great to out-
weigh alternative, governmental, or private investment programs. Furthermore, if equipment can be
justified on the basis of a cost-benefit analysis,
an investment program in such equipment can be re-
paid by user charges.

Small airports with few departures do not suffer
disruptions to the extent that larger airports suffer
them. Therefore, simply using the total departures
in the United States to estimate the market leads to
an overestimate. Only airports which fall into the
classification of hubs, that is, those airports with
over 26,975 passengers, may be used to obtain the
value of ineffectiveness costs. The airports listed
in Table 11.10 account for 85 percent of departures
from hubs.

Departures for all hubs in the United States in fiscal year 1961 totaled 2,573,541.[24] As stated above, the market for aviation-support equipment can approach the product of the present value of disruption costs per departure and the expected number of departures as a limit. Under these conditions the estimated market for aviation support equipment is therefore $495.62 times 2.573 million departures, or $1,276 million.

This, however, assumes that the cost of the equipment will really be as high as the disruption costs. In fact, as was also shown, the possible margin for the data processor is high, and it is thus likely that a data processor can be produced for less than the permissible maximum. Translated into an annual market extending over a ten-year life of the equipment would reflect an average of at most $130 million a year. In practice, most of the procurement and installation would probably be concentrated in a five-year period in the middle of the decade. Even so, however, the above considerations would seem to cast doubt on an annual market greatly exceeding that sum.

NOTES

1. Federal Aviation Agency, Air Traffic Control Systems Costs (Washington, D. C.: FAA, 1962), p. 19.

2. Block-to-Block time is defined as the number of minutes between pulling the wheel blocks at the departure station and putting them in place at the destination station.

3. Gary Fromm, Economic Criteria for Federal Aviation Agency Expenditures, prepared for Aviation Research and Development Service Federal Aviation Agency (Washington, D.C.: FAA, 1962), p. V-1.

4. Ibid., p. V-7.

5. Ibid., p. VI-1.

6. Ibid., pp. VI-2 - VI-4.

7.   Airborne Instruments Laboratory, Analysis of Capacity and Staging of Runway Construction at Chicago O'Hare Airport, (Deer Park, Ill.: A.I.L., 1963).

8.   Federal Aviation Agency, Digest of Economic Criteria for Federal Aviation Agency Expenditures, (Washington, D.C.: FAA, 1962), p. 10.

9.   Ibid., p. 10.

10.   Fromm, op. cit. pp. VI-8, VI-10.

11.   Fromm, op. cit. p. VI-10.

12.   United Research Inc., A Method for Determining the Economic Value of Air Traffic Control Improvements and Application to All-Weather Landing Systems, prepared for Bureau of Research and Development, Federal Aviation Agency (Washington, D.C.: FAA), pp. 5-8.

13.   "Fortune Airlines Study", Fortune Magazine, March, 1959.

14.   Fromm, op. cit. p. VII-5.

15.   Ibid., p. VII-7.

16.   Ibid., p. VII-7.

17.   Otto E. Kircher, Critical Factors in Approach and Landing Accidents, Part I, Statistics, Flight Safety Foundation Inc. (New York, 1960), pp. 19-21.

18.   Federal Aviation Agency, Elapsed Time and Costs in Air Traffic Terminals (Washington, D.C.: FAA, 1962), p. 1.

19.   Federal Aviation Agency, Economic Criteria for Federal Aviation Agency Expenditures, p. 31.

20.   Aerospace Industries Association of America, Inc., Aerospace Facts and Figures (Washington, D.C.: American Aviation Publishers, Inc., 1961), pp. 115-116.

21.   Federal Aviation Agency, Air Traffic Control Costs, p. 17.

22. Airborne Instruments Laboratory, <u>Topics in Electronics</u>, 1962.

23. Federal Aviation Agency, <u>Air Traffic Control Costs</u>, p. 19.

24. Federal Aviation Agency, <u>Air Commerce Traffic Pattern - Fiscal Year 1961</u> (Washington, D.C.: FAA, 1961), p. 1.

CHAPTER **12** COMMUNICATION
EQUIPMENT

by Stephen Gideon

INTRODUCTION

Private commercial communication systems and
satellite-communication systems have at times been
viewed as potentially extensive market areas in
which developments in advanced electronic techniques
could find wide and profitable application. Upon
analysis, however, it is found that the former cannot at this time be regarded as much of a growth
market for large-scale installations, mainly due to
the strong competitive response made by the established communication companies, notably AT&T. Satellite communications present a more hopeful picture,
but a number of potentially troublesome political
questions remain to be settled which might cut into
the markets for American-built equipment ultimately
installed in such a system. The problems of the
two types of installations will now be discussed.

POINT TO POINT COMMUNICATIONS SYSTEMS

The possibility of private operation of commu-
ication systems has arisen since the Federal Commu-
ications Division decision to allocate a band of
frequencies for private business use. Prior to this,
only public utilities and companies with a right of
way, such as oil and gas pipelines or railroads,
were permitted to operate their own broadband-micro-
wave system.[1] Since the time of this decision there
has been no rush to establish private communications
systems because companies as yet have not seen the
need for systems with the capacity necessary to make

211

such a system economical. One of the first was the
private-communications system of North American Aviation Inc. The network is used to transmit information required to control production, as well as
accounting data to a central office. Cost savings
up to $250,000 per year have been attributed to this
system.[2]

The alternatives to a private communications
system are services offered by common carriers.
These services have recently been greatly improved,
due in most part to the increased competition offered by systems manufacturers anxious to penetrate
the market opened by the FCC rulings.

Common carrier services which must be evaluated
against a private communications system are described below.

Wide Area Telephone Service (WATS)

Wide Area Telephone Service is an offering
which permits big users of long distance facilities
reduced rates. Charges are based on a flat rate
broken down by time and area. There is a full-time
service providing for unlimited, 24-hours-a-day use
or measured time service for a fixed number of hours
a month.

The country is divided into 6 regional bands
from the base area, and rates are fixed for each
area.[3]

Data-phone

Data-phone is a box-like instrument with a telephone attached, designed to permit communication
between business machines. A circuit can be established between two machines by dialing the proper
code. Installation charges plus usage rates are
applied for this service, which is expected to gain
increasing popularity with users who wish to transmit digital data.

The data-phone market is now still handicapped
by an old controversy concerning the use of "foreign"
equipment connected to the telephone system. AT&T,
particularly, has long maintained that it "cannot

guarantee reliable service" if any such device is
connected to its lines. Statements embodying this
prohibition are familiar to many individual subscribers, and the whole problem has concerned them,
too, sometimes in the past. It is possible, for
example, to buy ornamental phones (those of French
or Danish designs have been particularly popular)
and connect them to jacks installed by the telephone
company. Most of the telephones bought this way,
of course, are American instruments, some of them
originally made by Western Electric, the usual supplier to the Bell system. Still, the revenues to
the telephone company are much less because the company only imposes a (rather high) charge for installing the jack once, but levies a monthly charge for
an additional telephone instrument. The telephone
company claims that its prohibitions of foreign
equipment are a legal interpretation of the scope
of the Communications Act of 1934. In response to
many actual and would-be manufacturers of data-phone
and computer communication, the FCC has taken the
matter under advisement. AT&T still maintains its
rights and presented its views in an elaborate brief
to the Commission in March, 1968. Undoubtedly the
matter will now come to a head.[4]

Telpak

Telpak is a new AT&T offering which is now the
major competition to private communication systems.
It offers the user from 12 to 240 channels for any
or all of the following uses: telephone, teletypewriter, facsimile, telephotograph, data transmission,
telemetering, and miscellaneous signaling.

Rates start at $15-per-mile-per-month for 12
lines and go up to $45 per-mile-per-month for 240
lines plus terminal charges, according to equipment
type.[5]

Cost of a 100-mile private wire system connecting, for example, 6 voice channels, 4 facsimile units,
and a pair of typewriters would be $4,200 per month,
based on a cost of $3.50-per-mile-per-month for each
channel plus terminal equipment costs.[6] Under the
Telpak service the same facility would cost $2,160.[7]

This comparison may be generalized, using a
larger system as a basis for comparison. The cost

of constructing a microwave relay system of 1,000 miles with up to 600 4KC channels is estimated to be $260,000 per station, and terminal stations are estimated to cost $860,000.[8]

A relay station is usually required every 30 miles so that 34 relay stations are required for a 1,000-mile system. Total construction costs are, therefore, $10,040,000. The total annual cost including amortization and interest charges based on a 10-year life at 6 percent interest rate plus the annual operating costs of the equipment is estimated at $2,652,000.[9] This cost can be expressed at $4.42 per-channel mile per year. The cost of building a system with fewer than 600 channels would not be significantly different, so this can be treated as a fixed cost.

In general, the private microwave systems and the common carrier installations now in existence have little, if any advantages over the Telpak arrangement. This is true for all sizes of the system. Accordingly, microwave communications, except in special situations, have not made anything approaching a marketing breakthrough. As evidenced in the following Electronics News estimates the growth rate has been on the order of 5-10 percent per year:

Year	Common Carrier	Private	Total
		$ Million	
1967	78	52	130
1968	85	57	142
1969 Est.	93	62	155
1970 Est.	102	68	170

This is not a particularly impressive growth record.

Of the systems used, 55 percent of the capacity is for common carriers, 40 percent industrial (of which one half is for railroads) and the remainder indirect government use. The equipment industry is closely linked to the manufacture of radar equipment. A few firms, notably RCA, General Electric, Collins, Motorola and Lenkurt, share most of the equipment market. We thus have an industry highly sensitive to, and circumscribed by, regulatory policy, a relatively slow growth rate--or at least, little prospect of its immediate acceleration--and an equipment industry in which a small number of suppliers now predominate. Therefore, microwave communications could not be regarded as too significant a prospect for conversion entry, except, of course, for specialized components with necessarily small volume. A substantial increase in volume would have to be associated with a sharp upsurge in cable television--another prospect still stalled by regulatory conflicts.

COMMUNICATIONS SATELLITE SYSTEMS

Communications satellites have touched the imagination of the public as few recent innovations other than space flight itself. The prospect of instant TV communications across the world brought the concept to public attention, and TV viewers the world over are now familiar with the sometimes shaky pictures with the legend "Via Satellite." The often gory march of events can thus be translated in "real time" into the living room.

The most important organizational step in the creation of the present system was the establishment of the Communications Satellite Corporation (COMSAT), which is owned half and half by the communications industry and by the public. The corporation is organized to:

1. Plan, initiate, construct, own, manage, and operate itself, or in conjunction with foreign governments or business entities, a commercial communications satellite system;

2. Furnish, for hire, channels of communication to U.S. communications common carriers and to other authorized entities, foreign and domestic.

A public offering of stock worth $200 million was made in the first half of 1964.[10] There was keen bidding for the stock, a good deal of which seems to have been bought for sentimental reasons rather than a realistic expectation of profits.[11]

Steps toward establishing a global-communications system have also been taken in the form of two international agreements formulated in 1964.

These agreements established a partnership, later
named the International Telecommunications Satellite
Consortium (INTELSAT), which includes more than 50
countries and their designated communications entities, such as COMSAT. These member countries account for more than 80 percent of the international
telecommunications-traffic forecast for the next
few years. INTELSAT operates only the space segment
of the communications system. Since the opportunity
of industry in each member nation to provide equipment for the space segment of the system is assured
each member, U.S. corporations will share in only
a portion of this market.

The establishment of earth stations falls outside the international agreements, and is the responsibility of each member nation. However, the
Interim Committee, established by these agreements,
does have the authority to approve earth stations
for access to the satellite and in fact has been
excercising that authority. Member countries
throughout the world are building earth stations,
and as one could predict, U.S. corporations are receiving only a share of the market.

An additional important factor was introduced
in March 1964 by the proposed agreement between the
Department of Defense and the Communications Satellite Corporation for the use by the Department of
the network of the Corporation, rather than of a
separate system of its own. Better utilization of
frequencies and channels would give a shared system
of 29 satellites the same capacity as two separate
24-satellite systems.

As the communications satellite system concept
has developed and the initial steps in its implementation have been taken, basic technical decisions
have been made. First, a basic choice among satellite types has been made. Active satellites have
been selected rather than relatively simple passive
systems, as the Echo satellite, which require higher
power and higher cost-ground installations. Next,
the question of orbit has been decided in favor of
synchronous orbits. This approach uses satellites
in circular orbits about 22,000 statute miles above
the earth, revolving around the earth at the same
angular rate and in the same direction as the earth
rotates on its axis. In this way the satellites are

FIGURE 12.1

Overseas Telephone Calls Per Year
to and from the United States

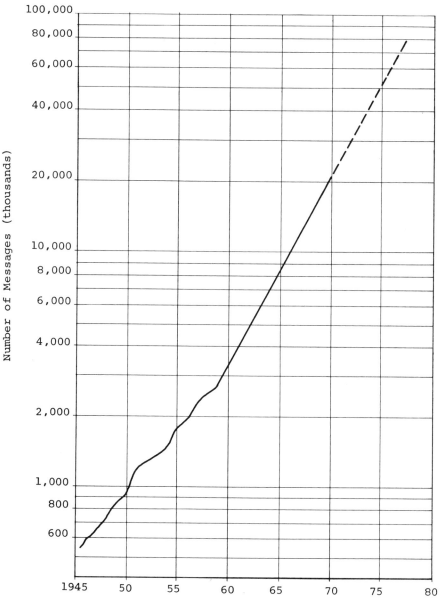

Source: William Meckling, "Economic Potential of Communication
Satellites," <u>Science</u>, vol. 133, no. 3468 (June 16, 1961),
p. 1891. Data after 1962 from Statistical Department, AT&T.

synchronized with the earth's rotation and remain
stationary with respect to a point on the earth's
surface.

A total of 608 satellite circuits were in use
in 1969.

While the transmission of television programs
has been most often brought before public awareness,
actually the largest single user of the system is
AT&T for its overseas telephone messages. These
have seen a most extraordinarily rapid growth. As
shown in Figure 12.1, the rate has actually been
increasing and is currently from 20 to 25 percent
per year. It is noteworthy that Meckling's original
data considered a 15 percent growth optimistic.
About one half of this volume of calls now uses satellite communications.

A powerful impetus toward this increased use
of overseas telephones has undoubtedly been a suc-
cession of rate cuts which have brought a three-
minute call to London from its 1950's level of $12
to $7.50 in 1969. The first service, established
in 1927, cost $75 for a three-minute call.[12] AT&T
has direct telephone access to 209 countries and
territories and in this service, satellites obviously play a big part, one that seems sure to increase as the reliability of the equipment is further
enhanced.

The technical, commercial, and political uncertainties that still surround satellite communications and microwave communications make meaningful predictions of a total equipment market rather
difficult. On the basis of the estimates in this
section, it appears doubtful that the new market for
electronic equipment will much exceed $30 million
a year.

NOTES

1. "Special Report on Major Business Problems," Business Week, (reprinted from Oct. 27, 1962 issue).

2. Ibid.

3. "Business Communications," Barron's National Business and Financial Weekly, (Apr. 17, 1961), p. 21.

4. "Telephone Company, Justice Department Answer Inquiry," Data Systems News, (Mar. 25, 1968), p. 14; see also editorial, p. 4.

5. "Special Report on Major Business Problems," op. cit.

6. "Business Communications," op. cit. p. 24.

7. Ibid. p. 24.

8. Rodney D. Chipp and Thomas Cosgrove, "Economic Analysis of Communications Systems." Paper delivered at the Seventh National Communications Symposium, Institute of Electrical and Electronics Engineers, 1962.

9. Ibid.

10. "Washington Trends," Electronic Industries (Dec., 1963), p. 23.

11. "Dial Cloud 7 for Paris and Rome," Business Week (Feb. 22, 1964), p. 78.

12. Information from AT&T rate listings.

CHAPTER **13** THE ELECTRONIC MARKET
POTENTIAL OF AUTO
INSTRUCTIONAL DEVICES

by Joseph Hoffmann

When this chapter was first written, it summarized the so-called "teaching machine" movement
and attempted to assess its market potential in connection with conversion of the defense-electronics
industry. It was concluded that, in general, the
potential of the field which in the early 1960's had
been expected to involve tens if not hundreds of
millions of dollars annually, would not, in fact,
realize anything near that amount and would, if it
existed at all, be associated with a general expansion of audio-visual and similar training devices
in schools and industrial training, generally. Such
views were rather controversial at the time and,
therefore, it was necessary to substantiate them at
considerable length.

In view of the fact that the bearish predictions
of the first edition have been borne out in the meanwhile, it hardly seems necessary to reiterate the
arguments at this time. Rather, we shall note that
the category "Teaching Machines and Aids," which accounted for sales of $7.6 million in 1963 and $7.8
million in 1964, decreased to $3.1 million in 1965
and has since decreased further. The principal reason for this appears to have been that the concept
of continuing feedback from, and response to, an
elaborate electronics system has not been found to
be the most efficient method of self-instruction.
Insofar as self-instruction is feasible at all, it
has frequently been accomplished by programmed text-
books and by simple devices more closely related to
the traditional audio-visual equipment. Moreover,
such machine systems contained little that was really
original but rather became aggregations of projection

equipment, tape recorders, and the like, with simple
synchronization. Much of this material, in fact, is
not of the typical programmed-learning type at all,
in which there is continual branching and in which
students are advised that they have made errors and
are given alternative instruction "loops" to help
them over their difficulties.

The market for audio-visual devices as such,
of course, has been increasing as has the use of
trainers and simulators incorporating such devices.
Sales of such equipment were given a considerable
boost by the increased federal contribution to
schools and universities during 1965 and 1966.
Grants became available for computers, calculating
machines, tachistoscopes for rapid reading instruction, projectors, closed circuit television, tape
recorder-equipped language laboratories, and the
like. Some of these items enjoy a significant
sales volume, but they are small indeed compared
with corresponding industrial or consumer products.
Consumer sales of tape recorders alone, for example,
are almost the same as those for all trainers and
simulators. The volume of phonograph sales is almost five times as big, and sales of electronic
toys--a small market--were still $10 million in 1966
as compared to the above mentioned $3.1 million in
teaching machines. Moreover, even in the educational equipment mentioned here the subsystems involved
tend to be quite standardized and to encompass products in which there are already many strongly entrenched manufacturers. For example, there was a
considerable increase in the sale of projectors,
but projectors, quite apart from their essentially
nonelectronic nature, continued to be supplied prin-
cipally by the firms that had always been prominent
in the field, like Kodak and Bell and Howell.

One of the few relatively complex systems now
under intensive study is the "talking typewriter,"
in which talking, projection, and typing are integrated in order to provide a single teaching environment for simple reading. These systems must still
be considered quite experimental. They incorporate
typewriters, projectors, and a simple computer, and
thus far they have been produced by the manufacturers
of these subsystems.

One such system was installed in the school district of Philadelphia by the Communications and Electronics Division of Philco-Ford. It has been in

classroom operation since last fall. It consists of
a Philco-Ford 2000 central computer, located in their
Willow Grove plant, and four clusters (central processor, data storage, and student terminals), located
in four schools in the district. Telephone data
lines tie the clusters to the central computer. Students respond to the lesson over the terminal, appearing as a combination TV monitor and electric typewriter with a light pen or by typing in the answer
in text form. While the computer works as a tutor,
letting the student progress at his own speed, the
teacher is free to work individually with each of
the students in his class who are not working with
the consoles, switching the process as the pupils go
from their desks to the terminals. When the lesson
is finished a teletypewriter prints out a written
record.

The point of the foregoing assessment is, of
course, that firms intending to diversify into the
educational field will find it exceedingly difficult
to sustain any significant product developments by
this market alone, especially since many of the
items proposed have thus far been assembled from
well known and virtually standardized modules.

One additional sector of the market which has
frequently interested firms looking for conversion
opportunities is the provision of software, e.g.,
programs. But these again do not have much to do
with the electronics industry as we now know it, any
more than the artistic input to his product can provide diversification to a manufacturer of phonograph
records. Certainly the cost effectiveness of equipment and the associated software has not been demonstrated to such an extent that financially hard-
pressed educational authorities are willing to spend
a great deal of their resources for them. Expectations held at one time that teachers, like production workers, could be in part automated out of
existence have failed to materialize.

A final comment must be made about the inter-
national-market potential. At various times UNESCO
and other international agencies have expressed considerable interest in the potential of auto-instruc-
tional devices as a means of decreasing illiteracy
and of fulfilling more advanced programs of cultural
improvement. While training devices have, of course,

been used all over the world, these tend to be voca-
tionally oriented in a very narrow sense and are certainly not designed to educate. The real problem in
the use of more sophisticated devices, however, lies
in certain cross-cultural difficulties which early
manifested themselves. We know that even in the most
industrialized and self-disciplined societies, self-
instruction is difficult for large parts of the population. These difficulties are multiplied enormously
in countries where there is an endemic estrangement
between the people and their government. Under such
circumstances anything the government says is automatically suspect, and a credibility gap enters even
the most innocuous programmed learning. In many
agriculturally oriented societies the very idea of
regular working hours is anomalous, as is the idea
of accomplishing something on one's own without see-
ing much of a tangible result. The prospects of
doing anything drastic about illiteracy, therefore,
by using anything less than "the human care of human
beings" also appear to be something of an illusion.

The emphasis away from the mechanics is evident,
even in American symposia and exhibitions in the
field. The Fourth Education and Training Equipment
Exposition of the American Management Association,
scheduled in New York in August, 1968, for example,
has many product exhibitors, but the extensive and
highly interesting program of lectures has very little on equipment as such; it again concerns itself
mainly with the problems of instruction on the human
level, and one whole session deals with these problems in the light of the urban crisis.

In summary, then, we can observe that educational systems with a heavy electronics content have
been general failures in the market and are in any
event composed of subsystems and modules drawn from
other sectors of the electronics industry in which
existing manufacturers are well entrenched. An infusion of federal funds gave an impetus to the
procurement of much audio-visual equipment over the
last few years, but this, in turn, is not something
which can continue indefinitely, as we must contend
here with market saturation with prospects of a replacement market only. Expectations of a smaller
school population are further "downside" influences.
As a significant factor in conversion opportunities
for electronics firms, educational systems as such
must therefore be discounted.

CHAPTER **14** THE
ELECTRONIC
LIBRARY

by John Baima

THE NEED FOR A NEW APPROACH

The flood of published material has multiplied
the problems of classification, interpretation, and
access beyond the capabilities of present systems.
The use of electronic computers has been proposed to
solve this problem. While the assessment of this
field as a business opportunity is still handicapped
by a considerable development gap, it is clear that
it has a sizable market potential.

In this chapter, the need for a new set of systems is first defined, followed by a description of
existing subsystems and total installations. This
is followed by a market estimate and an assessment
of the problems that still remain. It will be seen
that the electronic library has already attracted
many firms, not only those in the computer field itself, but also in office-copying machines, photo-
graphy, and others. The possibility of new entry
in this area by electronic firms is thus partly circumscribed by this considerable outside interest.

There seems to be little doubt that information,
like population, is experiencing an explosive growth.
It would seem that we now have a build-up of written
information of imposing proportions because of an exponential growth in literature generated by ever-
increasing numbers of authors.

It has been estimated that the average American will generate about 500
pounds of printed or written material
during his lifetime, of which about

10 percent will become permanent or
semipermanent documentation. Also
consider that it has been estimated
that throughout the world some
100,000 pages of information are generated every hour and that this volume is expected to double within 10
years.1

In 1967, estimated national expenditure for research
and development approached $18 billion--two-thirds
spent by the federal government and one-third by private industry and universities. Many people believe
that much of this money was wasted, because researchers and other potential users cannot retrieve and use
pertinent information already published:

As to cost, many companies are now
spending on the order of 1 to 2
percent of the cost of generating
technical information in assuring
that there is adequate access to
information. One company spends
12 percent of its research and development budget in an effective
information service.2

Unfortunately, the average researcher or in-
vestigator does not normally have access to any such
system. Many prominent men in both industry and government attest to the inadequacy of existing methods
of searching an information store that doubles in
size perhaps every eight or ten years. According to
Francis Bello:

Today there are more scientific and
technical journals in Russian than
in German, more in Japanese than in
French, and more in Chinese than
Italian. No accurate count exists,
but it can be said that there are
now between 50,000 and 100,000 technical journals being published in
more than 60 languages. New journals keep appearing at the rate of
at least 2 a day.3

The journals of 1968 alone will probably carry between one and two million scientific and technical
articles, a two- or three-fold increase over 1940.

To this, of course, must be added an increase in complexity of content so vast it cannot be measured.

Libraries have long been regarded universally
as evidence of mankind's cultural progress:

> From Assurbanipal in ancient Assyria
> to Thomas Jefferson in America, the
> men who created great libraries have
> been recognized in history for the
> intelligence and depth of their in-
> terest in the welfare of mankind.
> The threat that the great libraries
> of today may become lifeless monu-
> ments, choked by the pressures of
> exponential growth, is viewed with
> deep concern by many individuals
> and groups.[4]

It would seem that man has so far survived this
self-made document deluge, at least in the scientific
and technical fields, by specialization. Areas of
interest are constantly narrowing, and such a trend
is likely to continue. Since most forms of communication are both sparse and difficult among researchers and investigators, one tormenting problem is
omnipresent: Has this work been done elsewhere and
a satisfactory solution reported on in one of the
many journals or in other unpublished reports? For
several years U.S. experts struggled with the mathematics of an electronics-switching problem, extremely
important to military communications. Only after a
solution had been found did these investigators discover that the Russians had published this very
solution in 1950, just about the time the U.S. had
started its own investigations. Undoubtedly, this
has happened all too often.

Increasingly, the concept of an "Electronic
Library" utilizing high-speed computers for information storage and retrieval has seemed to present
an obvious solution to this dilemma. Unquestionably,
the application of mechanized techniques involving
computer-type devices offers a principal hope for
the future for rapid and reliable storage and retrieval of technical information.[5]

What is information retrieval? By definition,
it is:

The science and technology of receiving desired portions of previously coded and stored information.
In practice, this field involves the
study and development of methods
for acquiring, translating (if necessary), analyzing, selecting, cod-
ifying, reading in, storing,
searching, displaying and dissemi-
nating information.[6]

It seems apparent that the traditional library,
although certainly still of great use, must be improved upon if we are to cope adequately with the
"Infromation Explosion." The way in which recorded knowledge is organized determines the extent
to which interrelationships between units of information can be recognized and utilized. As the units
become increasingly specialized and more finely divided, so various classification and/or indexing
systems must become increasingly detailed, complex,
and finely structured. Herein lies the seeming usefulness of a system such as the Electronic Library.

Majorie Griffin, in discussing the "Library of
Tomorrow" has suggested eight general areas in which
an Electronic Library can assist man:[7]

1. Take over the proper cataloguing of information.

2. Take over the increasing problem of storage.

3. Properly interpret the request of the potential user so that the wanted information will be
searched and retrieved.

4. Automatically select for the requester information relevant to his specific needs and to anticipate his requests.

5. Answer a battery of questions at once, in
detail if necessary.

6. Print out a complete bibliography specify-
ing the library location of pertinent documents, or

7. Retrieve the documents upon request.

8. Pursue the search further as a reference librarian does. If necessary, follow through an interlibrary loan from a regional center.

In considering something such as this, however, it is obvious that problems appear immediately. It can be assumed that one of the chief functions of any library at present is to organize recorded knowledge for use; these uses can be varied and unpredictable. Obviously, it is physically impossible for any one person to remember all or even inspect all of the contents of a medium-sized library, assuming a normal acquisition rate. Hence, diverse methods of "remembering" the recorded material appear. Typically, requests for information are vague:

> There is consequent tendency for requests to be made not in terms of authors and titles, but in terms of subject interest. In stating such requests, the choice of terminology will be strongly influenced by the requestor's own background and vocabulary, and not necessarily by the text of materials collected in the library.[8]

The classification systems that develop must be flexible enough so that as contents and needs change, so can the system change. A more serious problem is the subject classification structure itself. As this situation grows increasingly complex, the cataloguing process becomes increasingly subject to error. As can be readily seen, the assignment of particles of information to any category is generally a subjective process. Invariably the cataloguer brings his or her own viewpoint into the process:

> It is at least plausible to suppose that the number of different categories to which a given piece of information can be assigned by different people with varying points of view is roughly proportional to the total number of categories in that subject classification scheme. That is, the difficulty of assigning something to the "right" pigeonhole is greater, the greater the number of pigeonholes.[9]

In any documentation system, the indexing function indicates if a source of information is available, and if so, where to find it. An index system may be either for the entire collection of information, for an abstract file, or a combination of both. At present, there seems to be a number of basic techniques for indexing. The first of these can be considered to encompass all of the traditional methods of indexing, such as the Dewey Decimal system, Library of Congress system, alphabetically arranged lists of document descriptors, and alphabetically arranged card catalogs of subject headings. It is quite evident that large and ever-changing collections make all of these methods too slow and complex for satisfactory searching by computer or other device. Moreover, it is extremely difficult, if not impossible, to classify survey-type books and articles dealing with a wide range of topics which cross lines of classification. For these reasons, the traditional collections of abstracts and indexes have also become inadequate. The proliferation of journals, reports, books, and other material has become too great for them to be up to date and cope with the volume of new information.

A second method of indexing is a system called "concept coordination" or "coordinate indexing." Probably the best-known example of coordinate indexing is the Uniterm system, developed by Documentation Incorporated in 1952-53:

> Coordinate indexing is based on the fact that the subject matter in a document can be represented by descriptive terms, often called keywords or descriptors. These keywords are, in a mathematical sense, coordinates which identify the document. A particular set of documents is defined by the intersection of some set of keywords.[10]

The approach is based on the premise that it usually is easier to get general agreement on the precise definition of the terms in a particular document than on the meaning of the document as a whole.

Terms are stored references to information and are of two basic types. Keywords are exact words taken directly from the title or text of the document; descriptors are arbitrarily labeled idea

units, derived by meanings or their analysis taken
from the text. In practice, each time a new document or piece of information is received into the
system, an accession number is assigned to it. No
two documents in the library have the same accession
number. Ther indexer decides on a list of the keywords which are representative of the subject matter
being considered. The accession number is entered
in the library location of each keyword. Descriptors
are formulated in like manner. Documents are filed
chronologically according to accession number so
that retrieval of a document is normally a matter of
mechanics whenever its accession number is specified.
Thus, a search for information is in essence a search
to determine the accession numbers of all pertinent
material in the library in answer to a query.

Many different versions of this system are in
use; means of expanding and improving its quality are
being sought by many different groups. Obviously
this system quickly becomes unwieldy if large libraries try to use it on a manual basis; it is, however, well-suited to automatic techniques. This
system has been used with handsorted edge-punched
cards, machine-sorted punched cards, and punched-paper
tape; but it would seem that its greatest usefulness
is with electronic data-processing equipment. Regardless of the technique being used, most present systems provide for the retrieval of the document
itself; the potential user, however, is not interested
in the document itself if he can acquire the desired
information without scanning all of it. This is the
goal of the more advanced information storage and retrieval systems currently under development:

> The user would like to have the in-
> formation within the documents pre-
> sented in a form which would allow
> him to make intelligent decisions
> concerning selective reading within
> the limits of his available time
> for reading. There are even further
> desirable features which should be
> provided by more sophisticated sys-
> tems.[11]

A third indexing technique that has had fairly
wide acceptance is KWIC--Key Word in Context. This
is a form of concordance that indexes documents by
title words:

A computer reads all the words in
all the titles, and alphabetizes
these words. Then it prints out
these words for all the titles in
alphabetical order in successive
lines but keeps with these words
the context of the titles and a
code for locating full information. No attempt is made to
associate synonyms. The user of
such a list faces the chore of
searching for synonyms himself.
The journal <u>Chemical Titles</u> is
such and index: it has been
published for several years and
serves as an express alerting
service to apprise chemists of
recent articles that have appeared in selected journals.12

A fourth method of indexing has been devised by
the Center for Documentation and Communication Research of Western Reserve University. If an information system must provide an answer to a question
expressed in words other than those of the text,
then the open language must be normalized somewhere
between input of index terms and the framework of the
question. The Documentation Center has provided this
normalizing by a device called the "semantic code,"
which is both a thesaurus and a multi-dimensional
classification of scientific terminology. A word
thus in the semantic code is made from units to which
have been assigned certain basic meanings. Words in
the English language are often constructed in much
the same way out of combinations of Latin and Greek
roots--thermo, meter, photo, phono, graph, and stat
are typical examples.

According to Jessica Melton of Western Reserve
University:

The semantic code, using three letter
units as roots, or factors, which
stand for general concepts, makes
possible a retrieval system where all
terms entering the system can be recorded on consistent principles to define the term and to relate it to
other classes of terminology with
which it shares common aspects of
meaning.13

Thus, in the semantic code a term such as "unionmelt process" becomes "a process of joining or fastening, specifically welding, by means of electricity and heat," and can be retrieved in a search for "electric welding" or "welding" or "joining and fastening." As can be seen, a matrix is created in the semantic code, such as in the coordinate-indexing system; the computer or machine, however, is not relied upon to make the association. The natural words are translated into the codes, which are then put on the index tapes. According to Western Reserve:

> We feel that at the present state
> of computer technology we are us-
> ing people for the tasks involving
> judgment that machines can be made
> to do only very expensively and
> fairly unreliably, and using ma-
> chines to do the repetitive tasks
> that people do only very expensively
> and fairly unreliably.[14]

Activities of the federal government in the field of research and development in scientific documentation were rather limited until 1958. At that time, directives from Congress and the President to the National Science Foundation extended its scientific information responsibility to the coordination of national activities and specified its tasks in some detail:

> One of these directives--Title IX
> of the National Defense Education
> Act of 1958--directed the Founda-
> tion "to provide, or arrange for
> the provision of, indexing, ab-
> stracting, translating, and other
> services leading to a more effec-
> tive dissemination of scientific
> information" and "to undertake
> programs to develop new or im-
> proved methods, including
> mechanized systems, for making sci-
> entific information available."[15]

Under this directive, the NSF Office of Scientific Information Service was established; the law also set up a 15-member Science Information Council, composed of research scientists, experts from the documentation and library fields, and interested, knowledgeable laymen.

The program of the National Science Foundation
has two fundamental objectives: to promote the development of improved techniques for handling scientific information and making it readily available to
researchers, and at the same time to make the existing systems more effective. In seeking to attain
these objectives, NSF carries on a wide variety of
activities, including making grants and contracts,
conducting surveys and studies, convening groups
of interested parties to discuss mutual problems,
and discussing gaps in service and areas of overlap
with those directly concerned.

NSF activities are grouped into certain definite,
but necessarily somewhat overlapping programs: Documentation Research; Support of Scientific Publications, Foreign Service Information, Research Data and
Information Services, the Education and Training of
information specialists, and the improvement of Research Library Facilities in this country.

Current Research and Development in Scientific
Documentation is a publication issued semiannually,
compiled by the Office of Science Information Service of the National Science Foundation, as a service to individuals and organizations interested in
scientific documentation:

> All pertinent activities in the
> United States and abroad that have
> come to the attention of the Foun-
> dation staff are included. The de-
> scriptive statements were prepared
> by the research workers themselves,
> with only minor editing by the Na-
> tional Science Foundation. In
> those cases where no significant
> change was noted in the descrip-
> tion of the project, a brief
> statement indicating the project's
> continuation has been included
> along with pertinent references.16

The descriptive statements are grouped under five
major headings:

1. Information Needs and Uses.

2. Information Storage and Retrieval.

3. Mechanical Translation.

4. Equipment.

5. Potentially Related Research.

Each section is preceded by an introductory summary which discusses briefly the work of organizations being reported on for the first time, to projects or studies which have been completed or discontinued, and to closely related research reports appearing in other sections. The National Science Foundation is currently preparing a cumulative bibliography of all publications and reports in this series.

Government officials are now considering a massive program to help researchers keep up with the great mass of information coming from U.S. scientific and engineering research and also are planning a still larger system for international information storage and retrieval. Doctor Chalmers W. Sherwin, from the U.S. Commerce Department, has proposed this plan:

> Just as the size of the track gauge
> standardized the railroad industry,
> international agreements on the in-
> formation exchange media, computer
> tape size, number of bits, and other
> basic standards would make it possi-
> ble for major abstracting services
> to begin to communicate with each
> other. A simple numerical code
> would have to be adopted to allow
> international retrieval. A long
> segmented number would be assigned
> to each article or communication
> by country and journal, or by source,
> sequence number, and index number,
> all in decimals.[17]

THE HARDWARE AND SYSTEMS

An electronic library utilizing machines alone can never solve the fundamental problems of information storage and retrieval; the machines normally can only provide the means for implementing solutions that would not have been practical using manual systems. Fundamental to any system consideration is the logical procedure of first defining system policy, philosophy and needs, and then considering the justification for such a system.

Fully automated systems that can be considered forms of an electronic library can be divided into two classes: document, in which document image and index are handled simultaneously, and aspect, in which a separate index is used to locate a stored image. Each will be considered as a group; general descriptions of the systems will be given.

Document Systems

1. Filmsort--The Filmsort system devised by Minnesota Mining and Manufacturing Company uses chips of film containing images of documents inserted into apertures created in regular punched cards. Searching can then be done on standard sorting and collating equipment. The U.S. Army Rocket and Guided Missile Agency uses the system to retrieve drawings from a general file of more than 2 million items.

2. Minicard--The Minicard system was developed by Eastman Kodak and utilizes film sliced into 16x32 mm. pieces, which can be handled like tiny cards. This system can now search at 1,000 cards a minute. More than 11 million document pages will fit on 900,000 Minicards. In a search, all cards are scanned electronically; those desired to answer the initial inquiry are deposited into a magazine fixed on the selector, and then are duplicated, processed, inspected, and cut; they are then stacked onto sticks for easier handling and delivered to the requestor, who can either study the film with a table viewer or make hard copies.

3. Rapid Selector--Index terms are encoded on punched cards, which are then photographed onto 35 mm. reels of microfilm, in the form of black and white dots representing bits, with the indexed document following immediately. Any desired documents can then be retrieved by means of a punched interrogation card and a patch panel, which specifies the search criteria and logical relationships that are required. The U.S. Navy's Bureau of Ships uses this system to locate and duplicate portions or entire volumes of desired information.

4. File Search--The File Search system utilizes a three-part basic arrangement, consisting of a recording unit, a retrieval unit, and a modified Flexowriter (a device used for punching both the index and request cards). This system allows requestors to retrieve documents in various forms: as an image on a screen; as a hard copy print; or as a duplicate film copy. This File Search system will automatically search a 1,000-foot reel of film (microfilm) containing about 32,000 documents at a rate of 64,000 pages a minute.

5. Rapid Access Look-Up--This system bacically is a quick catalog look-up system, with a print-out facility if desired. Each frame in a loop of 16 mm. film contains a catalog page and an alpha-numeric code for page identification; selection is normally done via a control keyboard. The film automatically stops when the proper frame is reached, and if desired the requested page is projected on a screen. Average selection time is normally about 1 1/2 seconds.

6. Magnavue--Magnavox has developed two systems based on the concept of the unit document. The basic storage medium is a 1x3-inch Mylar card containing coded indexing information. The earlier Magnacard system had no image of the original document, whereas the Magnavue system does have a photographic image of the original document. Each card in the system retains up to 1,000 decimal digits, or 600 alpha-numeric characters, and can be scanned at up to 5,400 cards a minute. Both systems are computer controlled; the newer Magnavue system, however, combines the advantages of high-speed electronic processing, high-capacity magnetic recording, and the ability of photographs to compress graphic information.

7. Media--This is another low-cost system developed by Magnàvox and utilized 16x32 mm. film cards containing up to 17 visually readable numbers, a machinereadable binary-coded counterpart of these numbers, and two or more pages of information reference by numbers. Any two-page document can be retrieved from a file of 10 million documents in one minute.

8. Microfiche--This is a system using basic 35 mm. microfilm:

Thomas Publishing's Thomas Micro-
Catalogue Division figures on
selling 1.5 mm Microfiche cards
this year (1967), up half a million
since 1965. The largest commercial
producer of Microfiche cards,
Thomas supplies new customers with
a basic library of 40,000 equipment
entries and a viewer made by Bell
and Howell for $350.[18]

Aspect Systems

1. Walnut--This system, developed by IBM for
the Central Intelligence Agency (CIA), is a photographic and electronic system able to retrieve any·
one of millions of typed or printed pages or photographs from a file center within five seconds. At
present there are no plans to market the system commercially. The Walnut system at present is the closest approximation to the concept of the electronic
library.

Documents first are microfilmed, then reduced
further with an image converter, and transferred to
strips of film, each strip containing 99 images. Each
document file contains 200 plastic cells of 50 film-
strips, a total of 990,000 images, or roughly about
3,000 average-sized books. The total Walnut system
can encompass more than 100 document files, or approximately 300,000 books. A form of "concept coordinate" system is used to search; images of the
desired card are returned to the requestor, who then
checks his choices on the list. From an existing
file pertinent search data are automatically punched
in an aperture card containing a blank film unit.

These unexposed aperture cards are then inserted
into the document file, which reads the location from
the punched holes and brings the filmstrip containing
the desired document image into lens position. The
card's film insert with up to four images is then
automatically developed in about one-half second by
a dry-heat process. The card is then returned to
the requestor, who may enlarge the images to original
document size for printing or for viewing with a
standard projection device.

2. Medlars--This is an acronym for the name "Medical Literature Analysis and Retrieval System." The sheer magnitude of medical literature is becoming impossible to deal with by present means. It has been estimated that 220,000 indexable, new medical articles are published each year. The gap between what the average doctor could and should remember about medical progress is growing continually. What really makes the situation alarming is the growing duplication in medical research.

Specific objectives of Medlars are:

1. Improve the quality of and enlarge the Index Medicus while reducing printing time.

2. Provide for computer compilation of bibliographic listings in a variety of rather broadly defined subject areas within the field of medicine.

3. Make possible rapid servicing of requests for bibliographic information.

4. Increase the depth of indexing of each article by adding more specific terms and by increasing the number of terms in the thesaurus used by the index in the analysis of the items.

5. Increase the coverage of the medical literature to about 250,000 items by 1970.

6. Increase screening activities to avoid needless duplication.

The following elements comprise each unit record:[19]

1. Names of authors.

2. Title of article in English.

3. Title of article in vernacular.

4. Journal title abbreviation.

5. Volume and page information.

6. Date of issue.

7. Language.

8. Subject tags.

9. Geographic tags.

10. Form tags.

11. Check tags.

12. Date of entry.

The system operates as follows: journals received by
the library are distributed to a staff of indexers
for the selection of articles to be indexed, the
translation of titles of foreign articles, and the
indexing of article citations with appropriate headings. Book material is handled similarly.

Unit records, such as shown previously, are
punched on paper tape for computer input; it is read
in, processed, compressed, and stored. Unit records
are ordered chronologically; once a month, for the
publication of Index Medicus, the unit records in
storage are expanded, sorted, edited, and rewritten
on tape. Once a year the material is merged for the
annual Cumulated Index Medicus. Information requests
are processed and read into the computer, instituting
a search for citations that meet the requestor's
specific requirements. Printout of desired information is effected in either of two ways: for most
requests a high-speed printer provides single font
copy; in special cases Graphic Arts Composing Equipment (GRACE) is capable of transforming the magnetic-
tape output of the manipulation subsystem into exposed
film from which, after processing, a printer expedites
the request.

> GRACE accepts electrical signals from
> a magnetic-tape transport operating
> fully under her control. These sig-
> nals arrive in bursts of coded char-
> acters which represent a full line
> of legible type across the multi-
> columnar page. This type is made up
> of a combination of 226 different
> alpha-numeric symbols which are set
> on film or paper at a rate in excess
> of 440 characters per second.[20]

Even at this great speed the annual Cumulated Index
Medicus requires about two weeks for composition. In

the general performance of tasks Medlars utilizes
computing equipment consisting of a Minneapolis-
Honeywell computer and associated tabulating equipment.

3. Verac--AVCO Corporation has built a model
of a fully automated system utilizing photographic
media to provide direct random access to designated
microphotographic fields of information. These document images are recorded on sheets of film. Using
reductions of 140 to 1, Verac can record images of
as many as 10,000 document pages on a single 10x10-
inch film sheet; the system-retrieval equipment can
store up to 100 film sheets.

A computer or a manual index can be used to
determine which images contain the desired information. Once this has been ascertained, the Verac
system can locate any image within 2 seconds and can
then produce a 35 mm. filmstrip of the desired image,
or even a full-sized hard copy.

4. CRIS--The Command Retrieval Information
System, by Information Retrieval Corporation, utilizes
mass micro-image storage combined with rapid automa-
tic-retrieval capabilities. The CRIS system divides
the retrieval problem into three specific areas:
index and search; storage and retrieval; and reproduction and transmission. The system itself has been
designed for compact, economical storage of many
millions of document images, and for rapid automatic
retrieval. Micro-images of any printed or pictorial
matter are stored on a scroll contained in a cartridge inserted into the CRIS unit. The unit automatically positions the image for display and/or
reproduction upon entry of a CRIS location number
corresponding to the desired image. Average retrieval time is under 20 seconds.

5. Cram--The Card Random Access Memory,
developed by National Cash Register, utilizes a
removable cartridge containing 256 magnetic cards
on which information can be stored in any order and
selected and read in only a fraction of a second.
High-speed accessibility and large-capacity storage
make it possible to sort data, update records on
either a random or sequential basis, make any random
inquiry, and store report data by use of only a
single unit.

Other systems currently under development include Microcite, a system being developed by NBS, which uses 15x15-inch sheets, each of which can record the images of up to 18,000 document pages or abstracts; another system is a computer-mass memory combination proposed by General Precision's Librascope division called the L-3000 system, which will abstract a document into a short 16-word list of the most frequently used words in each document. Inquirers, after rejecting unsatisfactory abstracts, can then request the actual documents via the code numbers of the relevant abstracts.

As can be seen there are many systems, both extant and currently under development; more sophisticated versions are under way. Of growing interest is voice response from a computer to an information request. This is not only the transmission of a recorded message, but is actually creating a reply by computer, which makes them up from stored syllabi:

> RCA recently announced a system to provide voice response over a party line to inquiries fed into its Spectra 70 system from as many as 100 remote points. In a banking application, for example, inquiries are transmitted to the computer by the bank teller who pushes appropriate buttons on a Bell Telephone Touchtone unit. The computer searches its memory, and by means of a prerecorded voice drum, replies orally over the same telephone unit.[21]

Any viable information storage and retrieval system would require a fast computer memory. The Polaroid Corporation has begun investigation of an unusual idea to minimize that problem, using a photosensitive, alkali halide crystal:

> The material contains ions that change when struck by light; given the myriad number of these tiny atomic particles in matter, a halide crystal with a volume of 1 cc. could, in theory, store 100,000 pages. In principle each page would be illuminated with a different wave length of light, or read into the crystal

> at a different angle. To get the
> image out it would be only necessary
> to illuminate it with light of the
> same frequency (color) or with light
> traveling in the same direction.[22]

Reproduction of material that has been searched
and retrieved is an integral part of any electronic
library and is a rapidly advancing science. As has
been seen, many different methods are used at present. Here are some of the more important systems:

1. The Diazo Process--commonly referred to as
the white print method, is one of the least expensive; costs per copy are about 1 cent.

2. Dye Transfer--or soft gelatin transfer.
This process requires a matrix. The first copy costs
about 9 cents, and next five copies 1 cent each.

3. Thermography--or the heat-transfer process.
It is very widely used in many systems; copies can
be made in 2 seconds at an average cost of about 5
cents each.

4. Diffusion Transfer Process--This process
produces high-quality, good-contrast copies. Costs
run about 9 cents each.

5. Electrophotography--includes two separate
processes, Xerography, and the Electrofax process.
Each makes high-quality reproductions at about 5 cents
per page.

6. Microphotography--microtransparencies may
utilize any one of three types of film: Diazo, silver emulsion or Kalfax. Transparencies can have five
sizes: 16 mm., 35 mm., 70 mm., 105 mm., and sheet
film.

Many of the techniques and devices utilized in
the various systems at present are of poor to fair
quality only. This is a field of extremely active
development; needed improvements should be forth-
coming rapidly.

PRESENT COMPLETE SYSTEMS

Small-scale starts in creating an electronic
library, without using something such as Walnut or
Verac, have been made by various corporations and
organizations. A typical example is the system at
the Knolls Atomic Power Laboratory of General Electric
Company.[23] The operation of the system is surpris-
ingly simple. Technical documents, reports, and
articles are abstracted by trained engineers, put
onto IBM cards, and read into a computer. A library
addition is made, plus a "current awareness" search
entry. To conduct a search the Technical Information
units engineer receives the inquiry, then selects
the most likely index codes. Punched cards are made
up, and the computer searches the file; a print-out
of the abstract plus its location in the files results from the search. A diagram of the present
system is given in Figure 14.1.

The success of the system rests on two factors:
the indexing and the system of formalized abstracts.
The index is based upon a combination generic classification and coordinate-indexing system. The system
essentially uses four basic indexing principles:

1. Conventional alphabetical indexing.

2. Classification of concepts into classes and
subclasses.

3. Coordinate system in which a document is
described by a set of terms.

4. Combinations of 2 and 3.

This simplifies use of the index for storing and
retrieving and avoids syntactic problems. There also
is a standard abstract format with a suggested list
of topics to be covered in the abstract. The
Technical Information engineer, who receives specialized training in this area, selects those best
suited to the particular document from the list of
suggested topics.

Two engineers and an administrative clerk comprise the Technical Information unit, specializing
in naval reactor design. Searches are conducted on
a Philco computer, using simple product or AND-type,

FIGURE 14.1

Knolls Atomic Power Laboratory Information
Retrieval System

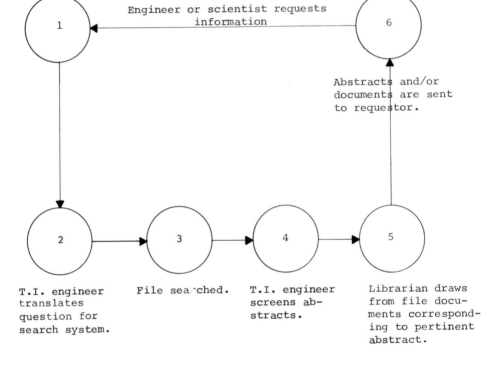

244

logic-search arguments. Results of searches are
high-speed print-outs of access numbers. Reference
copies of the documents are permanently filed in the
reference library and represent the primary source
of information. The index system is designed to
handle about 20,000 documents and can be refined as
required. Approximately 10,000 abstracts can be
stored serially on each reel of magnetic tape. For
all practical purposes the number of tapes which can
be utilized is unlimited. An "interest profile" is
maintained for certain staff members, who are automatically informed by computer-printed abstracts of
new documents and articles received by the library
which generally match their stated information requests.

No cost estimate of the system is available. In
practically all of the systems surveyed no accurate
cost information is available; in general, however,
it is acknowledged that even a small system is quite
expensive. For example:

> Major costs so far have been in machine
> time, keypunching, and programming
> involved in preparing, correcting and
> updating the tapes. These costs alone
> have been in excess of $20,000. Now
> the IBM 7090 is being used. The cost
> of this computer and auxiliary equip-
> ment runs around $500 per hour.[24]

It is felt that any increased costs generally
are more than offset by increased efficiency in
retrieving available information, resulting in
quicker results and better work accomplished by less
personnel. This is a matter of internal justification of new equipment and thus does not directly
provide a market estimate.

An estimate of potential capital outlay is also
complicated by the fact that the system can take many
different forms. There would, for example, be a
very considerable difference between a number of
independent installations around the whole country
and a central search computer, located in the Library
of Congress reached from other libraries by a simple
input-output device.

Because of these factors, direct-cost estimates
are practically impossible to make. In the next

section, therefore, an estimate of physical extent
of installations is presented, followed by a dollar
estimate based on imputed savings.

MARKET POTENTIAL

The question of market potential for the electronic library systems currently under development
commercially is enigmatic: it seems generally agreed
that a good potential does exist, yet there is a
total lack of information in the published literature.
It is only possible to deduce from figures presented
in the American Library Directory. All data exclude
small public libraries with annual incomes of less
than $2,000 or book funds of less than $500. Libraries from the Directory are as follows:[25]

	Number
Public Libraries	5,770
Branch libraries of these systems	823
Branch libraries of city, county, state systems	4,028
University and college libraries	1,379
Junior college libraries	645
Special libraries	3,473
Law libraries	434
Medical libraries	755
Total	17,307

At first glance this figure seems quite impressive. It is quite obvious, however, that very
few public libraries would want, need, or be able to
afford an electronic library, no matter how modest.

Here is a summary of size of collection for all public libraries serving populations above 35,000:26

	Number of Libraries
Below 100,000 volumes	527
100,000-499,999 volumes	252
500,000-999,999 volumes	23
1,000,000 volumes and over	21

In considering the number of university and college libraries, there are only 27 college libraries of more than 1,000,000 volumes. Undoubtedly, however, many universities and colleges have or will have general-purpose computers capable of being utilized in part as a form of electronic library. There is no realistic way at present to estimate the number of special libraries (including installations such as have been described) that would be able to utilize the services of an electronic library; the same statement can be applied to the law libraries and medical libraries. If one guesses that 10 percent of all university, college, special, law, and medical libraries eventually both desire and can afford an electronic library and that 50 percent of the public libraries of 500,000 volumes or over also fall into this category, there would be a total of 627 installations--a considerable market.

As noted, it is not readily possible to translate this into a dollar figure. However, assuming libraries to be concerned mainly with research, one can, as in the Medlars project discussed before, postulate an expenditure of 5 percent of all the present $18-billion research outlays for the kind of information generation and retrieval described. This would amount to $900 million annually, of which one could conservatively assume about $250 million might be in hardware. Of course, before such a market comes to pass, a number of important problems will have to be solved.

SOME PROBLEM AREAS

It is now necessary to define certain problems
that must be solved to make the foregoing potential
markets a reality. It would seem from all available
evidence that a promising start has already been
made on the concept of the electronic library; the
complex problems that have cropped up have not been
in computer technology at this point in development.
One major problem is conversion between natural and
machine language, even using programming aids such
as FORTRAN or COBOL. At present providing input to
a computer system is not only difficult technologi-
cally, but almost prohibitively expensive. Keypunch
costs alone run 1 or 2 cents a word.

The usefulness of the computer itself in establishing an electronic library has been questioned
by some. Libraries and especially research libraries normally contain large amounts of rarely used
material. Dead storage of this and/or searching is
most uneconomical. Even the most modern high-density
tapes cannot store as much alphabetical information
in a cubic inch as any conventional book.

According to Ralph Shaw:

> For the time being, the best that
> the computer can hope for is an
> opportunity to coexist with print,
> and to take over part of possibly
> all of the retrospective and pur-
> poseful searching of literature.
> Indeed it is a little difficult
> to see how the computer could
> achieve anything, even in retro-
> spective searching, if man did
> not continue to communicate in
> conventional form.[27]

As a literary aid, a form of electronic library is
well established already. Comprehensive glossaries
and concordances have been constructed.

The first efforts to computerize lexicography
were directed at indexing the Summa Theologiae of
St. Thomas Aquinas, followed shortly thereafter by
the "Dead Sea Scrolls." It should be understood that
the role of the computer in processes such as these

is entirely servile; it eliminates only the uncrea-
tive clerical and sorting work:

> The scholar's efforts are reserved
> for tasks he alone can do: drawing
> up exact instructions for the tape
> punching, parsing the strictly
> alphabetical indexing, separating
> homonyms, . . .[28]

Another related facet of the electronic library
is in the translation of languages. Substantial
research is being devoted to this area of translation
of one natural language into another by computer.
Many problems encountered in the mechanics of translation are quite similar to the overall problems of
the electronic library; for example, if translation
by computer could become a practical reality, it
would certainly be a major step towards the problem
of high-input costs if a form of "page-scanner"
could be developed initially for the translation
processes. The successful development of such a
device would facilitate the extraction of information
from within documents, rather than having the search
confined to an identification of titles alone.

It is felt by some authorities in the field
that perfect algorithms are available for elementary
arithmetic and logical functions, but none exist for
translation. Human translators can utilize their
background knowledge in order to resolve syntactical
and semantic ambiguities, which machines just cannot
handle. Any satisfactory input print-reading machine
would be difficult to develop for similar reasons;
in addition, type must be perfect, since the machine
is helpless against misspelled words, decimal points,
full stops, etc.

Insofar as machine translation is concerned,
cost is another major consideration. According to
Don Swanson, it is a tossup economically in considering man versus machine:

> For example, both machine and human
> translation of Russian to English
> cost in the neighborhood of one to
> several cents a word exclusive of
> the cost of machine input, and with
> the quality of the machine output
> leaving much to be desired.[29]

Thus, it would seem that before computers can process the texts of documents, books, and all other contents of the average library, more precise knowledge of syntax, semantics, and other aspects of language is needed. Such work is now being done extensively at MIT and Harvard, among other schools, where research programs on detailed knowledge of the grammar of several languages are being undertaken; one of the most recent findings is a "depth hypothesis," which seems to offer a possible explanation of several characteristics of language. Improved indexing techniques should become a reality as knowledge of language increases, thus greatly improving prospects for a true electronic library.

SUMMARY AND CONCLUSIONS

It would seem to be obvious that a way to cope with the "Information Explosion" is at hand: the development of the electronic library. As has been seen, many problem areas exist; none seem insurmountable at present, although much work remains. It is possible to visualize a future in which much of the library will be stored in a form of computer. Efficient classification, indexing, and searching techniques will make all of the stored information readily available. The Walnut system, developed by IBM, seems to be a real beginning of a complete system, as does the Knolls Atomic Power Laboratory system.

Behind this electronic library would stand a greatly modified local library and a national or regional lending library, holding rare, seldom-used available works and again serviced by computer devices, which can scan vast indexes rapidly and accurately on request. Perhaps the Library of Congress could do all searching on one giant computer, with other libraries only input-output centers. Once the desired information has been identified, the material could be sent out on loan from regional deposits or via facsimile transmission.

It is a generally accepted fact that the complex problems involved at present in the development of an electronic library are not primarily ones of computer technology; this science has advanced considerably beyond our current capabilities for adapting it to informational uses.

Typical of the technological advances is the "cryogenic store." Computer tapes in the past have had one real drawback: they cannot tell, as a human can, "yes" or "no" as to whether the requested information is known and available. Until recently this could not be done with any of the various types of computer store available, since the answer to any question involved looking at all of the stored material one item at a time. The late Dudley Buck, however, devised a form of storage by utilizing the phenomenon of super-conductivity, which takes place at temperatures close to absolute zero:

> This so-called "cryogenic store" has the interesting property that it can answer the question "is the information available" without at this stage actually locating it. The importance of this is that reference can be made to large areas of storage to find out whether it is worth scanning them at all, so that using a cryogenic store a detailed scan would only be necessary in that portion known from its statement to contain the required information.[30]

Another technological advance that seems extremely promising at this stage of development is laser storage:

> The Precision Instrument Company has reported the use of a laser digital recording system that has produced a storage capacity of 645 mm. bits of digital information per square inch packing density. One standard 2400 foot reel of the special tape used in this system can store as much data as 47,500 similar reels of conventional magnetic tape. Called the UNICON (Unidensity Coherent Light Recording) process, it is not a photographic method but makes use of the laser to burn minute holes in the tape storage medium.[31]

The company estimates that the entire Library of Congress collection of books could be included on 5 1/2 UNICON mass-memory cells. Retrieval is

accepted by a helicale-scan transport, with the tape
breaking the light path of a low-power laser.

In the development of a workable electronic
library the principal difficulties concern the problem of conversion between natural and machine language, indexing and retrieval. Current research
efforts in these areas are extensive, requiring the
combined talents of linguists, logicians, mathemati-
cians, computer scientists, and librarians. Substantial progress has been made; as has been seen, however, the problems are simplest when the information
being handled is quantitative, precise, and capable
of sharp definition:

> The difficulties are enormously greater
> when the material to be put into machine
> language and stored for subsequent re-
> trieval concerns complex interrelation-
> ships, concepts and ideas, which differ-
> ent people describe in different terms,
> and for which they have varying needs
> and uses.[32]

One rather interesting modification of a possible electronic library of the future is that a
computer would contain in coded form all of the original material available on a given subject without
any of the author's actual words. As is well known,
there is a great amount of redundancy and duplication in publication of original articles.

In a system such as this, upon presentation of
a question all of the relevant information would be
extracted, and, using some of the techniques of random sentence construction, a precis would be produced.
Such a system, of course, would not be at all popular among authors, since no reference will be made
to the originator of any given idea; but perhaps it
might in fact be to the good, since it would avoid
the hard feelings so often produced by inadequate
indexing and referencing.

Thus it would seem that the goal of a true
electronic library is attainable; present computer
technology, although suitable, will undoubtedly be
improved upon, as will the other associated hardware.
Better input, indexing, and classification techniques are being developed currently. Attention, however, should not be focused entirely on ways and

means; many of the systems described seem to suffer
from the weakness that too much attention is paid to
means and too little to ends. In the search for
solutions to the problems of development of the
electronic library, we should keep in mind what we
are really looking for and then make it easier to
find. Once these problems are nearer to a solution,
an appreciable market should develop, estimated at
about $250 million annually.

NOTES

1. Electronic World (March, 1967), p. 76.

2. B. E. Holm, "Storage and Retrieval of Technical Information," Mechanical Engineering (May, 1962), p. 62.

3. Francis Bello, "How to Cope With Information," Fortune (September, 1960), p. 162.

4. Science (Feb. 17, 1967), p. 803.

5. Joseph Karth, "Mechanical Translation," Special Libraries (October, 1962), p. 463.

6. William Bushor, "Information Storage/Retrieval," Electronics (June 29, 1962), p. 41.

7. Marjorie Griffin, "The Library of Tomorrow," Library Journal (Apr. 15, 1962), p. 1556.

8. Allan Kent, "Their Own Devices," Wilson Library Bulletin (November, 1962), p. 277.

9. Don Swanson, "Library Goals and the Role of Automation," Special Libraries (October, 1962), p. 467.

10. A. F. Glimn and R. D. Greenway, "Information Storage and Retrieval--Part I. Dogs, Cats, and Indexing." Conference Paper, American Institute of Electrical Engineers (May 12, 1960) p. 3.

11. Ibid., p. 5.

12. Ben-Ami Lipetz, "Information Storage and Retrieval," Scientific American (September, 1966), p. 234.

13. Jessica Melton, "The Semantic Coded Approach to Indexing Literature," MULL (March, 1962), p. 50.

14. Ibid., p. 51.

15. National Science Foundation Programs for Dissemination of Scientific Information (January, 1963), p. 1.

16. Current Research and Development in Scientific Documentation, no. 11 (November, 1962), p. 8.

17. Business Week (Jan. 17, 1967), p. 78.

18. Ibid., p. 66.

19. MEDLARS--Talk by Seymour Taine at the meeting of the New York Chapter of the American Documentation Institute held at the New York Academy of Science (Thursday, November 1, 1962), p. 10.

20. Ibid., p. 15.

21. "Information Storage, Retrieval, and Dissemination," Dun's Review (September, 1966), p. 209.

22. "Goodbye to Gutenberg," Newsweek (Jan. 24, 1966), p. 86.

23. C. L. Schmidt and R. G. Murdick, "Setting Up a Technical Information System," Machine Design (May 10, 1962), pp. 124-129.

24. Carolyn J. Krause, "The Use of Electronic Computers For Information Retrieval at the Naval Ordinance Test Station," Special Libraries (February, 1963), p. 91.

25. American Library Directory, 1962, p. xiii.

26. The Bowker Annual of Library and Book Trade Information (January, 1963), p. 17.

27. Ralph Shaw, "Electronic Storage and Searchi Searching," Times Literary Supplement (Apr. 1, 1962), p. 235.

28. R. A. Wisbey, "Mechanization in Lexicography," Times Literary Supplement (Mar. 30, 1962), p. 218.

29. Don Swanson, op. cit., p. 471.

30. Andrew Booth, "The Kinds of Machines Now in Use," Times Literary Supplement (Apr. 13, 1962), p. 252.

31. Electronic World, op. cit., p. 76.

32. Joseph Karth, op. cit., p. 463.

CHAPTER **15** MEDICAL ELECTRONICS
DIAGNOSTIC AND
HOSPITAL DESIGN

by Alfred A. Meltzer

INTRODUCTION

Science is now only beginning to understand some
some of the basic electronic principles that underlie
the functioning of our bodies and minds. It is already clear, however, that a whole new era of ex-
ploration and development is in the offing to meet
the demand for electronic methods of supporting and
controlling these functions. Electronic methods
will eventually supplant, to a large degree, procedures that are now chemical or mechanical, and many
concepts of automatic control successfully used in
industry will eventually be applied to medicine and
to hospital design and control.

This has led to exciting and challenging developments, to which many leaders in the industry have
already responded. The problem that remains is
whether present outlets and the potential markets
which can be developed will be broad and diverse
enough to offer the industry large-scale business
opportunities and encourage the entry of new firms.

The use of electronics to fight illness is
nothing new, but it has remained a relatively unde-
veloped area. As early as 1890, electric currents
of very high frequencies were being used for heat
therapy, presaging the present use of microwave and
infrared therapy. The x-ray was discovered in 1895
by William Roentgen, and he was followed eighteen
years later by W. D. Coolidge, who invented the pure

electron discharge tube and established modern methods for the application of the x-ray. Electrocardi-
ography, although often thought of as a modern
medical tool, stems back to 1903, when William
Einthoven recognized and recorded voltages generated
by the human body. This instrument and, later, developments of it were massive and cumbersome until
in 1935 the Sanborn Company perfected a lightweight
electrocardiograph, using radio tubes. Similar devices soon followed that recorded other bodily activities. The electromyogram revealed that the body
was virtually athrob with electrical impulses, and
the electroencephalograph recorded electrical waves
that were emitted by the brain.[1]

Even though this period of invention and development dates back to the 19th century, the use of
electronics in medicine is less widespread than one
might expect. Outside of a few specialized fields,
the medical profession carries on without benefit
of the extensive help which electronics offers to
other areas of science, industry, and daily living.[2]

The reason for this lag has been threefold.
Primarily it stems from the view that there is only
a limited potential market for specialized medical
electronics equipment which has minimized commercial
interest in its development. Private industry has
been reluctant to enter the field because of the
prevalent opinion that there is only a small market.
It is generally felt that unless a research and development program ultimately yields a profitable
commercial product, it occupies engineering time
that might be otherwise devoted to products that
would be much more profitable.[3] James Hiller of RCA
Laboratories has stated that the reason for this lag
in the application of this new technology to the
medical sciences and to public health is primarily
an economic one. For every dollar spent in explora-
tory work on a new device, $10 must be spent for ad-
vanced development and engineering, and about $100
more for product design, tooling up, and market development. Since the maximum potential sales from
laboratory and hospital devices range from a few
hundred to a few thousand, prospective sales cannot
cover the investment in engineering and production.
As an example of this, Hiller cites the electron
microscope which has been on the market commercially
for 20 years and has not as yet returned the manufacturer enough profit to cover its development costs.[4]

Secondly, due to the limited capital-investment budgets available to hospitals and medical schools this is a very cost conscious and frugal market. Of the 7,000 hospitals in the United States, 5,500 are private general hospitals. Only about half of these are big or solvent enough to afford any considerable amount of new equipment.[5] As a result of these financial restrictions, industry often finds it hard to price new equipment, such as the electron microscope, at a level high enough to return the development to the manufacturer.

Thirdly, the maximum application of electronic techniques to medicine calls for close cooperation between two groups of specialists who do not speak the same language. This professional barrier has inhibited a mutually understood awareness of the needs of medicine and the capabilities of electronics. It has resulted in a conflict over what instruments were needed, the means of testing these instruments in a clinical environment, and, as mentioned earlier, has inhibited the realization of the sales potentials of these products.[6]

It almost appears at times as if there has been a sustained mistrust of the machine by the medical profession. The x-ray and electrocardiograph remained the only electronic instruments in general hospital use until the burgeoning technology of World War II. Progress during the war and the new and exciting image given to electronics by early post-war developments began to change the picture. It was not until late in the 1950's that there was a new and quickening interest in applying modern electronics to medical and biological problems. Funds for the advancing techniques of medical electronics caught up with the demands of the profession. Foundation and government programs, which underwrote much of the research, helped get vastly improved x-ray and other basic apparatus into the capital expansion budgets of U.S. hospitals.[7]

The challenge that faced the electronics industry was to develop and improve equipment and systems in these seven major areas:[8]

1. Monitoring of sick patients in hospitals, i.e., recovery rooms, cardiac, and intensive-care areas.

2. Performing diagnostic studies on patients.

3. Testing laboratory specimens.

4. Treating patients.

5. Measuring and controlling the environment.

6. Preparing, transmitting, and analyzing records for clinical or administrative use.

7. Communications between hospital personnel, patients, and others.

The problem that had to be solved was to develop equipment without the large space and power requirements of most of the then existing instruments. Miniaturization both in dimension and power requirements became a reality through the use of solid state devices, such as transistors, crystal diodes, thermistors, crystal photoelements, and many others.[9] With them, whole new areas were opened. For example, electronic probes could now be introduced into the body to measure the function of various organs without interfering with their functions. Heavy apparatus was made portable, and its costs were reduced.

To monitor and record data, various techniques have now been developed. They cover a broad span, from a relatively crude direct write-out system which involves tedious information extraction and subjective data interpretation, to highly sophisticated integral-display systems. An integrated display not only evaluates the response of several physiological functions of organ systems in relation to the environmental conditions to which the organism is exposed, but it is also a comparatively flexible message-display unit that presents the final evaluation of the total situation for the information and action of those concerned.[10]

The following sections present a review of many of the more interesting new instruments that have been developed for medical diagnosis and hospital control and an analysis of the market problems and potentials of the industry.

ELECTRONICS IN DIAGNOSTIC MEDICINE

The field of diagnostic medicine and hospital
control has produced so many electronic instruments
that it is impossible to review them all in detail
in this report. Accordingly, the areas of greatest
interest are emphasized.

Adapting Television to X-Ray Techniques

The most common application of electronics to
medicine is the use of X-ray for diagnosis. An average $150,000 is spent on electronics to equip a
250-bed hospital today, and an additional $100,000
goes toward the cost of tables, tubestands, generators, film projectors, fluoroscopes, shields, mobile
units, and other items needed to outfit the radiolo-
gist. The present market of X-ray equipment is approximately $110 million a year, and there is a
promise of even greater demands, for newer and more
complex equipment.

Unfortunately X-rays have harmful as well as
useful properties. Overexposure may result in tissue burns, anemia, and eventually, leukemia. Since
the exposures required to obtain good x-ray photographs are short, this is rarely a limitation on
the X-ray as a diagnostic tool.

However, fluoroscopy, the direct observation of
X-ray images on a fluorescent screen, is an exception. This technique enables the physician to see
the effects of manipulation on the internal organs
and may give him guidance in complex operations, but
safe dosages may often lead to images that are so
dim that only a small fraction of the important detail may be visible.[11] Under the conventional X-ray
method for motion studies, the doctor observes a
fluoroscope screen which converts the X-rays into
visible light as they pass through the patient's
body. The doctor must work in a darkened room in
order to see the fluoroscope image properly. While
the patient being X-rayed is in very little danger
of excessive radiation, the technician and the radi-
ologist are always susceptible to a "build-up" of
radiation, which can have serious effects.

To repeat the viewing process, the patient must be X-rayed again. If the fluoroscopic image that the doctor sees is televised or filmed using conventional x-ray methods, increased amounts of radiation are required to receive a satisfactory picture. A technique has been developed by Dr. Russell H. M Morgaan of the Johns Hopkins Hospital that combines an RCA closed-circuit TV system with an X-ray image intensifier and produces pictures on a tape of high degree of clarity and resolution.[12] In a similar Westinghouse system, the beam from an X-ray tube passes through the patient and without striking the fluoroscope screen is picked up directly by an image amplifier.[13] This tube intensifies the motion-study image approximately 1,500 times.[14] An additional advantage of the video tape is that it is possible to keep records which can be used for conferences and clinical evaluation. It is faster and cheaper than cine, which had until recently been the only method of preserving a moving record of the fluoroscopic examination.

Future extensive use is anticipated through the possible routine use of video tape for chest X-rays and then ultimately reaching a point when all X-ray examinations can be recorded directly on tape. Not only can this technology replace the use of expensive X-ray film, but the physician may obtain immediate results of the X-ray examination without going through a lengthy developing and drying process, since tapes merely need to be played back and viewed on a TV screen. Storage of bulky X-ray radiographs, which must be retained as an integral part of the patient's medical record, has been a problem in most hospitals today.

At the Mount Sinai Hospital in New York City, as in most other hospitals, this problem is being obviated by reducing the X-ray photograph to microfilm. Cost of microfilming radiographs is approximately $40 per 1,000 images. Since Mount Sinai radiologically examines 65,000 patients a year and uses an average of 4 films per patient, 260,000 films must be microfilmed at a cost of $10,000 a year. When and if video tape can be developed to give the clarity and resolution of present-day radiographs, the cost of the film, processing, and eventual microfilming can be eliminated, since the tape can be stored in very little space and retrieved for viewing almost immediately by simply pressing coded-selection buttons.[15]

Improvements in X-ray equipment also offer the prospect of further progress in preventive medicine. Aerojet Delft Corp. of Plainview, N.Y. has introduced a portable X-ray unit for the detection of breast cancer. The unit can be placed on trucks, as are chest X-ray units. They expose the individual to less radiation, however. The unit costs only $19,000 compared with $35,000 to $45,000 for a conventional unit.[16]

Electrocardiographs

An electrocardiograph (ecg or ekg) detects and measures electrical potentials generated during contraction and relaxation of the heart muscle and makes a paper record of the events in time sequence. Recent trends here have been towards the use of transistor amplifiers to provide greater amplification without seriously increasing signal to noise ratio. In addition to increased amplification attention is being given to developing lighter, smaller, and more rugged portable models. Through the use of transistors, ruggedized tubes, and printed circuits, noteworthy advances are being made in this area.[17]

The leader in this field is the Sanborn Company, which derives nearly half its sales from ecg units and systems. Its line ranges from an 18-pound portable unit selling for $625, which is Sanborn's sales leader of several thousand per year up to an 8-channel console for about $10,000. A doctor can carry the portable on his rounds. The console, which resembles an electronic computer, enables a technician to monitor and record eight different body pulses at one time. Thus the cardiologist can obtain an invaluable picture in depth of cardiac activity.[18]

Lockheed's Missile and Space Division and the Heart Research Foundation have developed a 3-ounce transistorized transmitter, which is worn around the neck or carried in the pocket. Signals that are picked up are broadcast to a remote fm tuner that

drives a conventional ecg. By connecting the tuner
output to a telephone line, ecg signals can be transmitted anywhere in the world. The heartbeat can be
monitored while the patient goes about normal activity.[19]

Telephone transmission of the ecg impulse is of
great practical application when a physician can obtain long-distance consultation from a cardiologist.
The specialist can listen to the heartbeat while he
watches the tracing of an ecg by the recorder. Other
companies with similar transmission units are Electronic Medical Systems and the Mnematron Corporation, which use acoustical coupling to the telephone,
while Bell Telephone Laboratories uses a direct-line
coupling.[20]

Many of these new units have been incorporated
into complex multi-sensing monitoring systems. The
Chemetron Corporation, has a unit that visibly and
audibly monitors the heartbeat by beat.[21] This
sensor enables immediate artificial reviving of the
heart in cases of heart failure. A constant blinking
light indicates that the heart is beating. If the
blinking light stops and a continuous red light and
buzzer goes on, it indicates that the heart has
stopped. This unit informs the physician whether
the heart has actually stopped, or if the patient
is only in shock and the heart is still beating even
if only imperceptibly.

Electroencephalography and Anaesthesia

An electroencephalograph (eeg) detects the
rhythmically varying potentials produced by the
brain, using 15 to 24 pairs of electrodes placed at
various positions on the scalp. After amplification,
the signals from the pair of electrodes are simultaneously recorded. These records are used not only
for the diagnosing of neurological disorders but also to measure the state of consciousness of the individual.

This has been found to be of great practical
application today for the anaesthesiologist who is
thus able to use electronics to control the depth
of anaesthesia.[22]

The eeg produces an electrical waveform that contains frequency components whose amplitude is a measure of the degree of wakefulness of the patient. When filtered and rectified these waveforms can serve as the command signal to a servo system that controls the amount of anaesthesia supplied to the patient at a fixed rate proportional to the electrical activity of the cerebral cortex as sensed by the eeg.

Prior to miniaturization of this equipment with transistors, the eeg was restricted to large hospitals.[23] Greater simplicity and reliability now makes the eeg a commonplace instrument in smaller hospitals, clinics, and portable applications.

Instruments for Diagnosing Diseases of the Eye

There are about 200,000 sufferers from glaucoma in the United States, a major cause of adult blindness.[24] Increased pressure within the eye, if not detected and treated, is followed by permanent blindness. Electronic tonometers are replacing the old fashioned physical tonometers to measure the pressure of the eyeball. They are fast and gentle and do not respond to extraneous factors that lead to uncertain readings in the classic devices.[25] Other means of detecting glaucoma have been developed in which change in the amount of and alterations in color of the blood circulating in the eye are measured photoelectrically.[26]

Diagnoses by Electronic Computers

The instruments previously described rely on doctors or technicians for interpretation of results. Considerable attention has, however, also been given to simplifying and accelerating this process by electronic means. Specifically, it is possible to establish diagnostic centers where a computer can be programmed to read, measure, store, and analyze standard electrocardiograms automatically. An electronic computer is now making long distance "instant diagnoses" of heart diseases for the Veterans Administration.[27] Electrocardiograms of the patient can be transmitted to the computer in Washington, D.C. over telephone lines from any point accessible by telephone.

The computer has gone through a learning stage, taking into its capacious memory ecg's and associated clinical data on selected heart patients at a rate of up to 1,000 cases a month. On command, it can ask itself 5,000 questions about minute details in each lead strip of a twelve-lead electrocardiogram, get the answers, correlate them with its memory store in one minute, and print out its analysis in ten minutes, with an asterisk beside any measurement that falls outside normal limits. It never tires, forgets a question, or varies its standard of measurement. It takes a doctor a year or two simply to learn the rudiments of interpreting an ecg, and no two specialists ever wholly agree in their readings.[28] The computer can evaluate instantly all information about one patient; for an individual physician to do this would be an insurmountable task. The computer of the Veterans Administration is estimated to be right in 90 to 95 percent of the cases.[29]

Rapid progress is being made to develop the computer as a diagnostic tool in other areas of medicine. The application of current methods of computer technology to the processing of medical data can produce efficient storage, rapid retrieval, and accurate and immediate analysis of significant clinical information. One problem, that of efficient programming, appears to have been solved by the development of "Medlab," a software system developed by Control Data Corporation especially for medical data processing.[30] One project using computers of this type interprets X-rays of children's heads and establishes criteria of normal development. It uses a CDC 165-digital plotter linked with a CDC 160A computer.[31]

Instruments for Laboratory Diagnosis

The projects in the last section are of national scope. Even within a hospital, however, especially in laboratories, there has been progress in automating certain diagnostic procedures in addition to using electronic instruments common to many other kinds of scientific laboratories, for example, pH meters, photometers, etc. In this way, the quantity and quality of work of the laboratory can be increased at an economically justifiable cost. For

example, a blood-cell counter has been developed by
the Coulter Electronics Company. The Coulter Counter
is a high speed automatic counter that substitutes
for a technician who at best can count 20 to 30 samples of diluted blood a day, with a high sampling
error of 20 percent.[32] The counter makes a white
and red blood-cell count in minutes without fatigue
and within an error of 2 percent. The cost of the
counter is a little less than $4,000, but the in-
strument can pay for itself in a year or less, since
it can easily handle an increased workload that would
require one or more additional technicians. Technicians doing this level of work receive approximately $4,000 annually.

Another device which substitutes for a technician examining a slide is the Cytoanalyzer, which
examines the smear through a microscope and presents
on a television screen only the information that is
wanted. It incorporates a micro-scanner, which
senses electronically the size and absorption of the
nuclei of cells, making it particularly useful in
diagnosing malaria and cancer. This instrument,
manufactured by the Airborne Instruments Laboratory
Division of Cutler-Hammer Corporation, scans the
smear with a tiny beam of light. Any smear that has
an appreciable number of nuclei of abnormal size and
density is passed on to a skilled pathologist for
further examination.[33]

A device known as the Auto Analyzer is marketed
by the Technicon Company. This instrument enables
a laboratory to automate its analyses of blood chemical constituents at a great savings in time and
personnel. Through its use hospitals have been able
to meet the increased patient demands with a minimal
amount of personnel and physical space. This instrument and the Coulter Counter are becoming standard equipment in most laboratories today.[34]

Another new instrument that may hopefully out-
perform the Auto Analyzer is an automated high speed
multiple blood analyzer that is now being tested as
part of a vast health-screening program in the Varm-
land Province of Sweden.[35] Drs. Gunnar and Ingmar
Jungner have developed apparatus, consisting of cal-
orimeters, pumps, and other components, many of which
are American made. The samples are drawn into the
system at 90-second intervals, and the findings are
reported as a numerical print-out by an automatic

typewriter. The determinations performed give information about the amount of fat in the blood, the
level of serum iron, and signals tissue changes,
kidney malfunction, liver damage, and reports the
hemoglobin content of the blood. This apparatus can
process more than 4,000 blood samples a day, subjec-
ting each to 10 or more tests, and through automation the costs of these analyses can be cut about
90 percent.

Other products include an experimental system
by the Perkin Elmer Corporation that counts and identifies particular cells semi-automatically, using
a closed-circuit TV microscope and special-purpose
digital computer. Its present application has been
in studies of people whose blood has been exposed
to radiation.[36] An electronic hematocrit has been
developed that within one minute measures blood volumes, i.e., the concentration of red blood cells,
at the patient's bedside or in the operating room.[37]
This now requires a lengthy laboratory procedure.

This new technology has been progressing and
expanding in many directions. There is in the offing
the promise of even broader applications of medical
instrumentation. Harmless ultrahigh-frequency sound
waves are beginning to rival X-rays in probing the
body for defects and for diagnosis. Ultrasonic
scanning works somewhat similarly to radar and can
be viewed on a suitable screen (ultrascope). The
method has been used for detecting brain tumors and
similar growths.[38] It has been shown by a General
Electric research team that tiny electrodes implanted
safely in small animals can generate sufficient electricity from the body itself to run a 500-kilocycle
transmitter almost indefinitely. This may allow
micro-electronic devices to be implanted in the body
to regulate its functions or to monitor physiological
reactions without recourse to batteries or external
wiring.

The instruments discussed in this section are
useful in certain specific tests. However, a major
effort has also gone into products for hospital management in general. These developments will now be
reviewed.

HOSPITAL CONTROL AND DESIGN

Monitoring Systems

Since the development of single purpose devices which serve specific diagnostic needs there has been an increased demand for multipurpose devices capable of detecting and recording simultaneously a number of physiological variables. About a dozen or more of the large companies are already involved with monitoring devices. A few are actually developing monitoring systems, while others are merely surveying the market. These include RCA, General Electric Company, and the Minneapolis Honeywell Corp. (which worked out a system in collaboration with the Mayo Clinic). Smaller firms, such as Gulton Industries, have penetrated the field in part through space and military contracts.[39]

These systems are necessary to monitor the conditions of the critically ill, the cardiac patient during surgery, or the post-operative patient. The parameters measured are any combination of physiological phenomena, including temperature, pulse rate, respiration rate, systolic and diastolic blood pressure, electroencephalograph (eeg), electrocardiograph (ecg), electromyograph (emg), and pulse-pressure waves. Monitoring, analyses, and interpretation of a combination of variables provides an accurate picture of the overall condition of the patient, indicating not only imminent or sudden crises, but long-time trends as well.

The complexity of the instrument is proportionate to the number of functions the device can monitor and on the number of channels required for a patient. The cost varies from $500 to $20,000 for a one-bed unit, and to over $100,000 for a ten-bed unit, with the manufacturer installing the equipment and providing some maintenance services.[40] Among the cheaper devices, Medtronic, a specialist in heart equipment, has a basic meter that sells for less than $500. It is a mass-produced transistorized unit, the size of a pocket radio, that displays the heartbeat on a speedometer-like dial. An adaptation called the "telecor" and priced at $650 monitors both heart and breathing rates through a specially designed catheter inserted in the esophagus. For $1,500 the Sanborn Company has marketed a completely

transistorized 17-inch Montioring Oscilloscope for
visual presentation of up to 8-biophysical phenomena
simultaneously. Leads from the patient pass a junc-
tion-box switch with which the surgeon can select
the desired display.

Two of the more advanced monitoring systems are
the Gulton Hospital Monitor and the Honeywell Body
Function recorder. The Gulton Monitor is capable
of continuously checking 10 physiological functions
of 20 patients and sounding an alarm when a change
in a patient's condition exceeds limits set by the
physician. It keeps a continuous record of temperature, pulse, blood pressure, breathing rate, and
blood oxygen. In addition to this it can also measure ecg, eeg, respiration volume, audible heartbeat,
and galvanic skin response. The cost for a four-bed,
five-parameter unit is approximately $50,000.

The Honeywell Body Function Recorder, which is
a product of the Heiland Division of the Minneapolis-
Honeywell Regulator Company, is an intensive care
unit which automatically and simultaneously measures
and records 5 body functions every two minutes.

Three transducers are affixed to the patient
without any subcutaneous probes or catheters. A
clothespin-type transducer that slips over the ear
is a blood and pulse transducer that picks up the
pulse rate and the systolic and diastolic blood pressures via the blood circulation in the ear. A photocell measures the blood pressures through changes
in light intensity, and the pulse rate is obtained
by counting the beat-to-beat variation of light
coming into the photocell. The temperature transducer is clipped to the corner of the mouth, while
the respiration is recorded through an air detector,
about the size of a silver dollar, positioned in
front of the mouth under the nose.

When the recording and alarm systems are combined into a portable unit, they can be moved from
one bed to another. Although there is no technical
limit to the number of patients that can be monitored
at one time, there are physical limitations, since
the control station and the monitoring unit cannot
be separated by more than 500 feet. In addition to
the physical limitations there is a financial limitation, since each patient unit costs approximately
$7,500.[41]

Since a complete unit is a major capital investment, the administrator must consider the economic
returns and the justification for it. The purchase
of a recorder would not only have the effect of improving patient care by providing more frequent,
accurate, and permanent records of the conditions
of critically ill patients, but can free skilled
nursing personnel for more exacting tasks than entering and plotting graphs of patients' conditions.[42]

A recent installation of a critical care monitor system made it possible to monitor continuously
the condition of several patients in an area of the
hospital reserved for the acutely ill. When this
installation was made, at an investment of $20,000,
it was quickly demonstrated that there was more effective use of the nursing staff, already in pain-
fully short supply.[43]

In caring for the critically ill it normally
takes about twenty minutes each hour for a nurse to
read and record physiological phenomena required by
the physician. However, when a patient is in a monitored bed, these same tasks are accomplished by the
nurse in only five minutes. Thus the electronic
monitor saves approximately fifteen minutes each
working hour, or two hours per nurse per shift of
nursing time. Multiplying this figure by the average
staff of two nurses per shift in an 8-bed ward it is
evident that the "electronic nurse" makes available
to the hospital an additional twelve nursing hours
per day. In addition, the hospital is now able to
maintain instantaneous and continuous surveillance
of critically ill patients.

These statistics are significant because they
point to a practical method by which hospitals can
face the growing shortage of nurses and the increased
cost for operations. If a medical institution wished
to employ more nurses, it would, in many communities, be hard pressed to find them. As a result,
special nursing is often difficult to arrange, quite
apart from its high cost.

Enrollment at schools of nursing is growing
more slowly than the rise in patient population.
Immediate relief obviously lies in the use of "electronic nurses," especially for the critically ill,
where nursing activities are connected with routine

data acquisition. Nursing hours will thus be available where only a human nurse can satisfy the needs of the patient.

The economic gain realized by one hospital was that the electronic monitor freed one and one-half nursing days per diem, or forty-five nursing days per month per intensive care unit. This nursing time previously consumed in repetitive procedures, which are now done with the electronic monitor, has a dollar value. This sum, accumulated for less than thirty months (forty-five nursing days per month, at $15 per day, equals $675 per month), exceeds the full $20,000 cost of the monitoring system. It should be recognized that this system will have a useful life of more than seven years, which will release the equivalent of three times the total cost of the machine.[44] Since the time saved involves many staff members of similar qualifications, saved nursing hours can be readily translated into payroll savings or reduced staff needs.

At the Bethany Hospital in Kansas City, Missouri, similar monitoring units were installed in the intensive care wards and the cardiac rooms. Since the patients were given private rooms with constant electronic monitoring and 24-hour-a-day special nursing care, they were charged an additional $10 a day. In spite of the additional charge the patient saved $44 a day by eliminating special-duty nurses around the clock. Special-duty nurses in the Kansas City area are paid $18 for an 8-hour shift, or $54 for a 24-hour day. With an average occupancy of 60 percent the Bethany Hospital feels that it can recover their direct costs within a few years out of the extra charges alone.[45]

Although these units are financially self limiting there has been an increased demand by hospitals to have them installed into their recovery rooms and intensive care units. With monitoring equipment the patient can receive a higher quality of medical care and be under closer surveillance than that supplied by 24-hour-a-day nursing care. Records on each patient would be readily available, and nurses relieved of the routine of record collecting can devote more time to patient care. Not only may monitoring help to alleviate the nursing shortage but it can contribute to reduced nursing costs. It has been estimated that "monitoring might

cut by as much as half the number of nurses required
in critical-ward areas. One estimate even put the
average in savings in salaries at about $140,000 a
year per 12-bed unit."[46]

In a recent survey made at the Mount Sinai
Hospital in New York City it was estimated that a
12-bed intensive care unit would require the services
of 43 nurses a week.[47] At weekly salaries averaging
approximately $100, the nursing salary costs of this
unit would be about $224,000 a year. If the nursing
costs of this unit could be halved with the installation of a monitoring unit, then there could be an
annual saving in nursing salaries of $112,000 or less
than the cost of the unit, reckoned at $7,500 per
bed.

Closed Circuit Television

The closed circuit television camera is gradually being incorporated into the design of the
modern hospital as a means of improving efficiency
and reducing cost. Through the adaptation of television technology to its daily routine, every area
in the hospital is gaining in increased effectiveness.

Hospitals have found that a surveillance system that can view patients from a remote position
serves as a valuable adjunct to nursing care in the
acute and critical areas. It was originally feared
that this would contribute to decreased contact between the nurse and the patient. Actually it has
been found that it increased the nurses' effectiveness, since it allows for increased observation of
the patient. In this way the patients receive better care, since they are now under constant observation from the nursing control station in addition
to the regular nursing care.

Another important area for television is to
promote patient-visitor communications in special
cases where no visitors are allowed. Waiting rooms
can be equipped with two-way television facilities,
so that visitors, without actually going to the
patient's bedside, can "visit" and carry on a con-
versation.

Administrators are utilizing strategically placed cameras in the hospitals as a means of increasing their efficiency. With cameras in critical areas, the administrator need only flip a switch to maintain visible and audible contact with the problem area. In this way he can ascertain whether his personal attention is necessary and avoid a great deal of unnecessary time-consuming energy away from his desk. Cameras can be used for corridor surveillance and thereby eliminate the need for additional attendants during the evening hours. Similarly, when cameras are placed in boiler rooms to monitor gauges and machinery, many additional working hours are gained by maintenance men for other maintenance duties, possibly even reducing excessive personnel.

The installation of TV cameras in supply rooms can easily pay for their cost by the savings in supplies and the tightening of controls. The fact that there is a TV camera in the supply room is in itself a deterrent against pilferage. Video cameras in supply and stockrooms could also aid in the control of inventories.

Cameras placed in the operating rooms could allow responsible staff officials to judge procedures. Transferred to video tape they may well serve as an aid in the correction of poor procedures, or they may be used for teaching purposes.

The costs for these installations can be met by many factors. The administrative uses may be paid for in part by the man hours saved by the administrator and other personnel involved.[48] Although bookkeeping may not reveal it, there will be, over the years, a saving from this facility just as there is a saving now from the use of the telephone.[49]

Miscellaneous Devices

Other electronic devices of some importance that are finding widespread use in hospitals today are the electronic signaling systems and paging devices, which replace the old paging systems and eliminate disturbing the patient.

In another development Curtiss Wright Corporation has developed a "Gamma Sentry" that not only warns of gamma radiation, but also warns of dangerous

levels of radiation. Radiological sterilization has
been suggested to replace the steam autoclave. The
use of this gamma ray cold sterilization would substantially reduce labor costs and permit cold sterilization of heat-sensitive materials, such as plastics, bone grafts, cartilage, etc.[50] Meanwhile,
ultrasonic cleaning for instruments, syringes, and
"any mechanical unit small enough to fit into the
cleaner's container" has become an important product,
by now widely used in hospitals.[51] This, of course,
is also an electronic device.

There are many other electronic instruments,
but of them, only the electro-myograph is a major
product. It is used to measure the electrical characteristics of muscles and hence, muscular performance. Except for those described thus far in this
chapter, they have still to score a major breakthrough in the market. Of course, it may be precisely this which might make them attractive as units
in which a sound new idea can produce a viable
product.

Information and Data Processing

For the purpose of this volume, the data-processing market has generally been considered in previous chapters. However, data processing in hospitals
has its special characteristics and for this reason
warrants discussion here. To judge from the volume
of the literature in the field, it is obviously something which concerns hospital administrators to a
considerable degree. According to one estimate,
sales of data-processing equipment to hospitals now
run about $60 million, which while not much in re-
lation to the $2.5 billion data-processing market,
nevertheless reflects an interesting application
which, moreover, is expected to grow quite considerably. According to one estimate, the volume should
reach $140 million in 1970 and $325 million in 1975.[52]

One system recently described operates at the
State University Hospital of the Downstate Medical
Center in Brooklyn, New York. Using an IBM 1440/1410
computer system, the information center at the hospital operates a "total hospital operating and medical information system" within the hospital and
services an emergency bed-requesting system which
links nine participating hospitals to the computer.
It also maintains a complete medical library.

When the patient is admitted the computer assigns a bed, notifies the nursing station of an ar-
rival, orders his chart from the record room, and
enters vital statistics on the admissions form. Once
medical treatment has begun, the computer orders
drugs, laboratory tests, X-rays, supplies, and equipment and compiles complete medical records. The computer also works with the existing files and inte-
grates information with any previous data already on
file. Input stations are provided at all nursing
terminals from which instructions are relayed. The
computer has been programmed to adjust data in the
light of the results of clinical tests so that an
up-to-date report on the patient's condition may be
presented to the attending physician every day.

The emergency bed-requesting system rather resembles an airline reservation system and appears to
employ much the same methodology. One difference is,
of course, that for hospital admissions a great deal
more information must be gathered on each patient
than is required for each traveler in an airline
reservation system. The computer actually searches
for the hospital vacancy nearest to the patient's
residence so as to reduce transfer problems to a
minimum. Finally, the center also includes a computer-based medical library, much along the lines
described in an earlier chapter of this book. The
Downstate Medical Center has also incorporated a fil-
ing system designed to keep pace with its electronic
equipment. The system was designed by Supreme Steel
and consists of a series of joined modules containing both rollout cradles and stationery shelves.[53]
Another system, installed at St. John's Hospital in
Joplin, Missouri, uses an input system somewhat similar to that of despatcher in a production-control
system. To order anything, e.g., a test, the patient's card and a card pre-punched for the particular test to be ordered is fed into the card reader.
The system includes certain security precautions,
such as a key number for the person ordering the
particular test. The message is also printed at the
originating station as a further check.[54] Such precautions are necessary; one does not need an excess
of imagination to postulate any number of potentially
ghastly mistakes that could be made if such a system
were to be abused or even subject to any human error.
After all, even with the present presumably human
controls, one frequently hears of mistakes made in
hospitals, sometimes with dire results.

MARKETING PROBLEMS AND POTENTIALS

A market study of medical-electronic devices is limited by a general lack of published information on costs. Accordingly a major impetus to the market is hard to define. Moreover, in many instances, especially in the use of diagnostic instruments, there were no real economies that could be demonstrated by the purchase of these instruments. Actually, the machines are often expensive, and in some cases they add to hospital costs rather than save money. In describing one instrument, a hospital administrator stated that, "It costs $7 every time we use it, but the fact that we had it probably saved one woman's life already. How do you put a price on that?"[55]

Although economies derived should play an integral part in the consideration of the purchase of these instruments, they should not be the major consideration when human lives are involved. These instruments bring new ways of performing old tasks more accurately and, more important, add new functions that can save lives and relieve suffering.

A market analysis must, however, take the economic condition of its customers into consideration and define the conditions under which its product will be useful to them. In looking at American hospitals today and at their utilization of electronic equipment, two conclusions emerge: First, the hospitals are facing an increasingly critical financial problem, and secondly, they have not yet made full use of even the equipment available.

While the population of the United States has risen by 29 percent since 1945, hospital admissions have increased by 51 percent. Total hospital bed capacity has increased by 215 percent and is now at about 1.7 million. It would have to be doubled again by 1975 if past demand trends continue.[56] In many communities, the changes are even more rapid. The hospitals of Nassau and Suffolk Counties in New York increased their capacities by 11 percent in 1962/63 alone.[57]

Expenditures climbed 323 percent for all hospitals to $8.3 billion annually, with payroll alone accounting for exactly two-thirds of the total.58 Hospital charges have risen correspondingly for over a decade, from an average of $15.62 per-paient day in 1946 to $44.48 in 1965, according to Table 15.1. This has almost meant a tripling in costs over a 15-year period. Clearly, these figures point toward a crisis for hospitals. Patient costs are doubling every eight to ten years, and based on the average annual increase in 1960-1965, projected patients per day costs are estimated at $56.71 in 1970 and up to $72.30 in 1975. Contributing toward increased costs are not only increased wages, but also the number of personnel needed to maintain patient care. In 1950, each patient required the services of 1.78 hospital employees. By 1963, the average had risen to 2.41. Since that time, the rise appears to have halted somewhat; one would hope that this is due to some of the beginning benefits of automation, to architectural and layout features that reduce labor, and the phasing-out of some antiquated institutions; the possibility of declining extent of care in the face of rising costs cannot be ruled out, however. Certainly, the systems described in this chapter have considerable potential for alleviating the operational problems of hospitals. One should note, however, that some experts in hospital management have forecast a continual rise in the number of employees per patient.59

In addition to more bed capacity, more nurses, and more hospital personnel in general, hospitals need more and better equipment. With these problems in sight and the growing shortage of doctors to serve a sharply expanding population, the American Medical Association (AMA) concluded that "automation linked with preventive medicine appears to be the answer."60

These urgent needs have not thus far been translated into a large market for medical electronics. In 1966, sales in medical electronics stood at $307 million, of which $50 million were in hearing aids,

TABLE 15.1

Hospital Costs Per Patient Day and
Personnel Per Patient
Selected Years, 1950-1975

Year	Hospital costs per patient day[a]	Personnel per patient[a]
1950	$15.62	1.78
1955	23.12	2.03
1960	32.23	2.26
1963	38.31	2.41
1964	41.58	2.42
1965	44.48	2.46
1970[b]	56.71	
1975[b]	72.30	

[a]Figures shown are for non-federal short-term hospitals in the U.S.

[b]Estimates for 1970 and 1975 are based on the increase from 1960-1965.

Source: Statistical Abstracts of the United States, 1967 88th Annual ed. (Washington, D.C.: U.S. Department of Commerce, U.S. Bureau of the Census), p. 77.

a prosthetic device within the purview of the next
chapter. The items of interest here had sales as
follows:[61]

	$ million	Percent
X-ray equipment and accessories	150	61.4
Electrocardiographs	14	5.8
Electroencephalographs	4	1.7
Lasers	1	0.4
Electron microscopes	6	2.5
Ultrasonic devices (cleaning and therapeutic)	6	2.5
Clinical laboratory equipment	35	14.3
Closed circuit TV	3	1.2
Other standard and custom equipment	25	10.2
Total	244	100.0

Clearly, X-ray equipment still retains a dominant
position in this market. This is not, however, merely due to the fact that X-ray equipment has tended
to get more elaborate over the years. It is also
reflected in the fact that, in spite of much market
progress and substantial investment by hospitals,
many instruments are still little used.

The biggest reason for this, of course, is the
straitened financial position in which many hospitals
find themselves. However, government grants, notably
under the Hill-Burton Act, and gifts by foundations
and others have made some contributions towards the
purchase of electronic equipment, particularly in
the larger hospitals. In those with less than 300
beds, 90 percent of the cost of the items had to be
defrayed from operating costs.[62] Even in the larger
ones, in only a few cases did more than half of the
cost come from other sources.[63]

In Table 15.2 we examine the percentage of hospitals owning selected categories of medical electronic equipment. Since the table was compiled,
undoubtedly additional equipment has been procured,
and even from the table it is quite evident that the
largest hospitals are fairly well equipped. However,
as column 2 indicates, some 61 percent of all hospitals have fewer than 100 beds, and they really

TABLE 15.2

Percent of Hospitals Owning Selected Categories
of Medical Electronic Equipment, 1966

Short-term general hospitals	% of total hospitals	Electro-encephalography	Intensive care unit	Percent of Hospitals Owning		
				Operating room	X-ray diagnostic	X-ray therapeutic
under 25 beds	9.79	9.83	3.44	89.19	89.43	1.97
25-49	25.19	12.91	5.92	96.71	98.03	5.18
50-99	25.83	12.89	12.80	97.51	99.17	16.80
100-199	19.31	26.64	29.14	99.07	99.63	55.97
200-299	9.44	51.60	61.39	99.44	99.81	82.67
300-399	5.33	76.97	72.70	100.0	100.0	94.74
400-499	2.26	81.40	86.40	86.05	100.0	100.0
500 and over	2.85	96.93	89.57	100.0	100.0	100.0
	100.00					

Source: "Hospital Statistics" Guide Issue Part II, Journal of the American Hospital Association, vol. 46 (Aug. 1, 1966), p. 466.

appear to be poorly equipped, with items such as intensive care units or even electroencephalography, which has been around for many years. It is true that, as the source cited in the table shows elsewhere, hospitals under 100 beds only have 11 percent of the total hospital beds in the country, in spite of their very large number. However, large geographic areas have to rely on precisely such institutions for their entire hospital care.

Clearly then, the need is acute. As shown in Chapter 2, this is a market which has in the past responded very conspicuously to sharply increased government assistance. Between 1963 and 1965 under the impact of the considerable health legislation of the early years of the Johnson administration, the market grew from $215 million to $300 million. Between 1965 and 1966, however, the increment was only $7 million. The previously cited table does little to support the notion that this somewhat stagnant performance has been due to anything approaching market saturation. Certainly an increment of $100 million a year could be sustained for quite a few years in the future. After all, Table 15.2 only indicates that hospitals own such equipment; it does not evaluate whether the actual quantity installed in each institution is anywhere near sufficient for the needs of its patients. In medical electronics, therefore, especially that related to hospitals, there is a considerable prospect for substantial increases in needs and for meeting these needs through a generous infusion of government money diverted from military purposes.

NOTES

1. J. Richard Elliott, Jr., "Spark of Life," Barron's, 41, (Jan. 16, 1961), p. 3.

2. Dr. Vladimir K. Zworykin, "Magic Eyes for Medicine," Saturday Evening Post, 230, (May 31, 1958), pp. 26-27.

3. R. S. Ledley and L. B. Lusted, "Bio-Medical Electronics, Potentials and Problems," Science, 135, (Jan. 19, 1962), pp. 198-201.

4. "Atlantic Report, Science and Industry," Atlantic, 207, (April, 1961), p. 128.

5. Lawrence Lessing, "The Transistorized M.D.," Fortune, (September, 1963), p. 131.

6. E. F. Leonard, "Bio-Medical Electronics, Reply with Rejoinder," Science, 135, (Apr. 13, 1962), pp. 185-6.

7. Mark Blumberg, M.D., "Electronic Equipment Brings Problems in Purchase, Use, Design and Policy," The Modern Hospital, 97, (November, 1961), p. 78.

8. "Electronics in Medicine," Engineer, 210, (July 27, 1960), pp. 204-5.

9. Ibid.

10. H. L. Walkes, "Recent Developments in Bio-Medical Instrumentation," ARS Journal, 31, (October, 1961), pp. 1422-1428.

11. Dr. Vladimir K. Zworykin, op. cit.

12. "New Medical Electronics Technique," Franklin Institute Journal, 274, (July, 1962), pp. 72-73.

13. News Release: "New Westinghouse X-ray System Televises and Records Results for Doctors," (Dec. 6, 1960).

14. George C. Radcliffe, "Television in the Modern Hospital," The American Journal of Medical Electronics, 1, (July-September, 1962), pp. 208-211.

15. Interview with Bernard S. Wolf, M.D., The Mount Sinai Hospital, (October, 1963), and with Herman Block, Picker X-Ray Corp. (October, 1963).

16. "Medical Electronics Takes a Deeper Look," Business Week, (Feb. 25, 1967), p. 86.

17. William E. Bushor, "Medical Electronics," Electronics, 34, (Jan. 20, 1961), pp. 49-55.

18. J. Richard Elliott, Jr., op. cit.

19. William E. Bushor, op. cit.

20. "Phone Lines Transmit Data on Heart Beats," Electronics, 35, (Jan. 19, 1962), pp. 20-21.

21. "Study of Heart Action Makes Strides," Electrical Energy, 81, (Mar., 1962), p. 214.

22. J. Weldon Bellville, M.D. and G. M. Attura, "How Electronics Controls the Depth of Anaesthesia," Electronics, 32, (Jan. 30, 1959), pp. 43-45.

23. William E. Bushor, op. cit.

24. U. S. Department of Health, Education and Welfare, Selected Impairments by Etiology and Activity Limitation, a report prepared by the U.S. National Health Survey (Washington, D.C.: July, 1962); and R. S. MacKany and Elwin May, "Electronic Tonometer for Glaucoma Diagnosis," Electronics, 33, (Feb. 12, 1960), pp. 115-116.

25. R. Stuart MacKay, "Electronics in Clinical Research," Institute of Radio Engineers Proceedings, 50, (May, 1962), pp. 1177-1189.

26. K. D. Broodfoot, "A Photoelectric Apparatus for Examining Blood Circulation in the Interior of the Eye," Electronic Engineer, 34, (January, 1962), pp. 2-7.

27. "Computer Diagnosis Heart Ills in Seconds," New York Times, (Oct. 27, 1963).

28. Lawrence Lessing, op. cit.

29. New York Times, op. cit.

30. "Computers Start to Study Medicine," Business Week (July 9, 1966) p. 143. For an earlier comment, see Julius Korein, M.D., et. al, "Computer Processing by Variable-Field-Length Format," The Journal of the American Medical Association, 186 (Oct. 12, 1962), pp. 132-138.

31. "Computer Draws Diagram of Skull from X-Ray Data," The Medical Post (Apr. 11, 1967), p. 27.

32. "Hospitals, a New Market," Electronics, 32 (Sept. 18, 1959), pp. 22-23.

33. William E. Bushor, op. cit.

34. The Modern Hospital, op. cit.

35. "Sweden Pressing Health Check-ups," New York Times (Dec. 1, 1963).

36. N. F. Izzo and W. Coles, "Blood Cell Scanner Identifies Rare Cells," Electronics, 35 (Apr. 27, 1962), pp. 52-57.

37. Robert K. Okada and Herman P. Schwen, "Electronic Blood Analyzer," Electronics, 33 (Sept. 2, 1960), pp. 53-54.

38. J. B. Norman, "Medical Applications of Electronics Aid Patients and Physician," Hospital Journal - A.H.A. (May 1, 1966), p. 104.

39. Lawrence Lessing, op. cit.

40. "Patient Monitoring is More Than Just a Dream," American Journal of Nursing, 61 (November, 1961), pp. 100-102. See also, "Electronics at the Bedside," Medical News Weekly (Aug. 5, 1966), p. 57.

41. Ibid.

42. "New Electronic Monitoring System," Hospital Topics (September, 1961), pp. 38-40.

43. F. Gorham Brigham, Jr., "Evaluating the Acquisition of Capital Equipment for the Hospital," The Journal of Medical Electronics, 1 (September-November, 1961), pp. 24-26.

44. Ibid.

45.   Walter V. Coburn, "Bedside Monitor Keep Hearts Beating," Modern Hospital, 100 (April, 1963), p. 79.

46.   J. Richard Elliott, Jr., op. cit.

47.   Interview with Miss Lois O'Quinn, R.N., The Mount Sinai Hospital (December, 1963).

48.   Taker K. Robinette, "ITV a Versatile Tool," Hospital Management (October, 1958), p. 38.

49.   George C. Radcliffe, op. cit.

50.   "Hospitals, a New Market," op. cit.

51.   "Most Hospitals Own or Plan to Buy Ultrasonic Cleaners, Study Shows," The Modern Hospital, 97, no. 5 (November, 1961), p. 96.

52.   "The Medical Electronic Devices and Equipment Market," Modern Medicine Topics, 27, no. 4 (April, 1966), p. 1.

53.   Henry Korn, "Successful Prescription for Hospital Management," Data Systems News (November, 1967), p. 8ff; see also p. 9.

54.   L. Phillips, "A Hospital's Total Information System," Data Systems News (Apr. 15, 1968), p. 12.

55.   "Survey Shows a Widespread Acceptance of Electronic Instruments in U.S. Hospital," The Modern Hospital, 97 (November, 1961), p. 79.

56.   J. Richard Elliott, Jr., op. cit.

57.   Board of the Hospital Review and Planning Council of Southern New York, Hospital Review (1963).

58.   J. Richard Elliott, Jr., op. cit.

59.   Lewis, Cotton, Barland, op. cit.

60.   Lawrence Lessing, op. cit.

61.   Electronic Industry Marketing and Distribution Chart, Electronic News (1966).

62. "Modern Hospital Electronics," The Modern Hospital, 97 (November, 1961), p. 81.

63. K. C. Rock, Minneapolis-Honeywell Regulator Corp. Personal Communication (Apr. 26, 1963).

CHAPTER **16** MEDICAL
ELECTRONICS-
PROSTHETICS

by Vincent T. Turrini

INTRODUCTION

Medical electronics has long been regarded as
a potentially useful field in the conversion of the
electronics industry. It presents considerable scientific challenges and, therefore, has a high research content which, moreover, has been having
growing government support. In the last chapter
diagnostic and monitoring devices were considered.
In this chapter, the attention is focused on medical
prosthetics, at present the most novel general area
of medical electronics.

First, there is a description of the products
being developed and the organizations associated
with these products. The next step is to define the
requirements which must be met before a product is
marketable and the obstacles, both technical and non-
technical, which must be overcome before these needs
can be met. Finally, the potential market for these
selected devices will be explored.

Electronic prosthetics attracted considerable
attention in the 1950's and early 1960's, and many
of the devices described in this chapter were developed at that time. In the last five years or so,
however, there appears to have been relatively little
progress and certainly nothing that could be remotely
described as a breakthrough. One interesting device
was a means of steering a wheelchair by means of
movements of the eye, an important advantage to the
very severely paralyzed. This equipment was originally developed for space travelers. In general,

however, except for hearing aids, the products are
still in large measure experimental, and for some,
little information has been made public. Therefore
the present survey is not all-inclusive, and there
is no doubt that additional items could be described.
The purpose is rather to define the major products
in electronic prosthetics and to lay out the general
guidelines and requirements for their successful development. The principal systems discussed are sense
aids or replacements (e.g., devices for the blind),
organ aids or replacements (e.g., heart pacers), artificial limbs with electronic components (e.g., electronically controlled muscles), and chemical plants
(e.g., artificial kidneys).

The survey does not concern itself with hearing
aids, the only well-established product in the field
at present. These, of course, are electronic, miniaturized, and otherwise might be considered suitable products. However, two or three firms dominate
this $55-million market, and new entries are likely
to prove difficult. The existence of prior entries
in the systems considered in the present chapter
should not necessarily foreclose such entry. Very
few, if any, have thus far been developed to anything near their potential markets, and the existing
products could also, in general, still be extensively
improved. A substantial number of the devices are,
in fact, still experimental.

At present, much of the research and development
effort is being undertaken at the large research
institutes and university-associated hospitals. This
is naturally due to the specialization of this field
and the manner in which the research is financed.
To a large extent the research effort is underwritten
by the large national foundations, such as the Polio
Foundation, Foundation for the Blind, etc. The U.S.
Government is also a very heavy underwriter of this
type of research. The Veterans Administration and
U.S. Department of Health, Education and Welfare are
two of the main agencies which support this type of
effort. However, more and more private firms are
making efforts in this area.

Commercial success in this field, however, calls
for a very high order of competence. It requires
the integration of physiological and psychological
factors with electronic technology in ways that may

well be unfamiliar to most engineers and managements. There are many other unique problems.

Thus, it is a peculiarity of this type of product that, although one may seem to meet all the re-required technical criteria, it may not be a successful commercial product. For example, an artificial limb may meet all the required criteria, but because it requires a great deal of custom fitting in order to fit each individual, it may not be profitable to produce artificial arms on a production-line basis. Therefore the manufacture of the arm, itself, becomes a limited operation, although the electronic devices which power and control the arm could be mass produced profitably. Of course, all the devices concerned would have to be prescribed under medical supervision or other professional training. This is true even of glasses and hearing aids. However, the complexity of the fitting is obviously a factor. It also would require the establishment of suitable distribution channels and servicing facilities.

It is also obvious that since the prosthetic devices may be used to sustain important bodily functions--life itself, in fact--a high degree of reliability must be designed into them. Fortunately, present systems and components can be made to meet these requirements. The components themselves must be nontoxic, nonallergenic, nonflammable, nonexplosive, and spark free. The electronic devices must also be rugged. They are used by afflicted and handicapped people and thus see rough usage. There is also a question of training the users. In the design of reading devices for the blind, orthotic braces, and prosthetic limbs it is very important that training time be kept to a minimum.

It is important that these prosthetics be attractive in appearance to the user, especially in the case of obstacle detectors, orthotic braces, and prosthetic limbs. The potential user of such devices will probably not use them if they are distasteful in appearance, even though they are functional. As an example, artificial arms are being manufactured with a soft foam to imitate human flesh in softness and texture. Cost is also of the utmost consideration to the potential customer. In many cases the individual has no choice as to whether he wants to buy or not. He is a captive market, as in the case of pacemakers or artificial kidneys.

The engineer working on medical prosthetics
must obviously be qualified to integrate both the
physiological and purely technical aspects of the
system he designs. He also has two problems, in part
due to difficulty in communication. First he must
learn and know the end user of his equipment, the
customer. In this field the customers are handicapped
or afflicted in some way. Their psychological make-
up must be understood to some extent by the engineer
if he is to design a successful product. The difficulty and necessity of accomplishing this is pointed
out by Prof. Herbert Elftman who states:

> When an equation has been transformed
> into a device by an engineer and adap-
> ted to the human mechanism under medi-
> cal guidance, it still needs the skill
> of the prosthetist or orthotist and the
> skill of the therapist before it be-
> comes part of the personality of the
> human being.[1]

The second problem facing the electronics engineers is the difficulty of understanding the medical personnel they will be associated with during
the design and marketing phases of prosthetic devices.
In commenting on the difficulties experienced by
electronics people in marketing their prosthetic devices, David G. Kilpatrick stated:

> In general, electronics orientated
> people do not understand the very
> strange sort of selling and sales
> organizations that are required for the
> medical market. We are used to selling
> items by technical excellence, which
> is impossible since the average physi-
> cian refuses to even understand Ohm's
> Law.[2]

Mr. Kilpatrick goes on to discuss electronic
utilization in the medical field and states that:

> One of the largest limitations in de-
> signing and developing such devices is
> the unscientific manner in which basic
> physical measurements are made. For
> instance, the literature is loaded with

impedance measurements of the heart
which should be useful in designing
an electrical pacemaker. However,
almost all of the material is unus-
able because of the manner and preju-
diced methods of measurement.[3]

The problem of medical personnel understanding
the electronic engineer is in the process of solution. Programs are under way in which the rudiments
of electronics are being taught to physicians in both
undergraduate and graduate medical schools.

In spite of all these obstacles, there is an
impressive number of devices, as the following sections will show.

PACEMAKERS

Pacemakers are devices which serve to initiate
cardiac beating in cases of heart arrest, that is
when the natural electrical stimulus which keeps the
heart pumping in proper rhythm is not working properly. In some cases the natural rhythm is slowed
down, and in certain cases the heart stops beating
entirely. Heart blocks (cardiac arrest) or slowdown
can be caused by shocks during surgery, anesthesia,
adverse reaction to drugs, electric shock, drowning,
and diseases such as Stokes-Adams syndrome.[4] Many
other heart conditions can cause disorders of the
heart rhythm.

The pacemaker assists or replaces the natural
electrical stimulus which regulates the heart's
beating at a predetermined rate. In the human heart,
these electrical stimuli are generated at nodes, or
dense networks of fibres in the conduction system of
the heart. In the past, when this natural electrical
stimulus failed, internal or external cardiac massage
was instituted. Although this type of resuscitation
is successful if applied quickly by competent personnel, electronic pacemakers are much more reliable,
and the external pacemaker with externally applied
stimuli can be utilized by comparatively inexperi-
enced personnel.[5]

In the externally carried pacemaker with external simulator the impulses are applied between two

electrodes placed on the outside of the body. The
stimulating electrodes are placed over the chest wall
and deliver electric impulses with currents from 50
to 200 megamps and voltage from 20 to 100 volts.

Another type of pacemaker is the externally
carried instrument with an internal stimulator, where
the electrodes are brought into direct contact with
the heart by a stimulating wire attached to the heart
muscle. Advantages of the internal over the external-
stimulated pacemaker are that it is effective with
smaller currents, does not entail contractions of
the chest muscles, does not produce pain or local
skin burns, and, because of its small size, can be
carried.

A third type is the implanted pacemaker which
is placed within the chest wall. Artificial pacemakers that are connected to the heart by means of
a wire connection through the skin present the danger of infection as well as hindering mobility. The
above problems are overcome by implanting the artificial pacemaker within the chest cavity. A description of representative products follows.

The Medtronic Corporation manufactures a transistorized externally mounted pacemaker with an internal stimulator attached directly to the myocardium
(muscular tissue of the heart) for temporary stimulation, or with a bipolar patch for prolonged stimulation.[6] Shaped like an oversized package of
cigarettes and weighing 10 ounces, the unit uses a
self-contained 9.4 volt mercury battery, having a
flat voltage-discharge curve so that, for a given
setting, the pacemaker stimulator is relatively constant for the 1000-hour battery life. It is normally carried on the belt or in a shoulder holster. A
technique employed for placing the electrode is to
insert a braided wire through a vein in the neck and
into the heart. An alternate technique is to implant
stainless steel electrodes, insulated with Teflon
directly into the myocardium. A companion unit to
the Medtronic Pacemaker is the Cardiac Monitor, which
can be inserted into the same circuit with the pacemaker. This unit serves to activate the pacemaker
automatically should the patient's pulse rate fall
below a predetermined level. It also contains an
audio alarm.[6]

The pacemaker developed by the Atronic Corporation in cooperation with the Philadelphia General
Hospital, is attached to the heart by a wire in the
neck and running through the vein to the lower right
chamber of the heart.[7] The ground electrode is im-
bedded in the skin of the chest over the heart. By
using the jugular vein-insertion method, the piercing
of the heart muscle is eliminated as are the occa-
sional complications that result, i.e., hemorrhage,
fibrosis, and infection. The instrument, which is
the size of a small book and wrighs less than two
pounds, is a combination polarity and wave-rate monitor, impedance meter, and pacemaker. It can be us,ed
for monitoring and internally stimulating cardiac
activity in the event of an emergency, or as a pre-
cautionary measure during an operation.

Westinghouse Electric Corporation is marketing
a transistorized cardiac-resuscitation system, consisting of a cardiac pacer and bedside-monitoring
unit. Although it also generates periodic electrical stimuli, this system will respond to indications
of heart arrest by switching the pacer on and by signaling an alert to the doctor via radio.

The University of Buffalo School of Medicine
together with Buffalo VA Hospital and Wilson Greatbatch, Electronics Consultants, have developed a miniaturized implantable pacemaker for long-term
correction of heart blocks.[8] The pacemaker, which
measures 6 by 9 by 2 centimeters, including battery,
uses only nine components and has an estimated life
of 50,000 hours or more than five years. By potting
the unit in epoxy resin and then encapsulating it
in silicon rubber, satisfactory biological neutrality
can be attained.

Researchers at Boston Beth Israel Hospital have
also developed an implantable pacemaker. Highly stable silicon transistors are used together with special mercury batteries with a shelf life of five
years. As the batteries run down, the pulse rate of
the patient slowly decreases and surgery is required
to replace the batteries.

General Electric Company in cooperation with Dr.
Kantrowitz of Maimonides Hospital, Brooklyn, surgi-
cally implanted an internal pacemaker. External control of pulse rate was provided to permit temporary
increase in pulse rate for occasions when the patient

is engaged in strenuous activities. Completely self-
contained, the pacemaker uses simple circuits with
high reliability solid-state devices as active components and batteries with lives of three to five
years.

More elaborate devices are required for treating
more complex cases of heart arrhythmia. Thus far,
treatment has often been by drugs, which do not always work well. The "cardioverters" use an electrocardiograph for timing the exact instant in the heart
cycle when the stimulus is most effective and then
program the correct electrical current in correct
wave form.[9]

ARTIFICIAL LARYNX

The artificial larynx is a device which serves
as a mechanical substitute for the human vocal chords.
A sound of suitable pitch and quality is generated
outside the throat and then conducted into the vocal
tract, where it may be used in the normal manner to
form words and sentences.

As the name implies, the artificial larynx replaces the human larynx in those patients who must
undergo laryngectomy (the surgical removal of the
larynx). In a laryngectomy, the patient's lungs are
closed off from the vocal tract and they breathe
through an opening provided in the front of the neck.
All means of natural speech are lost. With modern
therapy, some laryngectomees can learn esophageal
speech, in which controlled vibrations of the tissues
at the top of the esophagus are produced by expelling
swallowed air. This is learned by exacting training
and many cannot do it successfully. Hence the need
for the development of an instrument such as the artificial larynx.

The American Telephone and Telegraph device
consists of a transistorized pulse generator, powered
by small mercury batteries.[10] This makes it possible
to package all components in a small unit that is
held in the hand. With the vibrator pressed against
the throat, a combined on-off switch and pitch control operated by thumb and forefinger regulates
speech inflection. The user forms his words by using
teeth, palate, tongue, and lips in the usual manner.

ORTHOTIC AND PROSTHETIC DEVICES

Orthotics is the medical specialty of orthopedic bracing. In certain illnesses, such as polio, arthritis, cerebral palsy, and also as a result of accidents, damage is inflicted on various parts of the human body. Arms and legs lose their muscular control and become flaccid, or in certain cases spastic. Orthotics is the science in which bracing for these injured limbs is designed and fitted by teams of orthopedic surgeons and orthopedists. It is a goal of orthotics to provide movement to these braces so that the patient may have limited use of his damaged extremities. Recently a great deal of emphasis has been placed on the application of electric power to these devices. In addition to experimentation being conducted on electrical motors, there is work being done on electronic controls and feedback systems for these orthotic braces.

Orthotic devices are used to assist the severely paralyzed limb to function in as normal a manner as possible. The need for better designed orthotic devices has become apparent as the number of patients with severe paralysis has increased.[11] The aim of orthotics is to help these patients regain some measure of personal independence and to care for themselves as much as possible. The devices are designed to provide basic functions to meet the individual patient's specific need.

As differentiated from orthotics, prosthetics is the actual replacement of a human limb or part of a human limb by an artificial device. Whereas orthotics is the bracing of damaged limbs, prosthetics is the actual replacement of missing organs. However, as in the field of orthotics, the externally powered prosthetic is undergoing a good deal of attention and experimentation. This renewed interest is due to several reasons, the main one being the reduction in incidence of paralytic poliomyelitis brought about by widespread use of poliomyelitis vaccine.[12] This enabled a great deal of money and professional skill to be redirected toward the rehabilitation of polio patients. Since the requirements for both orthotic and prosthetic devices are similar, they will be treated together in this chapter.

Several technical problems must be solved if
satisfactory electrically driven, electronically controlled, orthotic bracing is to be developed.[13]

Devices to provide linear actuation for moderate distances by electrical auxiliary power are required. A ball-screw infinite shaft actuator is
available in large sizes for airplane flaps, but
miniaturization of the commercial device is not
available. A major problem is gear reduction from
the extremely high rotary speed of the necessarily
small motor without introducing losses, bulkiness
or serious noise.

Devices to provide rotary motions, as of the
elbow, or finger or elbow flexion, directly from
electrical systems are necessary. Rotary solenoids
are available commercially for other applications,
but are not suited for use in orthotics or prosthetics. A number of designs were developed by the
Alderson Research Laboratories using reduction gears
driven by electrical motors. These were highly experimental and are not commercially available. Methods for attaining higher torques and ranges of motion
without undue weight are required. Further miniaturization of reduction-gearing systems is needed.

Instrumentation for control of electrical power
is required, initially with simple on-and-off control and then with increasing sophistication. There
is also a need for improved precision of control instrumentation, reduction of cost, reduction of bulkiness, better methods of patient training in use of
controls, improved freedom from accidental operation,
and, particularly, improved possibility of modulated
control.

The problems cited above are only a few of the
many facing the electronics engineer working in orthotics. However, they are similar in a great degree
to those in other product areas, such as pacemaker,
reading devices, obstacle detection, etc. The problems of miniaturization of components, motion trans-
ference, and control instrumentation are almost uni-
versal in the electronics field.

Some of the organizations active in this field
are the University of California, Texas Rehabilitation Institute, University of Michigan, Fairchild

Semiconductor Division, Alderson Research Laboratories, Rancho Los Amigos Hospital, Theratron Corporation, Case Institute of Technology, and Biotechnology
Laboratories.

At the above institutions, research is being
conducted in the areas of electromyographic control,
miniaturization of electronic controls, development
of high-speed motors and reduction gears, development of lightweight electronic muscles, and artificial limbs. This area, however, is still highly
experimental, and opportunities exist for major new
discoveries.

ELECTRONIC AIDS FOR THE BLIND

There are two general categories of devices for
the blind, obstacle and curb detectors and reading
machines. The former are often rather simple, but
reading machines may involve quite sophisticated
techniques. Electronic obstacle and curb detectors
are intended to permit a blind traveler to get about
more safely, more rapidly, and with less stress than
is possible with a guide dog or ordinary cane. They
employ ranging and proximity principles. They use
ambient and self-generated radiations. They use
sound, light, radio, and radar for their detection
beams.[14]

The Franklin Institute Laboratories have developed a cane which contains a few simple electronics
to aid in height assessment.[15] The cane is adjusted
so that with the top two inches from the ground it
gives no signal, but if the ground drops away an
additional two inches, as at a step down or a hole,
a signal cuts in, warning the carrier.

Bionic Instruments Inc. has developed an obstacle detector which uses a minimum of triangulation
and does not involve measurements of range or rate of
change of range. This company is also experimenting
with the design of an electronic detector, using a
powerful pulsed light source as an active obstacle
seeker. This steps up the basic sensitivity of the
device and enhances its detection capabilities, particularly for objects like narrow posts. This device
is presently undergoing field tests. Many methods
have been used to assist the blind in their reading

problems. There are some among these which have met
with notable success, for example, braille, talking
books, the manual alphabets for the deaf-blind, and
the Tellatouch, a unit which translates a letter from
a typewriter key to the proper pins in a braille cell.
However, in the above systems a sighted reader must
intervene at one point or another. The many disad-
vantages of these current reading methods--personal,
psychological, and economic--have given impetus to
research on devices which may eventually enable the
blind person to "read" ordinary printed, typed, or
hand-lettered material without sighted intervention.

The experimentation being undertaken falls into
two groups of devices.[16] The direct translator is
comparatively the simpler machine and relies heavily
on the human brain for effectiveness. It is cheaper
and smaller and could be useful in the home, office,
or school. The recognition type of machine is more
complex but requires less initial training and less
continuing mental work on the part of the user. It
is expensive and large in size and could probably
best be used in a library or other central facility.
The best approach would seem to be a combination of
both types. By developing several types of machines,
it is hoped that the specialists would be able to
prescribe a machine suited for an individual's needs.

Many machines for the purpose have been developed. Table 16.1 lists and classifies those devices
which are in existence and on which much experimentation is being performed to improve them. The
classification of electromechanical print-reading
systems into categories as shown on Table 16.1 has
been found generally useful. Systems with audible
outputs are set apart by the horizontal separation
from those with tactile outputs (useful for the near-
blind). A further separation in terms of mode of
operation is made by listing the methods in four
columns. Roughly speaking, at the left of Table 16.1
are the physically simpler devices, limited to slow
reading speeds and requiring considerable learning
and interpretative effort on the user's part and
perhaps best suited to intermittent use on specialized
tasks; while towards the right are the more complex
machines, capable of more rapid use with less psychological stress and hence more suitable for prolonged reading.

TABLE 16.1

Classification of Reading Machines for the Blind

Output	Simple Optical		Intermediate	Recognition
	Probe	Direct translation		
Audible	Orientierungs-hilfe fur Blinde Audivis Hear-a-lite	Optophone 1914 Optophone 1920 RCA Reading Aid RCA Optophone Battelle Aural Reading Device for the blind	Mauch Reading Machine recent developments tending towards letter recognition	Schutkowski System Sharples Apparatus Davis and Hinton Flory and Pike Recognition machine or TTS tape might control: Morse Code Tonal Braille, Frank "Spelled Speech", Prerecorded words, Speech synthesis
Tactile	Moon (University of Chicago) suggested finger-tip mounting of photocell and tactile stimulator	Naumburg Visagraph Snook Apparatus Sell Device "Faximile" Visagraph Kallmann Suggestion Surber Device	"Intermediate" systems with tactile outputs, if developed, might use conventionalized patterns suggestive of letter shape, like Moon type	Recognition machine or TTS tape might control: IBM Braille Reading Apparatus Zuk Reader

Source: National Academy of Sciences, Summary Report on 5th Technical Session on Reading Machines for the Blind.

Haskens Laboratories is working on the synthesis of speech-using techniques developed under a Veterans Administration contract. The output of recognition-reading machines for the blind will probably be letter-by-letter, and the work is aimed at producing an audible, understandable, speechlike utterance to convey the information to the blind user.

A more advanced machine also under development there is an interim word-reading machine. This device accepts punched paper tape, reads it, searches its memory for the word, and then plays back if it is one of those prerecorded. If the word is not one of those in the store, the machine spells it out in "spelled" speech as developed by Professor Methfessel.

The aim of the effort at Battelle Memorial Institute is the production of a practical, inexpensive, portable reading machine for the blind, which will give the user some capability to read ordinary typed or printed material without recourse to sighted help.

Mauch Laboratories is developing a more complex personal type of reading machine intended to recognize characters and then using tape recordings of the sounds of Methfessel's "spelled" speech. A trial recognition array has been built which recognizes all twenty-six lower case letters of an International Business Machine typewriter font at moderate scanning speeds.

CHEMICAL TYPE PROSTHETICS

In addition to the electronic prosthetic devices discussed previously, there are certain chemical and mechanical devices which may also be marketed. They may not be an easy field for the electronics manufacturer to enter, but the machines are briefly described here to indicate the range of prosthetic devices under development and to draw attention to the social issues which they have created. The electronic manufacturer desiring to enter the electronic prosthetic field may wish to add these additional devices to the product line. These machines, however, require competence in such fields as ion exchange, filtration, electrophoresis, etc., as well as conventional electronics.

A combination of a small oxygenator, a non-damaging blood pump, and a mechanism by means of which a baby may be suspended and his temperature maintained may be called an artificial uterus. It is designed to accept premature babies who would otherwise die and babies with temporary pulmonary insufficiency.

An artificial pancreas is being developed in which a commercially available autoanalyzer for glucose is connected with the bloodstream. A strip chart recorder that indicates the level of blood sugar automatically regulates the injection of insulin when blood sugar becomes too high and the administration of intravenous glucose when the blood sugar is low.

A variety of artificial heart-lung machines are presently under development. Some of them are simple and some are sophisticated and fully automatic. Although these machines have been used mainly in open heart surgery, they are now beginning to be used to treat medical heart failure.

The use of artificial kidneys is becoming more and more important in the treatment of kidney failure. In the artificial kidney the patients blood containing harmful wastes is pumped through sheets of porous cellophane immersed in a special cleansing solution. As the blood moves through the chamber, wastes are drawn through the cellophane into the cleansing solution by a complex process called dialysis. The cleansed blood passes through a rewarmer and back into the patient.

A great deal of controversy and discussion has arisen in the past year over the use of the several experimental artificial kidney machines developed at the University of Washington Medical School.17 The kidney machine was developed at the Medical School and an experimental program with human patients has been conducted for the last two years.

The patient visits the machine twice a week for an 11-hour period. He must do this for the remainder of his life. The patients with uremic poisoning who are selected for the program lead a normal life, those who are not selected die. The machines are expensive to build and, in addition, it requires $15,000 per year to maintain a patient on the machine.

There are approximately 100,000 people in the United States suffering from kidney disease, one out of 50 or 2,000 are physically and psychologically adapted to use a kidney machine. Assuming a machine cost of $20,000 and that it requires $15,000 per year per patient the United States would have to spend the following to save more than 2,000 lives.

New machines: 1 machine per 5 people-
400 machines x $20,000 = $8,000,000

Maintain patient: $15,000 per year x
2,000 people = $30,000,000 per year

The National Kidney Disease Foundation has since then estimated that it costs only $7,500 to $10,000 a year per patient but that many centers find such programs impossibly demanding of time, facilities, and personnel.[18] In part, this is a consequence of a relative national neglect of the life sciences, but it is clear that with an expenditure of $15 to $30 million a year, over 2,000 citizens could be kept alive whose chances are now zero. Indeed, further reductions appear imminent, by making a multiple unit in which some of the cleansing apparatus is shared, thus realizing economies of scale. A reduction of $1,500 per-patient-per-year is estimated, compared with the individual units.[19]

The Seattle program has only eighteen people in it, one patient for the fourth year. The Medical School of the University of Washington has appointed a lay committee of seven people to determine who should enter and who should not, that is, who should live and who should die. It seems regrettable that in this age, Bernard Shaw's "The Doctor's Dilemma" should have to be reenacted, with laymen as the judges. Here is one problem which public initiative should be able to solve, without waiting for drugs, transplants, and other developments not yet in sight. Poliomyelitis also called for a large iron-lung program before the advent of vaccines.

POTENTIAL MARKETS

A market estimate for the foregoing devices is not easily arrived at, mainly because several of the products discussed before are not developed to the

stage where even guesses at their final price can be
arrived at. However, by assuming a plausible price
for equipment and applying this to the number of
sufferers from the condition concerned, an order of
magnitude of the market may be arrived at.

Pacemakers

The markets for devices for stimulating and
regulating heart beats are likely to involve two
classes of equipment, the relatively simple individual units, used by individual patients and kept as
possible first aid devices and the more complex
"cardioverters," used primarily in hospitals.

There is no doubt that a substantial market for
the individual devices would exist if effective ones
could be produced at reasonable cost. It has been
estimated that there are about one million sufferers
from some irregularity of heart rhythm. A substantial number of them, perhaps as many as two thirds,
might benefit from pacemakers or other treatments.[20]
At present, there are about ten million cases of
cardiovascular-renal diseases in the United States.[21]
The death rate amounts to approximately 9 percent of
this number.[22] Applying this average figure to the
portion of the population suffering from arrhythmias,
it follows that there would be a replacement market
in these devices of about 60,000 units annually. An
initial spurt in equipping present patients should
provide a market of at least double this size for
some time.

It will be further assumed that the order of
magnitude of cost for a personal pacemaker can be
pushed as low as a hearing aid, with the hardware
involved set at $100 each. With the above reasoning,
this means a market of $12 million.

An additional very important group of customers
might well be the better and more highly skilled
First Aid Units. There appear to be no nationwide
statistics on the number of such units existing.
However, an inquiry to the New Jersey First Aid
Council brought the information that there were 300
units serving the 6 million inhabitants of the state.
Expanded to national need from this per capita rate
of one unit for 20,000 inhabitants, this means a
market for a further 9,000 units. However, in

addition to these groups, a real market should exist
at beach and lake resorts, swimming pools, etc. To
assure prompt application in case of electrical
shock, every line crew working with high voltage
might be equipped with a pacemaker. In all, an
additional $2 million in sales might well come from
these sources. Naturally, the use of these devices
would require extensive training as part of conventional first-aid courses.

There are also the more complex units used in
hospitals. Eventually, there may well be one in
every operating room. If the total number of operating rooms is conservatively estimated at twice the
approximately 7,000 hospitals in the United States,
14,000 units would be needed.[23] At $1,000 each, a
market of $14 million is the result; it may be ex-
pressed as approximately $2 million a year, assuming
a seven-year installation time.

For the heart devices, therefore, there is a
total potential market of about $16 million a year.

Orthotic Braces and Prosthetic Limbs

There is a potentially sizeable market for both
orthotic braces and prosthetic limbs. Table 16.2
indicates the large numbers of persons afflicted
with conditions possibly requiring outside aids or
braces. Only a limited number, however, would find
electronic devices useful. For example, there is
only a small number of arthritis sufferers who are
crippled badly enough to require externally powered
bracing. On the other hand, almost all those suffering from spastic and flaccid paralysis might
eventually utilize an externally powered orthotic
device.

As shown, there are about 3 million persons in
this group. Assuming that 25 percent of this group
cannot adapt to the new devices because of age and
other problems, there would be a potential market
for about 2.25 million devices. At a very conservative $200 per brace, this would reflect a total of
$450 million, or, translated as above into annual
requirements, about $60 million.

Details on the absence of major extremity are
given in Table 16.3. There are 260,000 persons

TABLE 16.2

Conditions Potentially Requiring Orthotics
(Estimated Incidence in the United States)

Spastic paralysis: Hemiplegia	2,000,000
Quadrilateral spastic paralysis:	
Cerebral palsy cases	100,000
Other spastic conditions	500,000
Flaccid: polios & Guillain-Barre	100,000 (with one or both arms involved; of these about
	15,000 are very severely involved in one or both arms)
Comparable flaccid paralysis:	
Peripheral-nerve lesions	500,000
Quadrilateral quadriplegia from cervical (C-5 or C-6) lesions	20,000 to 25,000
Arthritis	11,000,000 (including
	4,000,000 with rheumatoid deformities, most including some upper-extremity involvement)
Myopathies, muscular dystrophy	250,000
Burns, fractures, trauma	
Dyskinesia: athetosis, Parkinsonism	Unknown but substantial numbers.

Source: National Academy of Sciences—National Research Council, Orthotics Research and Development. A report prepared by the Committee on Prosthetics Research and Development, Chicago (June 4-5, 1962).

Table 16.3

Average Prevalence, Percent Distribution, and Rate
Per 1,000 Population of Cases of Absence of Major
Extremity by Etiology According to Age

United States, July 1959-June 1961.

Etiology	Age								
	All ages	Under 45	45+	All ages	Under 45	45+	All ages	Under 45	45+
	Average number in thousands			Percent distribution			Rate per 1,000 population		
All causes	259	87	172	100.0	100.0	100.0	1.5	0.7	3.4
Injury	196	68	127	75.7	78.2	73.8	1.1	0.5	2.5
All other causes	64	19	45	24.7	21.8	26.2	0.4	0.2	0.9

Note: Data based on household interviews and refer to the living, civilian, non-institutional population. Absence of major extremity is exclusive of fingers or toes only.

Source: U.S. Department of Health, Education and Welfare, Selected Impairment by Etiology and Activity Limitation. A report prepared by the U.S. National Health Survey, Washington, D.C. (July, 1962).

306

involved, two thirds of whom are over 45 years of
age. Assuming a market of 70 percent of potential
in the under-45 group and 30 percent in the older
group gives a total of 90,500 units needed, neglec-
ting the statistical effect of multiple amputees.
A full prosthetic limb could probably not be built
below $500. There is, accordingly, a potential of
about $45 million, or on an approximate annual basis,
$6 million.

Artificial Larynx

It has been estimated that there are between
23,000 and 25,000 laryngectomees living in the United
States.[24] At the present time there are approximately 3,000 new laryngectomees each year. Less
than 5 percent of laryngectomees are physically unable to learn esophageal voice. However, psychological problems raise the figure to about 35 percent.
If it can be demonstrated that the artificial larynx
can produce a better voice sound than esophageal sp
speech, the market for artificial devices should
grow accordingly.

A note of caution should be sounded for anyone
who considers entering this market. Western Electric Company makes a highly satisfactory device which
it sells through the Bell System, at cost as a public service, at $45. While there are other firms
in the field, it is clearly highly competitive and
one cannot therefore postulate any appreciable additional market.

Obstacle and Curb Detectors for the Blind

There are almost a million persons with severe
visual impairment (two thirds aged 65 or over).[25]
385,000 are defined as blind,[26] only about 60,000
of these people are generally capable of traveling.[27]
For the rest, age, psychological difficulties, and
lack of training cause immobility. While the primary market for obstacle and curb detectors undoubtedly lies within this group, it can be assumed that
good devices of the sort described would enlarge it,
for the time being, therefore, a market of 60,000
devices is a conservative assumption.

The price of obstacle and curb detectors thus
far produced in limited quantities is from $300 to
$400. Simplification and cost reduction to about
$200 would appear to be a necessity. On that basis,
about 10,000 units a year might be sold, for a value
of $2 million.

Reading Devices for the Blind

As was discussed previously, reading devices
may range from comparatively simple aural output devices to complex tape-to-aural-output machines.
These larger machines must utilize computers for
word storage and retrieval. The prices will probably vary from a target figure of under $1,000 for
the simpler devices, to over $150,000 for the larger
machines. The larger type of recognition machine
will find a market at universities, foundations, and
large libraries, where its use can serve many individuals. It might also serve as an important link
in a system for gathering, duplicating, and distribu-
uting information for the blind.

One cannot, however, look at statistics on
blindness and decide that by sheer numbers alone
there is a market for reading devices. True, there
are a great many blind people in the United States,
but there are other considerations besides just numbers. It takes a great amount of tedious training
to enable a blind person to use some of the present
types of reading devices. Even with this training,
a blind person can only read at a slow rate, which
is due to the inherent inability of the machines to
scan quickly. Therefore, a blind person must recognize his need for such a device and really want to
use it; he must be psychologically suited to use such
a device. As the more advanced machines are developed, those which take less skill to operate, more
blind people will take advantage of their availability. Therefore statistics are inadequate as a basis
for judging market potential. Rather, one would have
to determine the number of educated, well-adjusted,
psychologically adapted blind people who may be able
to utilize these devices if available.

Undoubtedly, the number would be very much
greater than the 60,000 presently "mobile" blind persons. It may be as high as 250,000 which would still

be only 65 percent of the total number of blind.
Making due allowance for sharing facilities, a market of $15 million a year could supply 15,000 of the
simpler machines or 100 of the more elaborate units.
Either would represent a strong beginning in the
task of helping the blind to a less handicapped life.

Chemical Type Prosthetics

As was already shown, there is a real need for
many more of the blood-cleansing machines described.
An expenditure of $5 million a year in equipment
does not seem excessive for the critical conditions
described, but clearly, there is also a question of
availability of other personnel and facilities.

ENTERING THE MARKET

It has been shown that there is a potential
market of about $104 million a year in the prosthet-
ic devices, which have been described in this chapter. It is made up as follows:

	$ millions a year
Pacemakers and other heart devices	16
Orthotic braces and prosthetic limbs	66
Obstacle detectors	2
Reading machines for the blind	15
Chemical type prosthetics	5
Total	104

The inadequacy of data, of course, makes this
estimate highly tentative. Nevertheless it appears
to be plausibly related to the physical extent of
the markets for each device.

To enter this market is not an easy matter and
would require considerable reorientation of the marketing effort in particular. First, the Food and
Drug Administration and the Federal Trade Commission
both are sharply alert to any devices that are not
efficacious or that make extravagant and untrue
claims. Beginning with the "Perkins' Patented Metal-
lic Tractor," which was bought by George Washington,

there has been a lush market in fraudulent devices in the United States.[28] The manufacturer must thus be ready to stand by his product and shoulder his increased responsibility in products that directly affect health and personal welfare.

Secondly, the roles of institutions and of large hospitals are crucial. They and the large national foundations that have long supported research on the afflictions described, would have to be convinced of the worth of a new product. They have or support training facilities, if not for patients, then for the technicians and therapists, to whom the task would ultimately fall. The long clinical tests of products would have to be accepted by the manufacturers. The cost of the training would, in fact, probably have to be borne by an agency other than the manufacturer. It does not seem feasible to add it to the cost of the product.

This raises the general question of support for research. The federal government, largely acting through the National Institutes of Health, already finances 57 percent of all health-connected research in the United States.[29] While support for the kind of research outlined here has been growing, it is still far from adequate. Still, as was shown in the last chapter, there is real difficulty in recapturing any investment in research made by the firm itself.

Whether sponsored by the government or by foundations, moreover, outside financing of research may compromise even further the patenting of devices. Electronic prosthetics cannot, any more than anyone else, make use of nonpatentable physical phenomena to secure protection. They are also precluded from the composition of matter patents that have been the principal types of drug patents. Hence patents are often of little use. Mr. David G. Kilpatrick, Medical Electronics Consultant with General Atronics, writes:

> As a result, the investors in the research end up with a device which is extremely beneficial but has a limited market and is extremely easy to copy since physical phenomena cannot be patented. My pacemaker was copied by no less than eight small companies within the first six months.[30]

Once all these initial hurdles have been cleared, a general-market organization would be required to sustain the product pipeline. Here, fortunately, there is an opportunity of possibly making use of an existing and well-established method. In the past, a unique method of selling to the medical profession has been developed by the drug and medical equipment companies. This type of selling has made use of the "detail man." A detail man is a highly trained salesman who makes the rounds of doctors and institutions, dispensing samples of his products and generally keeping the doctor informed of the latest advances in his field. The medical profession is used to this type of selling. This type of selling is foreign to the electronics companies, but to be successful in medical prosthetics they must adapt to it. It should not be very difficult for them to train experienced detail men in the basic electronics necessary to sell their prosthetic devices, and the results would be well worth the initial cost.

Another important consideration is to expose as much of the medical profession to medical electronics as possible. This can be accomplished by electronic firms sponsoring formal courses in undergraduate and graduate medical schools. They will find it very beneficial to indoctrinate the physician with electronics as soon as possible.

There are also some peculiar problems in pricing. One might think that a handicapped person would pay virtually anything for a device which will alleviate his handicap. However, most handicapped persons are also poor and must depend on foundations or government agencies for at least some support. Under present conditions, this limits effective buying power. The market postulated here would, in fact, have to be supported by public or charitable funds, quite apart from initial research, as mentioned before.

Another facet to be considered is the humanitarian decision of Bell Telephone to market their artificial larynx at cost. IBM is working on reading devices for the blind; other large companies are working in other prosthetic fields. If they also decide to market at cost the problems of competition would be immeasurably complicated in the absence of a major design breakthrough.

In fact, the latter phenomenon must be carefully weighed. It is clear that this is a fast-moving field and although, unfortunately, many of the afflictions are such that no easy solution by way of "miracle drugs" seems in prospect, this is a possibility in the case of a few, such as heart and kidney diseases. An even more plausible danger is, of course, that a drastically better machine is invented by a competitor. In devices, moreover, in which the performance of single components is often crucial, a small advance may spell a large competitive advantage.

In all, then, this market has its considerable risks. Nevertheless, in its emphasis on research, its market, in part, supported by public organizations and its requirement for high precision, reliability, and miniaturization of complex devices, it may have considerable prospects for the more inventive defense-electronics firm.

NOTES

1. National Academy of Sciences--National Research Council, The Application of External Power in Prosthetics and Orthotics. A Report prepared by the Committee on Prosthetic Research and Development (Washington, D.C.), 1961.

2. Letter from Mr. David G. Kilpatrick, Medical Electronics Consultant, General Atronics Corporation, West Conshohocken, Pa. (Apr. 9, 1963).

3. Ibid.

4. U.S. Department of Health, Education and Welfare, Highlights of Heart Progress (1960).

5. James R. Jude, M.D. et al., "Cardiac Arrest --Report of Application of Cardiac Massage on 118 Patients," Journal of the American Medical Association (Dec. 16, 1961).

6. C. W. Lillehei et al., "Transistor Pacemaker
for Treatment of Complete Atroventricular Disassocia-
tion," Journal of the American Medical Association
(Apr. 30, 1960).

7. S. Bellet et al., "The Use of the Internal
Pacemaker in the Treatment of Cardiac Arrest and Slow
Heart Rates," Journal of the American Medical Asso-
ciation Archives of Internal Medicine (March, 1960).

8. W. Greatbatch, and W. M. Chardack, "A Mini-
aturized and Subcutaneously Implanted Pacemaker for
Long Term Correction of Heart Block," 13th Annual
Conference on Electronic Techniques in Medicine and
Biology (October-November, 1960).

9. R. K. Plumb, "New Device Halts Wild Heartbeat," New York Times (Jan. 22, 1964), p. 39.

10. F. E. Haworth, "Electronic Artificial
Larynx," Bell Lab Record (October, 1960).

11. National Foundation, Orthotic Devices for
Upper Extremities (New York, 1958).

12. K. Landauer and G. Stickle, "An Analysis
of Residual Disabilities (Paralysis and Crippling)
Among 100,000 Poliomyelitis Patients," Archives of
Physical Medicine and Rehabilitation (March, 1959).

13. National Academy of Sciences--National Re-
search Council, Orthotics Research and Development.
A report prepared by the Committee on Prosthetic
Research and Development (Chicago, 1963).

14. Howard Freiberger, Electronic Obstacle and
Curb Detectors for the Blind. A report prepared for
the Veterans Administration (Apr. 6, 1961).

15. Howard Freiberger, Conference on Electronic
Obstacle and Curb Detectors for the Blind (April,
1961).

16. Summary Report on 5th Technical Session on
Reading Machines for the Blind, National Academy of
Science.

17. S. Alexander, "They Decide Who Lives or Dies
--Artificial Kidney Center," Life (Nov. 9, 1962).

18. H. C. Schmeck, Jr., "Public Help Sought as Fatal Kidney Diseases Arouse Wide Concern Among Physicians," New York Times (Jan. 10, 1964), p. 88.

19. H. C. Schmeck, Jr., "Kidney Machine Can Treat 15 Patients at a Time," New York Times (Apr. 13, 1964), p. 22.

20. R. K. Plumb, loc. cit.

21. Department of Statistics, American Heart Association, New York, N. Y.

22. American Heart Association, Cardiovascular Disease in the U.S.(March, 1958).

23. American Hospital Association, Hospitals – Journal of the American Hospital Association (August, 1962).

24. Letter from Mr. Jack L. Ranney, Executive Secretary, International Association of Laryngectomees (May 2, 1963).

25. U.S. Department of Health, Education and Welfare, Selected Impairments by Etiology and Activity Limitation, Report of U.S. National Health Survey, Washington, D.C. (July, 1962).

26. R. G. Hurlin, Estimated Prevalence of Blindness in the U.S., 1960 (New York: National Society for the Prevention of Blindness (1962).

27. H. Freiberger, op. cit.

28. M. Gardner, Fads and Fallacies in the Name of Science (New York: Dover, 1957), Ch. 7.

29. U.S. Department of Health, Education and Welfare, Resources for Medical Research, no. 1 (August, 1962), p. 2.

30. G. Kilpatrick, op. cit.

CHAPTER **17** THE DIMENSIONS
OF CHANGE

by John E. Ullmann

THE STATE OF THE INDUSTRY

In the first part of this book, the present
problems and resources of the industry were surveyed. The central problem lies in the present
concentration of the electronics industry in military markets, amounting to at least 60 percent of
the total. The objective of the study was to determine the extent to which alternative markets in
industrial, commercial, and consumer fields could
be found to make up for this very high market
commitment.

The background and outline of the study were
presented in Chapter I. It was shown that political
and military developments have induced a high degree
of insecurity in the markets of the electronics industry. Current and prospective cuts in defense
spending have created a clear need to plan for
conversion.

In Capter 2, the structure and organization of
the industry were examined. It was shown that the
electronics industry has grown at a very rapid rate
throughout but that much of this growth was due to
the expansion of military rather than nonmilitary
markets. In recent years, the industrial and commercial sector has exhibited the fastest rate of
growth, followed by the military, consumer products,
and components. The latter, consisting mostly of
spare parts, have expanded relatively little, probably in response to the development of reliable
semiconductors and the displacement of tubes for
many purposes. The task of finding a substitute
activity for the military electronics industry is
indeed formidable. To replace the entire defense

market would require an increase of 114 percent in
the present nondefense sector of the industry.

In Chapter 3, the policies of the industry
with respect to product design and production methods were reviewed. It was found that the industry
is generally organized around small-quantity production and as a result of this, it has found itself unable to take advantage of many of the labor-
saving devices of modern industry that are based
on large-scale production. Although the electronics industry has been able to standardize certain of its components, it has still not fully
taken advantage of such techniques of simplification
as modulization for which its product is, in many
respects, ideally suitable. In fact, even in such
external relationships as computer language, much
remains to be done along these lines. While a
good deal of this lag is undoubtedly due to the
rapidly evolving technology of the industry, it
adds to the cost pressures faced by the industry
and, by keeping lot size low, adds to the problem
of establishing mass-production facilities and,
hence, the realization of economies of scale.

The electronics industry is also in the middle of profound changes in its production processes.
It has developed new technologies, largely of a
chemical and metallurgical nature, to produce the
novel types of miniaturized circuitry. This has
two important implications.

First, the line of demarcation between systems
and components is becoming blurred. A systems manufacturer working with integrated circuits must, per-
force, make his own components. A components manufacturer unwilling to design his own circuits, if
not whole systems, may find that his markets are
evaporating.

Secondly, the probable concentration of the
electronics industry on the manufacture of miniaturized circuits by chemical and metallurgical
means is likely to leave it with an excess of capacity in conventional machining and assembly facilities, that is, with a substantial capital investment
that can no longer be fruitfully used. Even if it
is, much of the machinery used by the industry is
relatively old. It thus shares a characteristic
of the American durable-goods industries in general,

but it is somewhat better off in this respect than
some of the older industries of this group.

The industry is also beset by other problems
that have put pressure on its profit margins. The
gradual reduction in the award of negotiated contracts and especially the sharp decline in cost
plus fixed-fee contracts have resulted in retrench-
ments by many firms. The standardization of the
relatively few weapons systems now under production
has further reduced the need for and ability to
support new engineering effort. These problems are
strongly reflected in Chapter 4 in which the financial performance of the publicly owned firms of the
electronics industry is scrutinized. In spite of
increased commitments in the form of higher investments per worker and per dollar of sales, the industry has not been able to maintain its profit
margins. Whether one considers firms largely dealing in components, systems producers, or large
diversified firms, the median-profit levels have
exhibited a decline, and the proportion of firms
running at a loss has sharply increased. Many of
the firms appear to have had a fairly brief "golden
age," brought into being by contracts which, in the
perspective of their later history, turned out to
be windfalls. In consumer products, and now even
in industrial products, we are witnessing, for example, the sort of price competition which one typically associates with a relatively mature industry.

NEW MARKETS, 1968-1973

The objective of the marketing chapters of
this book was to determine what increments in
industrial and consumer markets could be foreseen
within the next five years and how they compare
with the size of the present market for defense
electronics. The simplest way of accomplishing
this in an overall sense is first of all to consider a time series for the four major sectors of
the electronics industry. Time series as such, of
course, are not particularly satisfactory as pre-
dictors of future economic performance, because
time is not truly an independent variable which
"causes" anything to happen to the sales volume.
Rather, within that period of time a variety of

economic factors act upon the industry and produce
the sales volume in its various sectors. Table 17.1
gives the results of an exponential time series derived from Table 2.2 of Chapter 2, using the 17
years from 1952 through 1968 as a base.

It is quite clear that if all of these forecasts were to come to pass they would produce an
increment of $11.3 billion in 1973 over the 1968
market. Since, as will be recalled from Chapter 2,
the expected sales to the government in 1968 are
$12.7 billion, such an increment would go far to-
ward absorbing any reasonably expectable displacement of the military electronics industry. The
question, however, is how realistic are these
forecasts?

Clearly, the most important part depends upon
what happens with industrial products. Their
growth rate has truly been extraordinarily high
and, moreover, has been going on for the past 17
years with a 17.3 percent high coefficient of correlation. Nevertheless, it is by no means certain
that such a growth rate can be sustained indefinitely. A total of almost $15 billion would re-
flect a 25 percent share of a $60-billion level of
spending for plant and equipment. This in itself
would be some 25 percent higher than the 1968 level.
While the American industrial establishment, to say
nothing of other sectors of society, could easily
absorb expenditures of that order of magnitude, the
realization of such levels of business cannot be
regarded as certain, and what must be open to even
more doubt is whether the electronics share of cap-
ital-equipment spending can be raised from its
present level of about 8 percent to the 25 percent
mentioned before. Nevertheless, the growth rate
is certainly both consistent and high.

The commercial industrial market can be visua-
lized as a "natural sector," largely consisting of
automation equipment and a stimulated sector largely
concerned with equipment for which government expenditures would furnish the principal procurement
incentive. As far as the automation market is concerned, we have drawn attention to the decline in
computer costs, and, therefore, the probability that
the fully to be expected increased use of computers
will lead to many products of lower specific value
and, therefore, to a relatively reduced rate of

TABLE 17.1

Market Summary, Growth Rates and Forecast to 1973

Item	Consumer products	Industrial products	Components	Total
	(amounts in $ billion, rates in percent)			
Sales, 1968	5.0	5.5	0.6	11.1
Sales, 1973 (est.)	6.9	14.9	0.6	22.4
Difference	1.9	9.4	0.0	11.3
Growth rate, 1952–1968	9.0	17.3	3.0	--
Coefficient of correlation, r	0.968	0.993	0.765	--

increase of dollar volume. There are also some
indications that automation itself is facing some
physical limitations in that the number of actual
installations is beginning to approach that of potential ones. This is so even in the case of computers, in which the number of units installed is
already greater than the number of offices with 25
employees or more. Accordingly the market must
increasingly concentrate on smaller units or more
sophisticated shared-time systems, all of which
have capital saving implications. Certainly, computer manufacturers can no longer expect their customers to justify computer acquisition on the basis
of massive automation of relatively simple clerical
tasks.

One area of interest remains, of course, that
of truly large record and surveillance systems,
such as the proposed federal government data bank.
Such a computer which, in W. H. Auden's phrase "may
say alas but can offer neither help nor pardon,"
raises important aspects of civil liberties and has
already led to Congressional demands for the aban-
donment of the project. Such a system, however,
even when installed can only be regarded as a par-
tial offset to the business that might be lost if
the market for the present highly sophisticated
military computers is diminished.[1]

Automation of distribution is in some respects
similar to the office automation market. In fact, it
is part of it. At present the most important prospective change is the further extension of computer
operation into credit transfers, i.e., the "cashless
society" concept. Under these conditions, the physical handling of checks, for example, would be eliminated, and the present magnetic ink character recognition system would then take its place in history
as only an intermediate stage between manual check
handling and totally electronic finances.

The market for process automation is also limited by the physical number of plants to be equipped.
The import of this numerical limitation is that
development costs typically have to be amortized
over relatively few units so that the savings which
they realize must be truly impressive in order to
justify their acquisition.

Without doubt, the largest single potential
market lies in numerically controlled machinery.

If only a small proportion of the aging machine-
tool stock of the United States were to be replaced
by numerically controlled machines, the market
potential would be enormous. As it is, the field
has seen very rapid growth, and we may certainly
expect that it will continue to grow much faster than
industrial-commercial products as a whole.

Nevertheless, both process automation and numerical controls have also been subject to some capital
saving influences. It hs been found possible, for
example, to use a computer to determine process settings rather than leacing it permanently connected
to the system (on-line, real time controls). One
computer can then serve several purposes. A similar
development appears to have occurred in numerically
controlled systems in which it may also be possible
to have several machines time-share a single computer.

Finally, there are the various stimulated markets
as shown in Chapters 6 to 16 of the book; several of
these contain some rather new concepts which would
have to be worked out before there can be anything
like sizeable market breakthroughs. Some tentative
estimates are presented in the following table; as
noted, these are subject to deliberate manipulation,
upwards or downwards.

Item	Amount $ Million
Road Traffic Automation	20
Rail Automation	35
Air Traffic Control	130
Satellite Communications	30
Education	50
Electronic Libraries	200
Medical Diagnostics and Monitoring	52
Medical Prosthetics	100
Total	617

Turning now to consumer products, it is seen
from the above that they too have maintained a very
steady growth rate, averaging 9 percent per annum
compounded between 1952 and 1968, again with a high
degree of correlation. The growth rate, of course,
is markedly lower than that for industrial products
so that its extrapolation over five years cannot

possibly bring as wide a discrepancy as could arise
in the case of industrial products. Still, in as-
sessing its significance, it is necessary to consider some of the determinants of consumer-product
sales which have been found helpful in the past.

    One of the major influences has been found to
be the rate of primary-family formation, because
many consumer durable items are bought shortly after
marriage. While this measure is perhaps better for
this reason, for other household durables, such as
refrigerators, washing machines, and the like it
has a major influence on such "big ticket" items as
television sets and stereo equipment. At any rate,
when the marriage rate declined sharply in the
1950's due to the small population increment at the
time in the prime marriage age, the sales of appliances dropped correspondingly. The current cohort
balance in the U.S..population leads to a prediction once more of a rising number of marriages, but
at the same time a corresponding decline in the average family size may well lead to a long-term diminished growth rate in such items as personal
radios, multiple TV sets, and other equipment of
the affluent young.

    The new families can, of course, only make an
effective contribution to new markets if their earn-
ing power is maintained. Over the years, there has
been a general improvement in the earnings of the
young compared with their elders, especially in
occupations with some technical content. However,
unemployment among the young, especially among those
poorly educated, is and remains high. If as a result young people are forced into low paying service
jobs, the good prospects of the consumer market are
not likely to be realized.

    The growth of consumer products in the past 20
years has, of course, taken place against the background of a steady introduction of new products.
At the beginning of that period, television had yet
to make a good deal of its market progress. There
were no transistor radios and high fidelity sets,
and tape recorders were practically nonexistent as
consumer items. In part, the relatively small increase in the dollar volume of consumer products
is due to the success of the industry in offering
more performance for less money, that is, smaller,

lighter, and more economical products that can give
the same service to the customer. There has been,
in short, the type of technical economic pressure
discussed elsewhere in this book, which leads
toward capital saving, the wide dissemination of
the products of the industry with only moderate
increase in value.

The relatively more favorable increase in dollar volume of the consumer sector in the last few
years has been largely due to the market breakthrough of color television which, being a relatively expensive item, also reversed the trend toward lower value per unit. Nevertheless, from what
we know of current research activities in the television industry, we can delineate some future
developments which are almost certainly likely to
lead to lower cost per unit for color television
sets as well. For example, we are likely to have
integrated circuits together with such developments
as a semi-conductor video screens, which may result
in much lighter and simpler television sets with
declining costs. Radios will probably continue a
similar development, with AM-FM sets becoming comparable in cost to, and physically smaller than,
present portable AM radios.

The question now arises what "entirely" new
products appear in the offing which could do their
share toward realizing substantial new markets.
One such group of new products which, because of
the volume involved, might give rise to an entirely
new sector of the electronics industry is that of
electronic components of personal vehicles. If an
electric automobile or other conveyance ever becomes the order of things, its speed controls are
bound to employ solid-state technology and would
inevitably lead to very substantial business for
an industry familiar with manufacturing such items.
Indeed, electronic-ignition systems are now under
development for automobiles and are already available on an experimental basis; while they are a
rather expensive extra at present, it is very possible that they will make their mark before long
and become standard equipment. The criterion here
appears to be whether or not they can be made cheaply
enough so as to save manufacturing costs relative to
the present systems. Another suggestion which has
been made is the use of an electronic anti-skid
device as an option on some 1969 models. The Ford

Motor Company is the first one to announce that it
will offer one in some of its most expensive cars.
This device would be directed by a book size solid-
state computer under the glove compartment.[2] In
view of the safety implications of such a device,
it is very likely that before long it would be made
standard equipment under national automobile-safety
legislation, provided, of course, that it can prove
its worth.

Two other potential new items are the microwave oven and the television tape recorder. The
micro-wave oven promises virtually instant warming
up of food and thus has prospects of becoming a
generally accepted household appliance. Its main
strength appears to lie in the defrosting of foods;
it cannot, for example, roast meat on its own, unless combined with a conventional broiler. In any
event, considerable cost and safety problems must
still be solved. One cannot be sure whether this
can be done within the next five years, although
prospects appear to be favorable for the long run.
The device might in part tend to replace other
ranges in the nation's kitchens and would not, therefore, result in as significant an increase in the
total appliance market as if it were a truly new
appliance.

The television tape recorder could be used to
record television programs and play them back or to
produce tapes from the user's own camera. They can
then be played back through the user's modified
television set. This system is an interesting one,
but one must compare it to certain functionally
similar alternatives. Its video part, for example,
would certainly have to be able to reproduce color
if it is to compete with the extraordinarily cheap,
light, and well-established movie camera and color
film. At present, certainly, the still considerable
maintenance and performance problems of color television, even in stationary applications at home,
argue against a speedy resolution of the design
problems which would have to allow for a portable
camera able to take a certain amount of abuse and
which would certainly have to be lighter than present portable TV cameras. In summary, then, the
sort of major new product which has been responsible
for so much of the consumer sector's past growth,
is much more likely to come, if at all, from the
transportation field than from micro-wave ovens
and TV tape recorders.

In the "personal" electronics field, there is, in any case, the question of whether in its present relatively deprived state (in respect to technical talent) the American consumer electronics segment is not excessively vulnerable to imports. Over the last two decades, Japanese and other Far Eastern imports have all but monopolized the personal radio and tape recorder field, accounting either for whole sets or for major components of "American" ones. British and German hi-fi and stereo components have long since been highly competitive with American ones. Japanese imports have also achieved a dominant position in electronic desk calculators (again, both in complete models and components, such as large-scale intergrated circuits and metal oxide semiconductors). The Japanese electronics industry is, moreover, engaged in an intensive development effort for large computers as well, so that its capabilities will, before long, extend from the simple four-rule machines to programmable desk calculators, mini-computers and the largest machines. Conversion in the direction of consumer products will therefore have to contend with a more competitive environment than was the case, say, in the late 1950's, and the industry will have to expend considerably more energy in product development, producibility studies and the like than was then necessary. This may well turn out to be an advantage to research-oriented firms.

We have, therefore, quite a wide variety of choices in new products, both consumer and industry oriented, as well as fields in which government decisions, funding or other market stimulation is essential. The real restriction on the realization of any of these possibilities lies in the totally disproportionate use of the best technical talent of the industry for military purposes. This raises the issue of occupational displacement, to which we shall address ourselves in the next section.

In summary then, it may very well be that the total estimated increment may be produced between 1968 and 1973. Even if two-thirds of this new business were to be produced, we would still be able to make up more than half of the current military business.

A second imponderable is the future of foreign trade. On the one hand, American competence in

integrated circuits may enable the industry to further increase its exports of industrial equipment
and may, in fact, produce more exports of consumer
items as well. On the other hand, the transistor
radio was developed into a viable consumer product
in Japan and some manufacturing of integrated circuits, and similar fine electronics work has already
begun intensively, both in Japan and, even more
rapidly, in Hong Kong.

Finally, there is the important point that the
increment in electronic markets is bound to attract
firms outside the industry whose prospects in their
own, under conditions of conversion, would be even
less bright than those of the defense-electronics
industry. The airframe industry is a clear example.
It has already entered heavily into electronics, although perhaps under present conditions in the aircraft market this development has run its course.
The trend is bound to be renewed, however, if aircraft procurement is reduced once more. Such a
development seems likely if the Vietnam war is liq-
uidated, because aircraft losses have been quite
heavy and have had to be replaced during the course
of the war. One factor against the airframe industry is, of course, its heavy capital equipment and
the disproportionate overhead which a venture into
the relatively light electronic industry would have
to carry. Another danger comes from the machinery
industry.

As controls of machines become more electronic
and less mechanical, the proportion of value added
by electronics increases, and firms in the field
will accordingly become tempted to take a share of
the electronics business themselves. Therefore,
any projections that we make in this book will
still demand a considerable degree of aggressive-
ness and enterprise on the part of electronics firms
themselves.

OCCUPATIONAL DISPLACEMENTS

Significant reductions in the military sector
of the electronics industry would result in major
shifts among the occupational categories of the
industry, with most of them being drastically affected. To derive these effects, certain simple

calculation must first be performed on the data of
Chapter 3 and on the results presented in this chapter. We know the present occupational breakdown of
the industry; assuming it to remain approximately
the same for the next five years, it is possible to
estimate the future distribution of workers by
occupation, given future total employment.[3] Again,
given the employment for 1966 and computing the
value of shipments per worker, one could estimate
the future workforce by direct proportion, but such
a procedure would be grossly in error. It would
neglect all actual reduction in the rate of increase
of the workforce, due to productivity improvements
and inflationary price changes. Since our underlying series of dollar volume is based on current
dollars, the latter must be considered. Accordingly,
based on past changes in dollar output per worker,
and assuming a price escalation due to inflation of
3 percent-per-annum until 1973, we may consider
that the volume for industrial and commercial products will be $10 billion and that for consumer
products $6 billion, both corrected for productivity
changes and for inflation.

The result is total employment for 557,000
workers in industrial work in 1973 compared with
285,000 in 1966, including a prorated share of
those in the components sector. Therefore, there
will be an extra 272,000 workers by 1973. Similarly,
the increase in those employed in the consumer field
is 308,000 - 243,000 = 65,000 workers. The effects
of these changes related to 1966 employment in the
military-space field are presented in Table 17.2.
Part A. assumes that all military and space spending has been eliminated and thus gives an extreme
and quite unlikely situation. Obviously, all categories are severely affected, especially engineers
and scientists and technicians, in which over 70
percent would be displaced and administrative and
clerical, in which close to half would be affected.
A second alternative, involving a 50-percent cut,
would still affect engineers, scientists, and technicians quite severely, the former to the extent
of over 50 percent while administrative and clerical
workers would remain roughly stable. Substantial
increases would be required however, both in the
number of skilled and unskilled workers, the latter
mainly as assemblers.

TABLE 17.2

Estimate of Possible Labor Displacement

A. Elimination of Military Space Products

	Military space products, 1966	Indust. comm. products est. increase (in thousands)	Consumer products 1966-1973	Total est. excess (deficit)	Est. excess (deficit) percent of military space employment
Engineers & scientists	118.1	21.9	5.8	(90.4)	(79.5)
Technicians	75.0	18.6	3.8	(52.6)	(70.3)
Administrative	96.0	40.1	8.9	(47.0)	(49.0)
Clerical	84.4	36.9	7.2	(40.3)	(47.8)
Skilled production	58.7	33.4	6.9	(18.4)	(31.4)
Unskilled workers	119.8	121.1	32.4	33.7	28.1
Total	552.0	272.0	65.0	(215.0)	(38.9)

B. 50 Percent Reduction in Military-Space Products

	Military space products, 50 percent of 1966	Indust., comm. and consumer products, est. increase 1966-73 (in thousands)	Total est. excess (deficit)	Est. excess (deficit) as percent of half of 1966 military space employment
Engineers & scientists	59.0	27.7	(31.3)	(53.1)
Technicians	37.5	22.4	(15.1)	(40.3)
Administrative	48.0	49.0	1.0	2.1
Clerical	42.2	44.1	1.9	4.5
Skilled production	29.4	40.3	10.9	37.1
Unskilled workers	59.9	153.5	93.6	156.2
Total	276.0	337.0	61.0	22.1

329

Obviously, such predictions must remain highly
speculative. They may be upset, for example, by
greatly increased demands for scientists and others
able to extend and improve computer systems, for,
as has been recently shown, many firms still find it
difficult to derive measurable profit from their
computer operations.[4] For the rest, however, occupational conversion will be in order. The subject has
been dealt with elsewhere by the author[5] and is considered in detail in another volume in this series,
The Defense Industry by Seymour Lielman.

Basically, it is a question of individual versus
collective skill transfers. Military industry itself has generally not been optimistic on the subject,
in part by taking a possibly erroneous view of its
own capabilities. For example, Mr. William P. Gwinn,
President of United Aircraft Corp., asserts[6] that:

> Years of emphasis on reliability and
> durability have resulted in develop-
> ing a work force carefully trained
> in a tradition of precision produc-
> tion that just would not be competi-
> tive in making every-day products
> for the consumer market.

The vicissitudes of the F-111 aircraft, to cite
but one example, suggest that perhaps a little skep-
ticism is in order here, but it is undeniable that
the capabilities of defense engineers require careful scrutiny and that we should not accept self-
evaluations uncritically. In a recent article,
perceptively entitled "Apollo and the Decay of Technical Excellence," Rep. William F. Ryan cities not
only the F-111, but also the Skybolt missile, the
submarine Thresher, and, he might now be able to
add, the Scorpion. He also points to major degrad-
ing influences in the sort of large-scale technological efforts which are typical of military
contracts:[7]

1. Sheer size and growth rate of
    organizations.

2. Insulation of the engineer or
    scientist from credit or respon-
    sibility for the results (or
    lack thereof) of his contribu-
    tion.

3. Suppression of internal criticism through devotion to an unblemished public facade.

4. The use of the ditch digger fallacy as a management tool for planning and controlling programs.

5. The availability of excess funds for glamorous projects.

The latter, of course, has resulted in overruns on cost by factors of three or more in several major contracts. Mr. Ryan defines the "ditch-digger fallacy" (i.e. 4 men can dig a ditch in half a day if 2 men can dig one in a day) as manifesting itself in the accumulation of excess personnel--"warm bodies," as he says--and the measurement of technical output by the "man-months" thereby expended.

A large proportion of engineers employed on military work are in fact, mainly engaged in various forms of documentation. One authoritative study considers this group one of the hardest to "convert."[8]

A second set of conversion alternatives is the utilization of the so-called systems capability. Some preliminary efforts in having erstwhile military experts tackle urban problems have been made, but the results so far have not been commensurate with the expenditures and have also shown that "systems work" has no relevance remote from its subject matter; in urban affairs, for example, the "systems approach" is merely an extension of conventional city planning and must rely on the latter's professional cadres for its principal inputs.[9] This point too is considered again in volume II of this series.

IMPEDIMENTS TO PLANNING

It has been shown in the book that a need for conversion planning exists and that the prospects of the industry are such that not all the task can be accomplished out of its own resources. At the same time, action toward effective planning is still limited. Certainly, the difficulties set forth in various parts of this book must be a factor, but

it is appropriate to look further into the problems
which have beset conversion planning in the past.

First, one of its principal enemies appears to
be a complacent belief that, somehow or other, matters will sort themselves out, since, after all,
conversion after World War II did not present any
major problem. It should by now be almost tautologi-
cal to point out that there are now no pent-up demands that cannot be met from other enterprises now
in existence, and no accumulation of cash able to
make that demand effective. It has been amply shown
in this book that the methods of working followed
in the defense industry are so different that even
if other products could readily be developed, severe
structural adjustments would remain. Yet this type
of sentiment still occasionally crops up in high
places.

Unfortunate as this is, there is probably no
human problem that does not have to face the type
of complacency that denies its very existence.
The really troublesome roadblock in conversion
planning is rather to be found in certain patterns
of circular reasoning at practically all decision
levels associated with the defense industry, with
the result that nothing is done because nobody knows
where to begin.

First, there is the view that if conversion
planning is loudly proclaimed a national task of
high priority, the American people will think the
Cold War over and, in the usual cascading processes
of American politics, refuse to support a wide variety of other policies (and, possibly, politicians).
On the other hand, drastic steps for arms reduction
are inhibited by the fact that no plans have been
made to cushion the economic shock. There are, to
be sure, frequent statements that the United States
feels able to sign any kind of agreement without regard to such considerations, but when the closing
of a defense factility, however obsolete, or the
cancellation of a major defense contract bring forth
the wrath of local and regional political representatives, such statements remain brave words. The
Congressman or Senator, incidentally, is faced with
corresponding conflicts. He too may support cuts
in spending or peaceful political initiatives, yet
he is bound to push the stake of his constituency
in the economic benefits of existing arrangements.

These conflicts are paralleled by others within the Department of Defense itself. There are conflicts as to what cuts to make or whether to make any at all. From a technical viewpoint, every weapon can be improved, yet there are gnawing suspicions that many of these suggestions are designed mainly to keep things going rather than to produce even remotely proportionate increases in the nation's security. Thus, the partisans of the manned bomber at times almost echo the sentiments of union leaders faced with the threat of automation, such as, for instance, the Brotherhood of Locomotive Firemen. Contractors are often drawn into these conflicts between the Services, the civilian direction of the Department of Defense and the political alignments that have grown out of these controversies. Thus the circular reasoning once more is brought into play. It is not known what will be cut or who will be affected, therefore nobody can plan. On the other hand, if proposals for cuts are made, fierce specialist opposition is immediately aroused which, in turn, may jeopardize other enterprises.

These uncertainties are strongly reflected in the behavior of the managements of defense contractors. They are, of course, keenly aware of the risks to their business, although such awareness tends to diminish after years of prosperity under political protection in which risks are reduced to vanishing point. They also realize their handicaps in planning for the future when they do not know what the government wants. If, on the other hand, conversion planning is resorted to, then many managements take the view, often expressed to the writer, that they would be regarded as a species of "underserving poor" by the defense-procurement agencies and no longer treated favorably in relation to competitors who have no other products. This view, it should be added, is strongly rejected by Defense officials, but it still persists. At any rate, it does seem to create a further impediment.

There is yet another set of such self-canceling policies. When times are good, the firm concentrates its financial and intellectual resources on more defense business. When times are bad, it lacks money for any meaningful effort in conversion planning. Of course, Armed Forces Procurement Regulations allow firms to charge certain cost of conversion.

Deputy Assistant Secretary of Defense Arthur Barber
is quoted as follows:[10]

> We have advised defense contractors
> to utilize Section XV of the Armed
> Services Procurement Regulations to
> establish long-term marketing and
> conversion studies. Many have done
> so, others have not. Any contractor
> can include the cost of "reasonable"
> conversion studies in his overhead
> allowance on DOD contracts.

The chargeable expenses specifically exclude development of new products. Even if chargeable, moreover, the cost of conversion becomes part of the
overhead and thus increases the cost structure of
the firm just at a time when it must cut its prices
even to stay in the defense business.

Lastly, the managers, as individuals, are beset
by conflicting emotions. Many of them are, of
course, convinced that nothing drastic can or
"should" happen to end or reduce what many regard
as permanent conflict, but even if they do not have
this view, this does not mean that they can formulate effective actions. On the one hand, they are
generally interested in the perpetuation of their
firm. A few managers are able to contemplate
liquidation of the enterprise and view the future
more in terms of a favorable sale as a tax loss to
somebody else than of any continued existence as a
manufacturing enterprise. For many senior managers,
however, personal assets are involved. Much of
their personal wealth may consist of the common
stock of the firms concerned, quite often hypo-
thecated as a result of a stock-option deal. This
gives the holding the characteristics of a margin
account, in which a decline may have a dispropor-
tionately severe effect on the manager's equity in
his investment. From a personal viewpoint, therefore, the managers are often strongly committed to
securing the future of their firms.

However, there is always a secondary problem
involving their own status. A manager typically is
reluctant to support a course of action which calls
his own personal future in the organization into
question. A change as drastic as that involved in
conversion, as amply documented in this study,

cannot help but bring about shifts in the relative
importance of departments and hence, of their managers. If new men with experience in nondefense
programs are brought in, or discovered within the
firm itself, they are likely to maintain a strong
ascendancy over those with knowledge only of a much-
reduced defense market. In fact, many existing managers would have to consider whether the need to
cut overhead would not result in the elimination
of their own jobs. Therefore, the sponsorship of
conversion in the councils of management may be a
difficult personal matter, even if the manager concerned otherwise regards it positively.

These problems of management have their counter-
parts in those of labor organizations and individual
employees. When business was good, labor organizations concerned themselves with the usual bread-and-
butter issues of unionism, with wages, working
conditions, and job security. It was not realized
until late in 1963 that in a defense firm, "job security" is meaningless unless it includes conversion planning. In part, the reluctance of labor
organizations to take a strong stand has been political. Part of the high command of the AFL-CIO has
been hostile to relaxation of international tensions
and has therefore insufficently considered the possibility of defense cuts arising not from disarmament
but from internal technical developments and the
resultant conditions of saturation. (Of course,
business has similar conflicts between "hard liners"
and pragmatists, for example, in matters relating
to Vietnam or trade with Communist countries.)

When a union is faced with cuts and steps, such
as political pressure for the continuance of the contracts have been exhausted, conversion necessarily
becomes an issue and has recently taken the form of
proposals for labor-management conversion committees.
However meritorious such suggestions are, they are
difficult to incorporate into union contracts at
times of bad business when the bargaining power of
the union is much reduced and when it thus feels
itself unable to make the matter a strike issue as
long as other conditions are met. As a result, attempts thus far to establish such conversion committees have proved unsuccessful.

The individual is also handicapped by circular
reasoning. When times are good he does not move,

especially when going to a nondefense job means a
pay cut. When times are bad, he lacks the resources
to make the move and may be tied down by property
ownership in a depressed area.

It is clear from the foregoing that, quite
apart from the Vietnam war, the reasons for the
present immobilisme in conversion planning are complex and involve practically everyone in the defense
industry and its market. Nevertheless there is a
need for action. Some modest proposals toward that
end follow in the next section.

THE WAY TO ACTION

To find a way out of this general inaction is
not easy if it is not to be countered immediately
by the same arguments that created it. Since a federal government market is at issue, the federal government has an important responsibility, though not
the only one. The following suggestions may offer
some first steps out of the difficulties.

First there is a need for a strong and unequi-
vocal announcement at the highest level that conversion represents a national need and that
consequently planning initiatives are required at
federal, state, and local level.

It was shown in this book that the electronics industry cannot solve the conversion problem
within its own structure. Similar findings have
been reported for other impacted industries. Hence
certain major government plans must be made that
would redirect the resources involved. Among these
are the attack on poverty, international industrialization, intensified health care, and social rehabilitation, urban and agricultural renewal, the
improvement of education, and many others. It is
not the shortage of ideas that is at issue but how
to translate them into viable plans.

For this it is suggested that no attempt be
made initially to devise these projects primarily
in order to convert specific defense-related resources. Rather, programs for each should be formulated in relation to the nation's needs and
translated into the resources required to fulfill

them. Then the claims of defense and nondefense
activities on the nation's finances and manpower
can be adjudged in the light of national priorities,
which can and should be the subject of national de-
bate. This procedure gets around the problem of
not knowing what to plan, because it is not known
with certainty what defense resources will be released. Many necessary projects are at issue here,
and they should not depend for their planning or timing for what might be termed the "table scraps" of
defense spending. This suggestion also implies that
the Department of Defense should not carry the burden
for such planning. It is not qualified for it and has
repeatedly disclaimed its desire for such work.

Accordingly, the government agencies most appropriate for this work would be units of the Departments of Commerce, Housing and Urban Development,
Transportation, Interior, Agriculture Health, Education and Welfare and Labor, national and international development agencies, state, regional, and
local planning authorities. By making the plans in
some detail, an array of plans is obtained from
which projects can be chosen on their merit and as
an integral part of allocating available resources.
A varied set of plans could meet many different
types of adjustment, and, being available, would
cut the long-lead time otherwise required.

Since defense procurement takes place within a
framework of detailed government regulations, some
of them require re-examination. One of the first
tasks would be a study of the present method of
charging overhead in relation to its encouragement
or hindrance of conversion.

When both defense and nondefense products are
made in the same factory, there should be a method
of charging realistic overhead rates for each, without on the one hand burdening the nondefense products with charges that would not be incurred if
there were no defense business and on the other
hand cause the government to subsidize the firm to
the extent that its commercial products are, in
effect, "dumped."

The shortage of funds for conversion may also
require action. In 1964, Senator Jacob K. Javits
suggested the creation of a government agency for
this purpose, which seems to be similar to the old

Reconstruction Finance Corporation.11 Dr. Murray
L. Weidenbaum has suggested a series of steps to
support research and development programs by better
tax treatment of expenses and by loans.12

On the individual level, there is first of all
a need for the support of individual training steps
in the form similar to the GI Bill, directed, however, more exactly to the kinds of occupations
likely to be in demand for the conversion process.13
To be effective such a scheme must include much
more generous living allowances than were paid in
the past, since the issue here is not the care of
a predominantly young and vigorous group with
limited responsibilities but rather the maintenance
of men who had sizeable incomes and now have responsibilities and commitments scaled accordingly. Indeed, the rates of unemployment insurance should be
increased considerably, preferably by raising the
maxima which can now be paid.

Given the above framework, the task of planning
by the individual firm is much simplified. Even in
the absence of some of the recommendations made, it
is possible to plan. It would seem that a first requirement is to reassert the principle of private
enterprise, which holds that a true entrepreneur
does not merely passively respond to a market but
tries to promote its growth, if necessary by establishing a virtual "lobby" for the purpose. Defense-
oriented firms do this now, and it is perplexing to
encounter the contrary view when conversion is at
issue, that in the absence of a "master plan" for
the economy, nothing can be done.

The first step would be for the company to
assess its own capabilities very thoroughly, with
respect to its finances, production facilities,
existing skills and skills formerly practiced by
its employees. In part, reliance should be placed
on suggestions for new products emanating from the
organization itself, but decisions on them must be
made not on the basis of an internal poll of this
type but on the assessment of a national need made,
as suggested earlier in this chapter. Here it may
be necessary for individual members of managements
to revise some political prejudices and view public
projects as desirable rather than as the sort of
government spending to be strongly deplored, as op-
posed to the government spending which supports the
firm.

Once decisions have been made that useful projects exist for which the firm has capability, a strong marketing effort must be made to sell the idea. This means applying political initiatives, enlisting other local business interests which depend on the continuing prosperity of what often is the largest local employer, coordinating initiatives with labor organizations, etc. In short, the same type of effort must be made to influence the course of history that has to be made by any industry which tries to grow or maintain itself in a mixed economy. The fact that not all firms can be successful should not hamper efforts; the race, as frequently pointed out in this book, is to the swift.

The problem has been raised of how to judge the adequacy of a conversion effort. It is not an easy question to answer but the efforts which have been brought to the attention of the writer, often consisting only of a few "part-time worriers," are certainly insufficient. It is better to judge by results, and this can be done by knowledgeable market experts, management consultants and even, if need be, by government agencies. It is very likely true that the Department of Defense and other security-connected agencies cannot adequately make such judgments, but then, as aforesaid, they should not be expected to. If the conversion experts of a firm feel that they have the backing of management, their work is much facilitated. If their task is largely window-dressing, public relations or otherwise badly regarded, if the unit is staffed with the least capable engineers and market analysts in the firm and if it cannot logically look forward to the adoption of some of its ideas, the chances of success are minimal.

Lastly, perhaps a word to theoreticians in the field is in order. It is true that everything in a complex society interacts, but this must not lead to overcomplication of the issue. For example, the creation of jobs is more important than more elaborate studies on work motivation, etc. Automation and civil rights are closely related to the major economic problems of our time, but this does not absolve industrial managements and their advisers from aiming at more limited objectives. In conversion, as in so much else in our troubled times, it is better to light a candle than to curse the darkness.

The challenge of industrial conversion deserves
to be taken as part of the mission of the United
States in the modern industrial world. The United
States has established the greatest industrial society ever seen, based on its own genius and the effective and imaginative use of discoveries made
elsewhere. In advancing, it has also encountered
some of the greatest problems of industrialization.
Perhaps it owes to the less well-endowed an attempt
to come to grips with these problems. Such a task
involves, in part, a national decision, whether to
be parochial and restrictive or farsighted and ex-
pansive, whether to display a mature grasp of the
issues or espouse the politics of frustration and
whether to promote understanding and compassion or
perish in war. The choice begins with the way in
which conversion is approached, for it requires
the formulation, at long last, of ways in which
the scientific and technical growth of the past
decades can be turned away from man's destruction
to the enrichment of life.

NOTES

1. John E. Ullmann, "Automation and the Price
of Progress," American Journal of Orthopsychiatry,
vol. 36, no. 1 (January, 1966), p. 70.

2. Business Week (June 8, 1968), p. 88.

3. Electronics Industries Association, 1967
Yearbook (Washington, D.C.: EIA, 1968), Tables
60, 61.

4. Business Week (June 15, 1968), p. 87.

5. John E. Ullmann, "Occupational Problems in
Conversion" in U.S. Senate, Subcommittee on Employ-
ment and Manpower, Convertibility of Space and De-
fense Resources to Civilian Needs: A Search for
New Employment Opportunities, 88th Cong. 2nd Session
(1963), p. 1126. See also Chap. XVIII of J. E.
Ullmann (Ed.) Conversion Prospects of the Defense
Electronics Industry (Hempstead, N.Y.: Hofstra,
Yearbook of Business, 1965).

6. Hartford Courant (Sept. 15, 1967); quoted in Consumer Reports (April, 1968), p. 170.

7. William F. Ryan, "Apollo and the Decay of Technical Excellence," American Engineer, vol. 38, no. 1,(January, 1968), p. 19.

8. U.S. Arms Control and Disarmament Agency, The Transferability and Retraining of Defense Engineers (Washington, D.C.: U.S. Government Printing Office, 1967), p. 6-9.

9. U.S. Arms Control and Disarmament Agency, Defense Systems Resources in the Civil Sector (Washington, D.C.: U.S. Government Printing Office, 1967); see also D. Bird, "Rand Men Tackle City's Problems, Big and Little," New York Times (Apr. 29, 1968); for a critique, see J. E. Ullmann, "Humanizing Modern Technology," New University Thought (Special issue 1966/67), p. 79-80.

10. Quoted in D. Allison, "The Civilian Technology Lag," International Science and Technology, (December, 1963).

11. Sen. J. K. Javits, address to Leadership Conference on Industrial Conversion (Washington, D.C., Apr. 23, 1964).

12. M. L. Weidenbaum, "The Economic Impact of Changing Times on the U.S. Defense Industry," symposium on Changing Times in the Defense Industry, Electronics Industries Association (Washington, D.C., Mar. 12, 1964).

13. Ibid., see also, the author's independent suggestion to the same effect, in "Full Employment and Peace," address to the 38th Semi-annual convention of the New York State Council of Machinists (Elmira, New York, Mar. 7, 1964).

ABOUT THE EDITOR

John E. Ullmann, Professor of Management and Chairman of the Department of Management, Marketing and Business Statistics at Hofstra University, is a mechanical and industrial engineer specializing in technical-economic analysis, with a research background in the economics and design of machinery and production systems. Before joining Hofstra, he was Assistant Professor of Economics of Engineering at Stevens Institute of Technology, and Lecturer at Columbia University.

Dr. Ullmann has acted as consultant in industrial marketing to several firms and is a consultant in industrial development and other community problems to various public agencies. He has written many articles and monographs on product development, industrialization, engineering economics, and operations problems of firms and has written and lectured extensively on industrial conversion. He is co-author of Manufacturing Management: An Overview (1969).

Dr. Ullman received his B.Sc. in Engineering from the University of London and his M.S. and Ph.D. from Columbia University. He is a Professional Engineer in the State of New York.